CONTENTS

A Mirror publication
Act. Head of Syndication & Licensing: Fergus McKenna
Mirrorpix: David Scripps and Alex Waters
020 7293 3858

Produced by Trinity Mirror Sport Media,
PO BOX 48, Liverpool L69 3EB
0151 227 2000

Executive Editor: Ken Rogers
Senior Editor: Steve Hanrahan
Senior Art Editor: Rick Cooke
Editor: Paul Dove
Editorial: Steve Myall
Designers: Colin Sumpter, Barry Parker, Zoe Bevan
Sub Editor: Alan Jewell

Part of the Mirror Collection
© Published by Trinity Mirror
Images: Mirrorpix, PA Photos
Printed by William Gibbons

A NATION PREPARES FOR A

FAIRYTALE

WEDDING

BY STEVE MYALL, DAILY MIRROR STAFF

IT is the announcement that has made the nation smile. It comes after a courtship of more than eight years and the culmination of a fairytale romance of which every girl dreams. When Prince William weds his sweetheart Catherine Middleton on April 29 she will take the place in the world's hearts left by the tragic death of his mother Diana, Princess of Wales.

The union will bring an unparalleled feel good factor to the country and a huge boost to the image of the royal family. The eyes of the world will once again be following a young Prince and Princess full of love for each other and on an adventure the like of which most people can only dream.

Their names will drift into the lexicon of terms for the perfect romantic match. As families tighten their belts across the globe the sight of two sweethearts showing their love for each other could have even the biggest sceptic sharing in a positive opinion of the couple.

Theirs is a classic tale of love against the odds as each come from very different backgrounds and defy convention. They have managed not only to have a long and meaningful relationship but to marry in an age when fewer couples do.

Kate, 28, is the everywoman, the country girl, "a commoner" in Royal circles, who met her handsome Prince at university and fell in love. Her family background is unremarkable, just like hundreds of other girls.

Her mother Carole is a former air hostess and her father Michael, a former airline pilot, who now run a mail-order business selling toys and games for children's parties from a converted barn close to their home in Bucklebury, Berks.

The eldest of three children, Kate was educated at the exclusive Marlborough College in Wiltshire, where she was described as level-headed, popular and talented. He is the dashing future king of England with a tragic past who attended St Andrews University in Scotland to escape the prying eyes of the world and discovered his Cinderella.

His story is a tragic tale of his parents publically broken marriage and subsequent death of his mother in a car accident. Yet he has overcome all and avoided the pitfalls of the privileged to find a woman who he wants to spend the rest of his life alongside.

It is a heart-warming tale that rails against the stories of easy come easy go relationships which characterise the new millennium.

When the 28-year-old Prince popped the question in Kenya, in October 2010, using his beloved mother's dazzling oval blue 18-carat sapphire and diamond ring it was a sign of how deep his love for Kate had become.

Instead of an expensive bespoke jewel costing millions he opted for the one memento he valued most from the memory of his mother. Fittingly in the early 1980s, no single piece of jewellery represented a fairytale romance more than Princess Diana's engagement ring.

The ring, which Kate will twist on her finger like every other bride to be, signals the creation of another Princess of Wales. The marriage of Wills and Kate, as they are known popularly by the public, will be the biggest royal event since the wedding of Prince Charles and Diana in 1981.

There will be a public holiday and parties in the streets, already the Prime Minister David Cameron has admitted he slept out to watch the 1981 wedding procession. This event will be a star studded celebration expected to be attended by heads of state from around the world.

There will be an associated feel good factor expected to give a huge boost to the nation and the economy as crippling spending cuts hit home. There are details of dresses, menus, guest lists and presents to come for the couple just like any soon to be weds.

In their first television interview the pair looked calm and relaxed as they spoke of their shared sense of humour, William's failed cookery attempts, Kate's occasional frustrations and her happiness.

But what came through most was the normality of their lives, William's nerves about proposing and what she might say, her respect for his mother and also their wish to start a family.

Their candour will only bring more good wishes upon them from a public already won over by brave William, who revealed he hid the ring in his rucksack on holiday for three weeks.

The outpouring of love for William and his bride stems not only from the quiet dignity with which he has carried himself since his mother's death but also from the hope that he will secure the future of the monarchy.

William is a great advertisement for the royals, he avoids controversy, is diplomatic yet approachable and seems to have inherited many of his mother's traits. He has not allowed himself to take a free ride on his status like many of Europe's other young royals do and instead opted for a life in the military.

Once married he and his bride will live as a couple in North Wales, where the Prince will continue to serve with the Royal Air Force as a pilot of search and rescue helicopters.

There they share a secluded cottage and apparently live a modest life once behind closed doors not dissimilar to many young couples watching television and cooking for each other.

Their enduring romance has been characterised by discretion, with courtiers anxious, after their experience of watching the Prince's mother hounded to her death in a Paris underpass by paparazzi photographers that they should be left alone.

Kate first came into the public arena when the Prince while at university was pictured at a fashion show looking longingly at her as she modelled a revealing outfit. The die appears to have been cast for the future then and they were soon pictured out in public although it took until very recently for them to start appearing together at events.

Their friendship and then love was forged while studying art history, in Fife, where they shared accommodation for four years. She is credited with persuading him not to leave when he had a "wobble" at the end of his first year.

Their relationship then flourished further during weekends alone in the breathtaking scenery of the Queen's Balmoral estate. Unlike the normal celebrity relationship, their love was allowed to grow in relative privacy.

William has spoken of wanting to give Kate time to "back out" if he felt she was unable to cope but she made clear her determination to be with him. But the media silence did not last, and Kate was brought to the public's attention after she was spotted beside Prince William and Prince Charles at the Swiss ski resort of Klosters in 2005.

Kate's proud parents:
Michael and Carole

Kate moved to London shortly afterwards and despite a blip in their relationship in 2007, when they temporarily parted, the couple remained close.

So it was no surprise when after a very short time apart Kate was present when the prince received his RAF wings from his father at RAF Cranwell in April 2008 and in Windsor when he became a Knight of the Garter in June 2010.

The Queen is known to warm to her and the positive effect she has on William and his brother and father. She is viewed as a reliable person who is comfortable in the media spotlight and is deeply interested in the Prince's charitable work.

And it is there the future lies for them both, not just on commemorative plates, tea towels and mugs but in following the legacy of the Prince's mother in helping others less fortunate.

Several public divorces and stories of greed and bad behaviour have tarnished the reputation created by William's grandmother and beloved great grandmother. There have been calls for the institution to be scaled back and even scrapped yet now the future looks bright with a glorious couple getting married and the ultimate promise of a King William and Queen Kate on the throne.

Breaking the news:
All smiles during a
TV interview

13

That's our boy. Daily Mirror – Tuesday, June 22, 1982

The look on Prince Charles's face said it all.

"It's a grown-up thing to happen to you," said the proud new father.

The Prince was speaking soon after seeing the Princess of Wales give birth to a 7lb 1oz boy last night. The baby, who will be the second in line to the throne, was born at 9.03pm. Diana had been in labour for 16 hours.

An announcement said both were well and the baby "cried lustily" at birth.

The Queen, said to be "smiling at everyone", heard the news at Buckingham Palace.

News of the birth sent waves of cheers through a crowd of more than a thousand who had waited outside St Mary's Hospital, Paddington, since early morning.

They waved Union Jacks, sang, "it's a boy, it's a boy" and shouted: "We want Charlie". After continuous chants, the Prince stepped out of the hospital to greet the well-wishers. He had a lipstick smear on his right cheek and seemed slightly dazed.

Asked what the baby was to be called, he replied only: "We had a bit of an argument about it." Then he added: "I can't say who he looks like. It's too early to say. He's blond, sort of fairish, with blue eyes."

Almost deafened by the roar of the crowd, he said: "Can't you please quieten them down? My wife is trying to sleep."

Some of the crowd started yelling: "Give us another one." Charles replied: "Bloody hell – give us a chance."

Bundle of joy: Proud parents Diana and Charles leaving hospital with baby William

The Royal Wedding Album
CHILDHOOD MEMORIES

Special day: The Princess of Wales with Prince William at his Christening

Growing fast:
William in New Zealand,
April 1983

Toddling around: Kensington Palace, December 1983

Right: Prince William made his first public speech on Tuesday, June 12, 1984 at a photocall commemorating his second birthday! William measured in on the day at three feet tall and weighed two stone – both average for his age

16

Birthday boy:
William aged two

17

18

First day at school: William looks happy to be dropped off with Diana at his side

William and Harry return to school
after the Easter holidays in 1990

19

Bye bye mum: Being met by school
headmistress, Miss Frederika

Prince William on his
way to school

Looking the part: Prince William
in fancy dress at school, January 1987

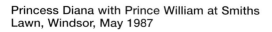

Princess Diana with Prince William at Smiths
Lawn, Windsor, May 1987

Racing ahead: Prince William in the cockpit
of a Formula One Benetton car at Silverstone

Young man: Arriving for his first day at Eton College

Fun day out: William sees Stig of The Dump at Richmond Theatre in 1989

PRINCE WILLIAM AT TWENTY ONE

WILLIAM AS HE APPROACHES 21: HIS MOST REVEALING INTERVIEW
DAILY MIRROR – FRIDAY, MAY 30, 2003

PRINCE WILLIAM has spoken for the first time about the moment he nearly quit university. He admits he was so overwhelmed by his first year at St Andrews that he considered not going back. And he says he was eventually persuaded to stay on after a long heart-to-heart with Prince Charles.

In an interview to mark his 21st birthday next month, William explained his early misgivings. "It's new surroundings, new scenery, and I wasn't quite sure what to expect," he said. "It's the same as starting school really and I was a little uneasy."

He revealed that Charles told him he, too, had been nervous when he first went to Gordonstoun. "My father was very understanding," said Wills. "He was very good and in the end we both realised – I definitely realised – that I had to come back."

William says it was the right decision – and he now reckons university life is "brilliant". He revealed he'd even had a go at Scottish dancing. "It's great – but I'm hopeless at it," he laughed. "I do throw my arms dangerously around and girls fly across the dance floor!" William said part of his early problem was being the most famous student at the university. But he added: "People relaxed very quickly about it and the students have been so good towards me." They let me get on with things to start with and realised that no one could settle in just like that. So they gave me a bit of space and it's worked – and I hope for them as well. It's been brilliant. I don't think I was homesick, I was more daunted."

William confessed that underneath his apparently calm exterior he can sometimes be very nervous. "Little do you know," he joked.

He agreed to give the interview – just hours after finishing an end-of term exam – as a thank-you to the media for respecting his privacy. It was conducted on behalf of all national newspapers by Peter Archer of the Press Association.

Archer described William – now midway through his four-year MA degree course – as "relaxed and unassuming" as they chatted in a university meeting room usually used for Bible studies or for counselling students.

William said most people in the town barely give him a second glance now – and that's the way he likes it. "They just treat me like everyone else – it's really nice," he said. "I'm able to lead a near-normal life. The people of St Andrews and the students have been so supportive. Basically, I feel very comfortable."

He went on: "It's quite interesting because when I'm walking around, you see people in their own little worlds – and I always go into my own little world as well. You don't really notice what's going on around you. But the local residents, I'm sure, know what I do. They know the routes I take. Yet, very kindly, they just get on with their lives." Tourists visiting St Andrews are a different story. "I think it's probably a little harder for tourists and foreigners who come up here to try and pretend, as it were, that they haven't seen me," he says. "That's a bit tricky sometimes, but

everyone else is very relaxed. I hope I'm not a tourist attraction – I'm sure they come here really because St Andrews is just amazing, a beautiful place."

William arrived at the university in September 2001. "I was very nervous about what was going to happen because I'd heard lots of stories," he recalled. "The exams are the tricky bit but once they're out of the way, the rest is a lot of fun.

"There's an immense amount of reading and lectures take up quite a lot of your time. But I love being at St Andrews. It has a community feel and the people here are brilliant." Asked how he was treated by the university dons, he joked: "Once they stopped trying to spy me at lectures then it was all very relaxed,"

William said he would recommend a university education – a message that has clearly been passed on to younger brother Harry, who leaves Eton College next month. "I would recommend it as long as you decide to work," he added. "You have a lot of time to yourself and you have to keep busy."

William admitted the last two years had flown by. "Living in a hall of residence for the first year was a good move," he said. "That's where I met most of my friends. It was a lot of fun.

"I think if you had gone into a house straight away with people you didn't really know, it would have been very awkward and you would have been isolated."

Despite having a share of at least £17million left by his mother and being a member of one of Britain's richest families, William appeared sympathetic to the plight of hard-up students. But, because of his position, he has steered clear of becoming actively involved in student politics. He said: "I do listen to what goes on and I know there are some students who have just cause to be worried about loans and fees."

William said he has no definite plans for when he leaves university but denied reports that he will go to America. He has revealed a taste for cider, R&B music – and food shopping in his local supermarket. But as far as his dad is concerned, William's dedication to his studies at St Andrews University still leaves a lot to be desired. "My father thinks I'm the laziest person on earth," William joked. The student Prince has a reputation in his family for liking to sleep late in the morning and has his leg pulled about it by the Prince of Wales. "But surprisingly, I do actually get up. I've had nine o'clock lectures all this year," William insisted.

At university the Prince is known as plain Will or William. Wearing a baggy jumper with holes under the arm and on the right elbow, he confirmed he is moving house – to a farm cottage on the outskirts of town – for the next academic year. And he talked about his comical attempts at traditional Scottish dancing, admitted he was "absolutely useless" at cooking and "the biggest idiot" at painting on canvas. He even described the inside of his bedroom.

23

24

Away from it all: Prince William (centre) carrying a surfboard as he walks with two friends along the shoreline at St Andrews in Scotland, in the last year of his four-year university course. Opposite, above: At his graduation ceremony. William got a 2:1 in geography. Kate graduated in the same ceremony

But during the interview, as he sipped mineral water, all he was really thinking about was the prospect of a boozy night on the town to celebrate the last of his end-of-term exams.

"Everybody thinks I drink beer but I actually like cider," William declared.

The Prince spent his first year living in St Salvator's Hall, before moving into a shared £100-a-week house with three other students, including close friend Kate Middleton. But he said he has missed the space and freedom the country allows him. He plans to decamp to a farm cottage on the outskirts of the town, which will give him the privacy to entertain friends discreetly and indulge his love of countryside pursuits.

"Most people tend to move houses and that was always my intention. In my third year I have fewer lectures and have to spend less time in the university and so I thought: how about moving somewhere different? I do think I'm a country boy at heart. I love the buzz of towns and going out with friends and sitting with them drinking and whatever – it's fun. But, at the same time, I like space and freedom. I like cinemas, bars, restaurants and lots of sport – on the beach, playing quick golf – just making use of everything up here. There's quite a lot to do here."

Weekends are sometimes spent in nearby Edinburgh with friends. He said: "There are so many people here from different backgrounds. My friends are made up of all sorts of different people – I've got lots of Scottish friends, American friends and English friends. I don't deliberately select my friends because of their background. If I enjoy someone's company, then that's all that counts. I have many different friends who aren't from the same background as me and we get on really well – it's brilliant."

And William's friends may admire his attempts at Scottish dancing.

"I love Scottish dancing – it's great. I'm hopeless at it but I do enjoy it. I usually make a complete muck-up of the Dashing White Sergeant.

"I do throw my arms dangerously around and girls fly across the dance floor. Scottish culture is very diverse and definitely very different." He admitted, however, he draws a line at wearing a kilt in public. "I haven't got into it yet – it's a bit draughty," he laughed, "I have worn a kilt in private and I'm not saying I never will wear one in public." Other royal men, notably the Prince of Wales, regularly wear the Lord of the Isles tartan when in the Highlands.

William's lodgings for the past year are typical of most students. He said: "I'm not particularly fussy about my room. I just want it to be somewhere I can relax – my own space.

"But I do have drapes up in my room. I like that because it makes it more cosy. I've got to have a stereo – got to have music – I love my music."

Friends say William likes R&B and plays it loud. "Then there's the odd book, just to make it look like I'm working – and a comfortable bed."

William admits to a bad habit: "I do a lot of shopping – I enjoy the shopping, actually. I get very carried away, you know, just food shopping. I buy lots of things and then go back to the house and see the fridge is full of all the stuff I've just bought. I cook quite regularly for them (housemates) and they cook for me.

"Although we haven't had a house supper for quite a while because everyone's been doing exams. I've got some very good cooks in my house but I'm absolutely useless as my paella experience, which was filmed at Eton a while ago, proved."

He added: "We tend to have chicken, curries and pasta," he said. "But we go out to eat quite a lot – whatever we feel like at the time."

Household chores were shared and, at first, organised with lists of duties. "We all get on very well and started off having rotas but, of course, it just broke down into complete chaos. Usually, you just fend for yourself."

Prince William, a student of art history, praised his father's talent as a painter but confessed he had not inherited his ability. He said: "I did do a couple of drawings at Eton which were put on display. Teachers thought they were examples of modern art but in fact I was just trying to paint a house!" But of his dad, William said: "He's brilliant. He's very modest about it and he's always criticising his own work. But I do actually really like it. His subject matter is particularly sensitive – he paints mostly landscapes – and his paintings make a lot of money for charity."

William said his younger brother, Prince Harry, is a talented artist.

"Harry can paint but I can't. He has our father's talent while I, on the other hand, am about the biggest idiot on a piece of canvas. I like traditional art. I love the Renaissance. It's fascinating because it's just so detailed and precise. I did my A-level history of art dissertation on Leonardo da Vinci's drawings which, of course, are in the Royal Collection, so I was very lucky."

William did admit he harbours a fear that other students do not have. "I'm slightly concerned that when I leave here the media could have a tendency to look into what I've done," he said. "I'm just hoping that they won't go round trying to do that. If they do, I think the people of St Andrews will be my greatest allies."

It could be that William just wants to protect his privacy. Then again, maybe, like any student, he doesn't quite want his father to know everything he's been doing at university.

26

A ROYAL
LOVE STORY

AS TOLD THROUGH THE MIRROR HEADLINES . . .

DAILY MIRROR, *Wednesday, March 2, 2005* PAGE 3

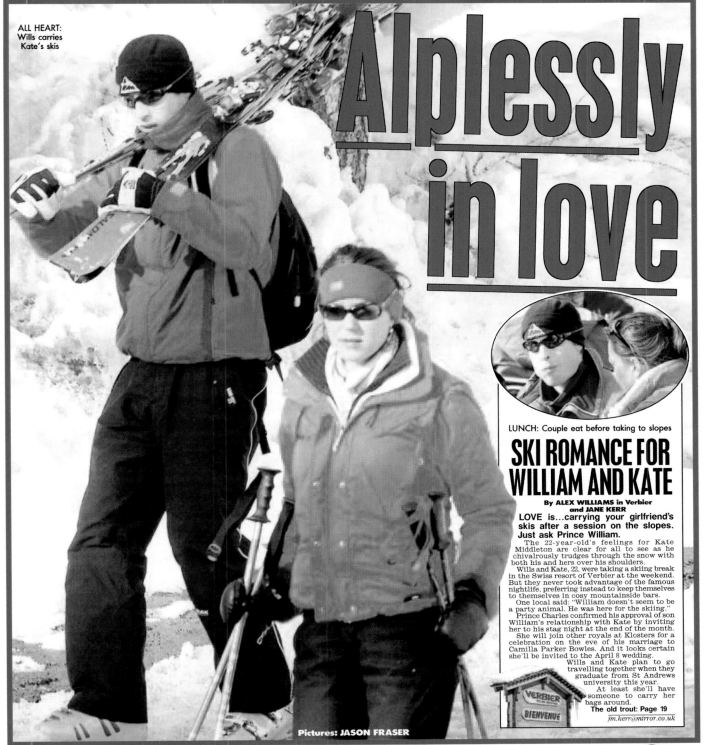

ALL HEART: Wills carries Kate's skis

Alplessly in love

LUNCH: Couple eat before taking to slopes

SKI ROMANCE FOR WILLIAM AND KATE

By ALEX WILLIAMS in Verbier and JANE KERR

LOVE is...carrying your girlfriend's skis after a session on the slopes. Just ask Prince William.

The 22-year-old's feelings for Kate Middleton are clear for all to see as he chivalrously trudges through the snow with both his and hers over his shoulders.

Wills and Kate, 22, were taking a skiing break in the Swiss resort of Verbier at the weekend. But they never took advantage of the famous nightlife, preferring instead to keep themselves to themselves in cosy mountainside bars.

One local said: "William doesn't seem to be a party animal. He was here for the skiing."

Prince Charles confirmed his approval of son William's relationship with Kate by inviting her to his stag night at the end of the month.

She will join other royals at Klosters for a celebration on the eve of his marriage to Camilla Parker Bowles. And it looks certain she'll be invited to the April 8 wedding.

Wills and Kate plan to go travelling together when they graduate from St Andrews university this year.

At least she'll have someone to carry her bags around.

The old trout: Page 19

jm.kerr@mirror.co.uk

Pictures: JASON FRASER

WOGAN: BBC TV STRICTLY CLUELESS

By FIONA CUMMINS

RADIO 2 star Terry Wogan has made a blistering attack on BBC TV bosses.

He slammed them for "beating an idea to death" with endless makeover and reality shows – and not knowing what do with stars such as Graham Norton.

The comedian, who has hardly been seen on the BBC since signing up for £3.5million last year, is due to host Strictly Come Dancing spin-off Strictly Dance Fever on BBC1 this year. But Wogan, 66, told Heat magazine: "Look what they've done with Strictly Come Dancing. It's a big hit – great.

"So then we have Strictly Come Dancing the ice skating version. Then you have Graham Norton doing one of them because they don't know what else to do with him."

A BBC spokesman said Terry was "entitled to his opinion".

CRITICISM: Terry

DAILY MIRROR, *Thursday, March 31, 2005*   PAGE 3

PRINCE TAKES KATE ON ROYAL HOL

TENDER: William and Kate yesterday

28

By JANE KERR, Royal Reporter

PRINCE William gazes tenderly at sweetheart Kate Middleton yesterday – and shows how much in love they are.

The couple shared a quiet moment during a ski holiday with Prince Charles, Prince Harry and around 30 of the royals' friends.

Kate's presence in Klosters – her second visit with the family to the Swiss resort – shows how serious Wills, 22, is about her.

It also indicates she has the royal seal of approval. At one stage the pretty student, 21, stifled a giggle as she sat next to Charles at a restaurant table.

Kate – who shares a cottage with William at St Andrews University in Fife – also joked with Harry, 21, as the group headed for their first day on the slopes.

Others on the trip include Tara Palmer-Tomkinson, her dad Charles, sister Santa and Santa's author husband Simon Sebag-Montefiore.

Harry's mate Guy Pelly, once wrongly accused of introducing him to cannabis, is also there.

And the group made a royal ascent up the slopes yesterday in a ski-lift called the Prince of

SKIING: Harry in gear

Head over Wills in love

Wales, its name emblazoned on the side. The holiday will also feature a stag night dinner to mark Charles's April 8 wedding to Camilla Parker Bowles.

The vacation highlights Charles's relaxed attitude to his sons' girlfriends. He has even offered to aid Harry's

Zimbabwean sweetheart Chelsy Davy, 19, in coping with the media spotlight.

A royal source revealed yesterday: "Harry has asked him for advice on how to protect Chelsy. The prince's media advisers are doing what they can to help."

jm.kerr@mirror.co.uk

GIGGLE: Kate with Prince Charles

Pictures: ELIOT PRESS/JASON FRASER

Church: I'll deck Gav if he flirts

CHARLOTTE Church says she will deck lover Gavin Henson if he flirts with "sluts" who try to pick him up.

Charlotte, 19, says she hates it when the rugby star is targeted by women.

She said: "I get jealous when girls are overly flirtatious. I just find it blatantly rude if I'm stood there and they can see I'm with my fella.

"Then I might just say a few quiet words – something like, 'Back off'.

"But what annoys me more is if a bloke flirts back. It is blatant disrespect – if Gavin did that I would flatten him."

She sent a text message to Gavin, 23, while she was away promoting her new record after he admitted being surrounded by female admirers in a bar.

It said: "You're not making me feel good with all these sluts in my man's company."

Drink nearly ruined my life

Says QUO'S RICK PARFITT

Pages 24 & 25

Great War vet gunner dies at 108

FIRST World War veteran machine gunner George Rice has died, aged 108.

His death, from pneumonia after a fall, leaves alive just nine of the 5.4million British soldiers who fought the Germans.

Mr Rice signed up at 17 and served with the Duke of Wellington regiment. In one skirmish alone he killed eight Germans with a single burst of fire.

He said later : "It was just my job as a soldier. I don't know what you felt.

"You were there to fight the enemy. Feelings didn't come into it in that sense, frightening or otherwise."

Mr Rice, who was born in Newcastle upon Tyne lived his last few years in Birmingham after his wife died, aged 93.

Dennis Goodman of the World War One Veterans' Association said: "It's sad but he was full of life – a very jovial man."

WILLS ♥ KATE: IT'S OFFICIAL

THRONE ROOM: William and Kate leave club apart
Picture: XPOSURE

Prince and his girlfriend to 'come out' on first public date

PROTOCOL: The Queen

EXCLUSIVE

By NATHAN YATES
Royal Correspondent

PRINCE William and his girlfriend Kate Middleton are to step out together at an official public occasion for the first time.

They are planning to "come out" as a couple after becoming frustrated with the secrecy surrounding their relationship.

The move will finally make Kate and William an accepted item in the royal household and is the next step on the way to a possible engagement.

A Clarence House insider said last night: "William has grown weary of the cloak-and-dagger operation surrounding his girlfriend.

"He wants her to be acknowledged as an important part of his life. He is planning to appear in public with her as

ANNE SNUB TO CHERIE

PRINCESS Anne delivered a withering put-down to Cherie Blair, it was claimed yesterday.

The PM's wife is said to have told the princess: "Do call me Cherie."

Anne replied: "Let's stick to Mrs Blair."

Cherie reportedly branded the Queen's daughter a "bitch" after the princess blanked her and is believed to dislike the royals.

Journalist Paul Scott also alleges in a book, Cherie gives Tony's toe-nail clippings to a new age guru. Downing Street said Scott's claims are "totally untrue".

a statement of intent and commitment to her. He has lost patience with his girlfriend being kept hidden, as if the family is ashamed of her.

"William is very much in love with Kate and he does not understand why this should be a secret."

Aides so far refuse to admit publicly that 23-year-old Kate is even William's girlfriend. But the prince – also 23 – wants her to be given the royal stamp of approval and has introduced her to the Queen.

One possible outing would be a visit to the charity Centrepoint, of which William was recently made patron.

A joint appearance meeting London's homeless would make William and Kate appear in a sympathetic role.

The insider added: "It is a question of choosing the right kind of occasion.

"It would preferably be a fairly low-key event where the couple can be themselves.

● PRINCE Charles is giving a rare interview on US news show 60 minutes to pave the way for his November tour to America with Camilla.

nathan.yates@mirror.co.uk

29

ANOTHER ROYAL EXCLUSIVE

WILLIAM: Will you marry me?

ROMANCE: Kate stars in a school play at 13

KATE: Yes, it's all I've ever longed for. Yes, oh yes, dear William..

DRAMA: Leading man William gets on one knee. Below: Kate and Wills

By DAMIEN FLETCHER

TENDERLY kissing her hand, William gazes lovingly into Kate's eyes before dropping down on one knee and pleading: "Will you marry me?"

Hearts melt as she gushes back to her Prince Charming: "Yes – it's all I've ever longed for." She adds: "Yes, oh yes, dear William...Ah, to think I am loved by such a splendid gentleman."

But hold on a minute. This emotional scene isn't really all it appears.

And as far as we know Prince William hasn't actually popped the question yet to girlfriend Kate Middleton.

By an amazing coincidence, Kate uttered the prophetic words at the age of 13 – when she appeared in an end of term play.

The royal sweetheart – now 25 – was starring in a Victorian melodrama at St Andrews prep school in the village of Buckhold near Pangbourne, Reading.

Her performance brought the house down. But no one in the audience realised that one day it could be played out for real.

At one point, Kate says: "I feel there is someone waiting to take me away into a life that's full, bright and alive."

Later a fortune teller reveals she will meet a "handsome, rich gentleman". Kate asks: "Will he fall in love with me and marry me? Oh how my heart flutters!"

At the time, nobody expected her to end up dating the second in line to the throne. Sadly the play ends with Kate holding the baby – as leading man William turns out to be a cad.

Former classmate Kingsley Glover, 24, remembers Kate's performance well.

He says: "Back then, she was completely different – shy, skinny and lanky. But just look how confident and beautiful she is now."

Actor Kingsley, from Reading, admits he had a crush on her when he was a 12-year-old boarder at the school.

But he blew his chances one night when a gust of wind caught his dressing gown in the corridor. He was naked underneath and Kate and her friends giggled at his embarrassment.

Kingsley says: "It made me cringe but now I laugh when I think the girl who might be the future Queen of England has seen my crown jewels."

● WILLS, 24, officially took up his role as vice royal patron of the Welsh Rugby Union yesterday as he saw Wales beaten 9-19 by Ireland at the Millennium Stadium.

damien.fletcher@mirror.co.uk

ACTING: Young mum Kate holding baby

30

Royal wedding: Prince Harry throws
confetti over Prince William after the
wedding of Laura Parker Bowles to
Harry Lopes at St Cyriac's Church,
Lacock, Wiltshire in 2006.
Inset: Kate was also a guest

WILLS ENDED IT BY PHONE

SPLIT: William and, right, ex Kate

Revealed.. final call to Kate in a car park

EXCLUSIVE
By GRAHAM BROUGH

PRINCE William confirmed to stricken Kate Middleton that their romance was over in a dramatic mobile phone call.

Kate, 25, was hoping for a reconciliation even though she and Wills, 24, agreed at an Easter meeting their four-year affair was on the rocks.

A colleague who saw her take the call in a car park at her work in London, said: "It was clear it was William – and definitely a tiff."

FULL STORY: PAGES 4 AND 5

The strain shows: Prince William and Kate Middleton pictured at Cheltenham after it was announced that they were to split citing intense media pressure as one of the reasons for the breakdown of their relationship

THRONE APART

WILLS
The prince casts a quick glance in the direction of his ex-lover

KATE
She stares away pointedly as the pair sit apart in the Royal Box

Picture: RICHARD YOUNG

① A cheeky greeting for Chelsy

② Joker Harry keeps his girl in fits of laughter

③ Pair have a snog as the gig begins

So near, so far for royal and his ex..

By TOM LATCHEM and VANESSA ALLEN

THEY were just yards apart, but Prince William and Kate Middleton may as well have been on different planets.

Yesterday's emotional Concert For Diana was the pair's first public appearance since their split in April.

And many hoped they would cap an amazing day by rekindling the romance.

Instead, they pointedly kept their distance.

Wills, 25, sat with best friend Thomas van Straubenzee, in Wembley's Royal Box, while Kate, also 25, stuck with Zara Phillips.

The future king occasionally glanced towards his former lover, but she kept her gaze firmly on the stage.

It was a different story for William's brother Harry, 22.

He and girlfriend Chelsy Davy, 21, looked very much a couple in love.

She gave him a lingering kiss as he and Wills returned after opening the concert.

And several times she rocked with laughter after he whispered in her ear.

So there may yet be a royal wedding after all…

Voice of the Mirror: Page 10

tom.latchem@mirror.co.uk

① Heir I go.. Wills is, er, dancing

② Grooving like papa, eh, bruv?

③ Well, one is enjoying it anyway

3AM ALL THE ACTION FROM DI CONCERT ON PAGES 16&17

35

Chased 'suspect' death fall

A MAN died after he jumped over a wall and fell on to a railway line as he fled from the police.

The suspect was being followed by two officers after reports of a group of men throwing objects at a shop window.

The police were following up CCTV footage showing the vandalism at around 11pm.

A police spokeswoman said: "On seeing the officers, the man made off on foot. The officers saw him run along a road and jump over the wall towards the railway line."

The unidentified victim's body was later spotted on the tracks.

The spokeswoman said he was not hit by a train.

The coroner has been informed and a postmortem examination will be held.

Two men held in connection with the earlier incident in Ormskirk, near Liverpool, were being questioned last night.

SHELLEYVISION

Never mind poverty, Syed wanted 'to make towels history'

Shelley on Syed Ahmed - Hot Air?

IN THE MIRROR TOMORROW

Cop fan plea to Doherty

JUNKIE rocker Pete Doherty claims he was once arrested and forced to the ground by a cop – who then begged for his autograph.

The Babyshambles star reveals: "The policeman had a badge saying 'Pete Doherty is innocent'."

He tells Jonathan Ross on his BBC1 chat show on Friday: "I was gobsmacked. I was face down before being asked, 'You wouldn't sign this for my son would you, Pete?'

"I said, 'Take the cuffs off and I'll do it now'."

Doherty also insists he and girlfriend Kate Moss are not married despite recent rumours they'd wed on holiday. He jokes: "Yes, we did it for the third time, ninth time."

Pete, who invited Kate to sing with him at Glastonbury at the weekend, tells Ross they escape the crowds by taking moonlit strolls around London.

He says: "When you get away, it's more special…"

KATE MISTAKE

Did Wills run back to her after realising what he was missing?

SOLO: Kate in London last month

COUPLE: Wills and Kate together in February

EXCLUSIVE
By LAURIE HANNA

PRINCE William rekindled his romance with Kate Middleton after seeing her partying with other men, it was claimed last night.

Wills was reminded of what he was missing when he saw pictures of a happy Kate enjoying nights out on the town without him, a source said.

Since their split in April, Kate has been spotted enjoying herself in London clubs. She has had no shortage of male company, including Charles Morshead and Henry Ropner. Both denied they had any romantic link to Kate, insisting they were friends.

But the source said: "Even if they were just pals, it was difficult for William seeing Kate out, letting her hair down on the arms of other men.

"He increasingly began to realise how much he missed her company."

It was revealed yesterday that the couple have been spending time together again two months since their split in April.

At a party to mark the end of his training course, William kissed Kate passionately.

As the end of the evening approached, the prince drew Kate towards him.

One source said: "William didn't care that people were looking. At midnight, he started kissing her. They just couldn't keep their hands off each other. His friends were joking that they should get a room together.

"It wasn't long before William took Kate back to his quarters."

The party, with a Moulin Rouge theme, was at Bovington Army camp in Dorset where the prince is training.

It was said to be the latest in a series of secret dates as the couple, both 25, took tentative steps to rekindle their romance.

A senior royal source said: "The relationship may look to have run its course to those on the outside.

"But to those who know William best, it is still clear he loves her very much indeed."

A friend of Kate added: "She knows if they do get back together permanently, there'll be no turning back. There will have to be an engagement and then marriage."

Meanwhile, William has been busy with his Army career and organising a concert in memory of his mother Diana.

Kate and William's shock split is believed to have been a result of his refusal to commit to her – and because Army life was putting pressure on the relationship.

They met at St Andrews University in Edinburgh and became a couple in 2003.

Kate, who works as an accessories buyer for fashion store Jigsaw, is expected to attend the Concert for Diana at Wembley Stadium next Sunday.

On William's birthday last week he became entitled to part of the inheritance left by Diana – an income of up to £300,000 a year.

l.hanna@mirror.co.uk

WHEN Wills and Kate split up,, I wasn't convinced that their hearts were in it.

It struck me that it was a decision driven by Kate, who needed a firmer commitment.

They didn't part because they no longer cared – quite the opposite. In both cases, absence has made the heart grow fonder.

When love is flourishing at the time of parting and longing fills every hour, it doesn't just re-blossom, it bursts with passion on the pair being reunited.

People can probably remember long partings, such as when a man goes to war, that can serve to fire up the relationship and

CAN LOVE WORK A SECOND TIME?
MIRIAM STOPPARD

give it strength. This doesn't always pertain – where the love is unequal the relationship can rarely take the strain.

When love is flourishing at the time of parting and longing fills every hour, it doesn't just re-blossom, it bursts with passion on the pair being reunited.

We tend to see our partner in a rosy glow when we're parted – only to be reminded all too forcibly of their shortcomings when you get back together and reasons for parting are obvious

again. In that case, getting back together gives you closure.

One of the more cheering aspects of Wills and Kate getting together again is that there is a subtle shift of power.

Any girl who attracts the attention of the heir to the throne will be in his shadow. And though the media loved Kate, she was in a subordinate position.

She no longer is. Wills is with a woman much more comfortable as his consort than ever. Kate's glowing in the knowledge that Wills made all the running.

In this case, their trial separation will be the making of them and their mutual love.

36

Separate lives: William and Kate sit apart from each other during the charity concert in memory of Diana at Wembley Stadium in 2007

ROW: Elton stopped in car by cop

Elton rant at police who dare stop him

By EVA SIMPSON

ELTON John's meeting with Princes William and Harry was delayed after he got into a row with traffic cops outside Wembley.

A fuming Elton was heard shouting at police who stopped his car: "You must be f***ing joking."

The singer, who opened the concert with Your Song, was stopped at the barriers by officers carrying out extra security checks as he tried to drive back in to the stadium.

Sitting in his car he jabbed his finger in the direction of the police.

His driver was told he couldn't bring the car into Wembley and his celebrity passenger would have to walk.

The officer wouldn't budge leaving the 60-year-old star to stomp into the venue.

A spokesman for Sir Elton admitted that he had words with the police officer.

He said: "He had been there for 10 hours, performed a brilliant set and it's a shame that people are concentrating on one petty moment. You can't expect Elton to start walking towards Wembley as 60,000 people are leaving. That's a security risk in itself."

FUMING: Elton

A police spokeswoman said Elton's car was wrongly driven down a road outside the stadium which is for pedestrians and made it turn around.

The spokeswoman added: "We can confirm a vehicle was stopped when it left Wembley stadium following the Diana memorial concert."

But things got worse for the singer when he arrived to find the two princes holding court with rappers P Diddy and Kanye West.

An eye-witness said: "Elton took one look in the room and immediately turned round and left followed by his entourage. He clearly didn't like the idea of hanging around for anyone."

Prince William paid tribute to Elton. Wills told us: "Elton was amazing. There's no way we could have done the concert without him."

Baby joy for Ed and Soph

THE "thrilled" Earl and Countess of Wessex announced they were expecting a baby yesterday.

Sophie, 42, who suffered a life-threatening ectopic pregnancy in 2001, is three months' pregnant.

A spokesman refused to comment on whether Sophie and Edward, 43 – who have a daughter, Louise, three – used IVF.

THRILLS

Wills celebrates the rekindling of their romance

3AM at the DIANA CONCERT AFTER-SHOW PARTY

By EVA SIMPSON and SARAH TETTEH

PRINCE William and Kate Middleton stunned revellers at the Diana Concert after-show party with a passionate smooch on the dance floor.

They celebrated the rekindling of their romance with a raunchy routine that had VIP guests whooping with delight.

At one point revellers looked on open-mouthed as Wills brazenly gave Kate's boobs a loving squeeze while the couple – both 25 – rocked to R'n'B grooves.

Meanwhile Harry, 22, and girlfriend Chelsy Davy, 21, spent most of the night snogging in a corner of the makeshift club constructed specially for the night at Wembley Arena.

The amazing scenes at the £250,000 bash were a world away from the lacklustre Concert For Diana watched by 15million people on BBC1 and tens of millions more around the world. As the 60,000 stadium crowd snaked home, the princes and their guests adjourned to the nearby arena for some serious partying.

The themed bash – a cross between Cirque du Soleil and a burlesque nightclub with scantily-clad acrobats and sexy dancers performing overhead and in cages – was in contrast to the prim and proper gig.

Hugging and kissing, Wills and Kate weren't shy about letting the world know their romance is back on. They began the night in separate corners, but as the dance-floor filled – a gigantic perspex rectangle with exotic fish swimming below – the couple began to make their moves.

As the Dom Perignon, lychee martinis and other cocktails flowed, Wills and Kate both received plenty of attention from wannabe suitors. The prince made a point of chatting to pop beauty Joss Stone for 15 minutes – right in Kate's eyeline.

At one point Kate hissed to a pal: "He's ignoring me!" She then took to the dance floor, showing off her toned figure in a clingy white lace minidress.

Kate was soon surrounded by male admirers as superstar DJ Erick Morillo pumped up the volume.

One man, slightly the worse for wear, was dragged away by a royal bodyguard as he appeared to get a little too familiar with Kate. Suddenly a sweat-drenched

EXCLUSIVE

Wills made his move. Waving one hand in the air, jumping up and down to the pounding music, the future king grabbed Kate and planted a smacker on her lips.

"It was amazing," said one onlooker. "They were really going for it on the dance floor. He was holding her close from behind and cheekily cupped her breasts. It was pretty X-rated stuff. I think he realised after a bit that they were becoming the show so they went off to a quiet corner."

The reunited couple kissed passionately over two Mojito cocktails.

Not to be outdone Prince Harry, 22, kept girlfriend Chelsy Davy, 21, close at hand throughout the evening.

One reveller said: "Chelsy was so excited by the glamour of the party she just hung by the bar sampling the pink cosmopolitan cocktails and pina coladas.

"She was gazing up in amazement at the burlesque dancers performing in giant cages above them and discussing their skimpy outfits with her pals.

"Then Harry came bounding over and she squealed in delight as he lifted her off her feet and snogged her. He followed her around, made sure her glass was always full, and gave her his full attention.

"He looked like a love-sick puppy when she left just after midnight, and he retired to one of the tables with a mate."

Guests – including Take That, Ricky Gervais, Duran Duran and Bryan Ferry – were treated to raspberry vodka jellies and cappuccino vodka jellies prepared by London's Embassy Club staff.

The food was extravagant. One section offered oysters, lobster, crab, squid, scampi tempura and rye bread. Also available were roast beef and succulent lamb, crusty loaves and creamy potato salad.

And for those who were still hungry as the party began to wind down at 3am, there were bacon butties, burgers and hot-dogs.

The room was decked out in decadent white drapes and white leather sofas to create a romantic boudoir theme, with private sections where lovers could hide away.

The mood was kept sultry with 200 candles in delicate glass containers with red rose petals scattered around.

But not all the guests were happy. Rapper P Diddy went into meltdown – because he didn't have any salt for his crab salad. The multi-millionaire was heard having a John McEnroe moment at the seafood counter, shouting: "What do you mean there's no salt? You cannot be serious!"

He left 20 minutes later, disappointed that the princes had not yet arrived.

Prince Harry was sorry to have missed him. He told us later: "P Diddy is so cool. I'd love it if he could teach me a few raps."

eva.simpson@mirror.co.uk

DAILY MIRROR, Tuesday, July 3, 2007   PAGE 9

& KATE

SOULMATES: Prince Harry chats to stunning soul singer Joss Stone at the after-show party

RESPECT: Wills greets P Diddy backstage. The star wore a T-shirt bearing a portrait of Diana

THE BOYS AND THE BAND: The princes thank members of Take That for their performance

ROYAL DATE: Chelsy and, below, invite

YOUR EYENESS: Harry shares a joke with Kanye

ADORED: Diana

She was a part of us – we miss her

James Whitaker

WILLIAM and Harry may have felt the concert was the perfect way to celebrate Diana's life.

But for many of us, it highlighted just how much we have lost. Why else would 15million people have tuned in to what was frankly a lacklustre show?

For Prince Charles, and more particularly Camilla, it must have been an uncomfortable day.

For the five and a half hours that Diana's fans rocked around the world, Camilla's name hung heavily with me.

Having been critical of her for many years I had recently softened in my attitude towards her.

I am happy she makes our future king content and that his sons apparently accept her. But do they really?

How can they forgive their step-mother not giving their mother a chance as she battled her demons?

And I do not exonerate Charles. Quite simply he didn't try hard enough to look after Diana.

He encouraged Camilla to "stay in touch" at all times. She was non-negotiable in his selfish life.

So in the end we all lost Diana. Hardest hit were her two sons. It is fitting that they think about her every day. But, with respect, we all miss her.

She was a part of us too as Sunday's concert showed. Establishment figures may have found her a pain; some even described her as being "mad".

But who would most of us have as our future Queen? Just how much good this extraordinary woman achieved in her brief life was emphasised repeatedly during the concert.

We saw Diana bringing hope and love to troubled souls. She was magical with the young, the old and the so-called "dregs" of society. Of course, Camilla can never match Diana, nor does she try to.

But 10 years on, the hole in the nation's heart is still very apparent.

39

4 **M** Daily Mirror
MONDAY 23.06.2008

Chas charity furious over Ed's balloons

EXCLUSIVE by RICHARD SMITH

PRINCE Edward is to release 300 balloons at a school birthday – but has infuriated a wildlife protection charity whose president is his brother Charles.

The Marine Conservation Society said turtles, dolphins, whales and sea birds could be killed eating the balloons – which they mistake for prey.

And it claims hundreds of thousands of sea birds die each year being tangled up in litter – including balloons. Spokesman Richard Harrington said: "If people release hundreds of balloons into the air the chances are some poor creature will die as a result. By all means use the balloons – just don't let them go.

The charity has been running a "Don't Let Go" campaign for 10 years to highlight the hazard. Charles has been its president since the 1980s.

Edward, pictured above, is to release the balloons on Wednesday to mark the 300th birthday of Lucton School, Herefordshire. School bursar Paul Thorne said: "There's no way we would show disregard for wildlife."

Wills lets his heir down as he

Tetbury
12.07 am
22/6/08

▶ PARTY LOVERS
Wills and Kate show off moves

It pays to be with the right insurer

DAILY Mirror
Monday June 23, 2008
A BETTER READ GUARANTEED 40p

100 NELSON MANDELA GIG TICKETS TO BE WON
PAGES 26 & 27

EXCLUSIVE: The Dancing King (and his Queen)

MORE MAD PICTURES
PAGES 4 & 5

COST OF LIVING UP 11.6%

By RUKI SAYID

Mirror index shock increase ▶ Food up 15% ▶ Transport up 16% ▶ Utilities up 13%

INFLATION has hit 11.6 per cent, nearly four times the official figure, a shock Mirror index reveals today.

40

celebrates with Kate

DANCING KING Kate and Wills get close

IT'S HIS HIGHNESS Wills sings at top of his voice

41

ROCK 'N ROYAL

IT'S the Royal wheeee! Party-loving Prince William hurls his arms in the air and sings his heart out as he celebrates his 26th birthday on the dance floor.

Our exclusive pictures prove Wills is a Royal who really does love to let his heir down as he twirls giggling girlfriend Kate Middleton around during a boozy celebration.

He began the evening sedately enough, quietly drinking and chatting with Kate, brother Harry and a few friends at the annual Beaufort Polo Club party on Saturday.

But once the music began to blare, Wills, in blue jeans and open-necked check shirt, could not resist the temptation to grab Kate and haul her on to the dancefloor in a huge tent in the club grounds.

He put in a couple of requests with the DJ – and as a string of hits by Nickelback, Rhianna, Bon Jovi and AC/DC began playing, the Prince started to show off his fancy footwork. Sadly, Wills looked more hip-op than hip-hop.

Even the faithful Kate, 26, could not suppress her giggles as the Prince gyrated about, throwing his arms aloft in what appeared to be an impression of a helicopter attempting to land in an unusually-fierce tailwind.

But he was not going to let her get away with being a spectator – and Wills was soon whisking Kate around the floor as she laughed out loud.

When the music finally slowed, he showed a more tender side – pulling her in close for a slow dance.

One fellow dancer at the party in Tetbury, Gloucs, said: "They both seemed really happy, just larking around and letting off steam.

"Kate looked amazing in her floor-length clingy dress. William could not take his eyes off her."

Meanwhile Harry seemed unusually morose without girlfriend Chelsy Davy at his side.

While friends climbed up on tables and chairs to dance, Harry, 23, slipped out of the marquee to chat with friends before wandering off alone for a stroll.

Chelsy did arrive at the club yesterday to watch Harry and Wills play in a polo match.

Wills, currently serving in the Royal Navy, is soon to join the frigate HMS Iron Duke on duty in the North Atlantic for five weeks.

Harry is carrying out civilian duties after leaving his Iraq posting with the Household Cavalry.

Voice of the Mirror: Page 10

TAKING IT SLOW They have romantic moment

NO ARM TRYING Wills gets funky in the tent

Dancing King and
Queen: Celebrating his
26th birthday in style

42

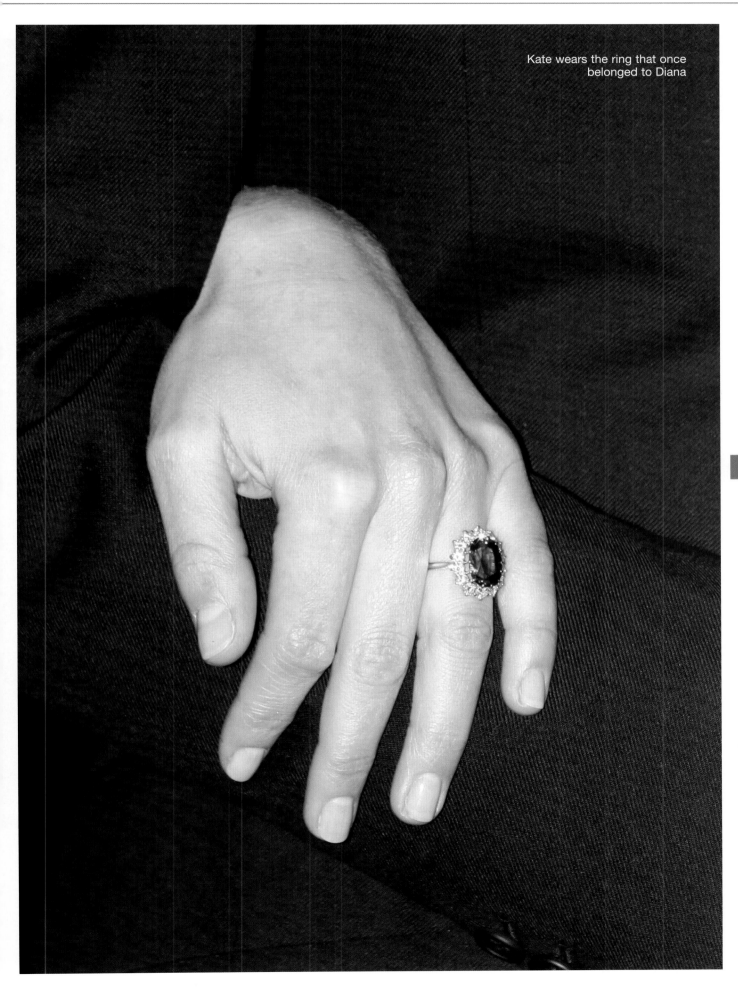

Kate wears the ring that once belonged to Diana

45

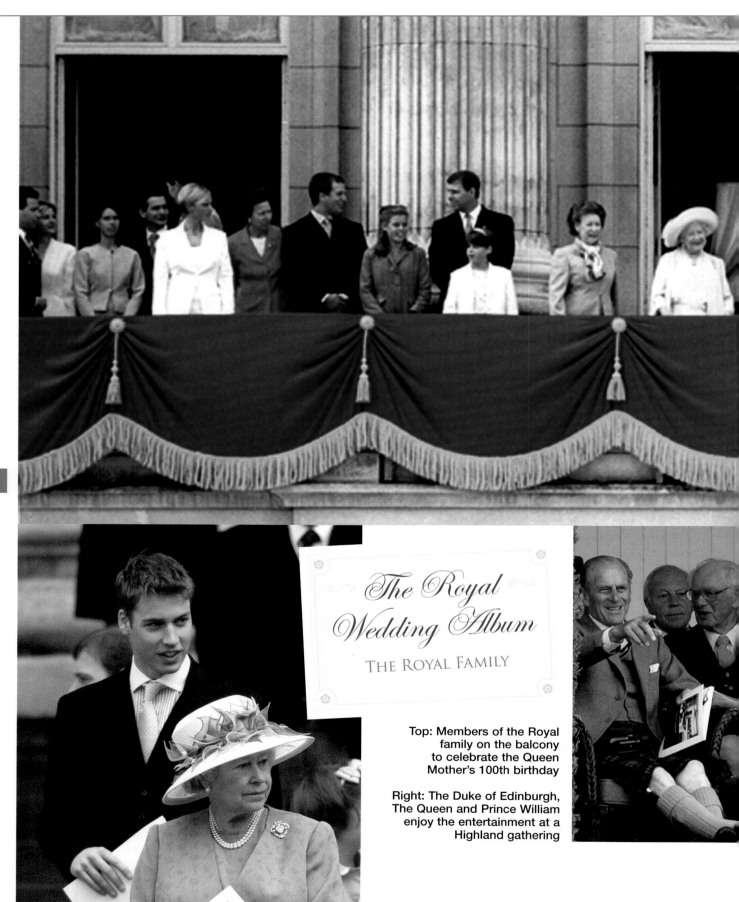

The Royal Wedding Album

THE ROYAL FAMILY

Top: Members of the Royal family on the balcony to celebrate the Queen Mother's 100th birthday

Right: The Duke of Edinburgh, The Queen and Prince William enjoy the entertainment at a Highland gathering

Right behind you Gran: Wills at St Paul's Cathedral

Iraq War memorial service:
Camilla is close at hand

Brothers in arms:
Wills and Harry

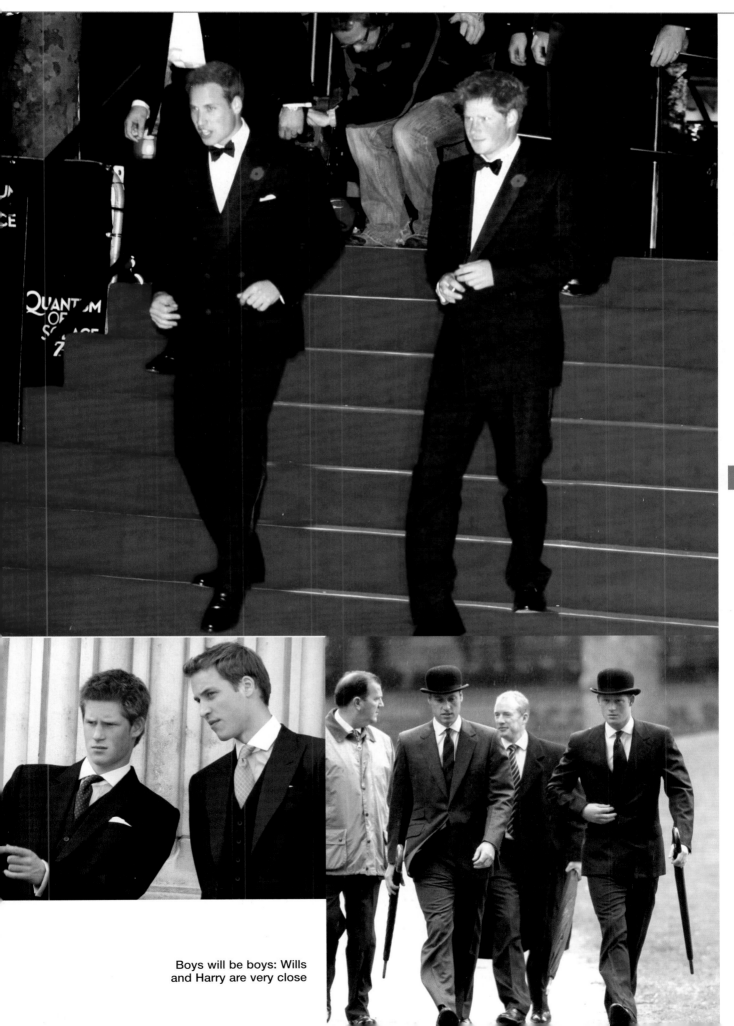

Boys will be boys: Wills and Harry are very close

Fatherly advice:
At St Andrew's University
with Prince Charles in 2001

53

Down with the kids:
Charles tries to impress
his son with his DJ skills

54

56

A nation in mourning:
The Prince of Wales and his sons view the
sea of floral tributes to their mother after
her tragic death in September 1997

64

Lest we forget:
At the Wellington War Memorial
in 2005, wearing the Queen's
Golden Jubilee Medal

Mixing with the stars: At the Princess Diana Memorial Concert in 2007 with Natasha Bedingfield, Tom Jones, Joss Stone and Prince Harry at Wembley Stadium and (left) with Duran Duran

Trying his hand: FA President Prince William shows off his ball skills during a 2009 visit to St Aidan's Primary School in Blackburn and (right) shares a joke with the pupils

Best of British: Meeting the Great British Lions team head coach Clive Woodward and his players Will Greenwood, Gordon Bulloch, Gareth Thomas and Brian O'Driscoll in 2005

A sporting life: Meeting up with the famous All Blacks; celebrating a goal (top) and consoling Cristiano Ronaldo after Manchester United's 2-0 defeat to Barcelona in the 2009 UEFA Champions League final in Rome. Below: With UEFA President Michel Platini

67

Paying tribute: Mixing with the crowds and speaking to Falklands war veteran Simon Weston at City Salute in London (above) and (below and right) visiting the Auckland Children's Hospital in New Zealand

Paying his respects: Prince William signs a book of condolence after 9/11 and (below) remembers the London bomb victims in 2005

Prince William during his time training in the Army at Bovington

Prince William (centre) being briefed by Major Andy Coulston, the Officer Commanding 20 Armoured Brigade Signal Squadron, under the watchful eye of the 20 Armoured Brigade Commander, Brigadier James Everard, and other staff officers officers of the 1st (UK) Armoured Division who he met during a visit to the Army in Sennelager, Germany

Above: Prince William shooting an Australian military F89 Minimi machine gun at Holdworthy Army Base with soldiers of the 3rd Australian Regiment

Left: With the family at Sandhurst Royal Military Academy after The Sovereign's Parade that marked the completion of his brother Prince Harry's Officer training in 2006. The Prince was one of 220 cadets passing out and receiving their commissions into the British Army

Right: Prince William talks to a member of the Afghan Army, before a remembrance day ceremony at Camp Bastion in southern Afghanistan

GETTING TO KNOW KATE:

1) Kate was born in Royal Berkshire Hospital, Reading, as the first of three children to Carole Elizabeth, an air hostess, and Michael Middleton, a flight dispatcher for British Airways. She was raised in Bucklebury, Berkshire and attended St Andrew's School in Pangbourne, followed by Marlborough College in Wiltshire.

2) She met Prince William in 2001 at University of St Andrews where they were both studying. She allegedly caught his eye as she strutted down a runway clad in a naughty see-through dress at a university fashion show.

3) Her relationship with Prince William was made public in 2004 after being pictured beside William and Prince Charles at the Swiss ski resort of Klosters.

4) In October 2005, Kate complained through her lawyer about harassment from the media, stating that she had done nothing significant to warrant such attention.

5) In November 2006, Kate happily accepted a position as an assistant accessories buyer with well-known national clothing chain Jigsaw.

6) Kate and William broke up during a holiday in the Swiss resort of Zermatt, which was revealed in April 2007.

7) Kate and Prince William insist they're "just good friends" in June 2007 as she and her family attend the Concert for Diana at Wembley Stadium. She sits two rows from William.

8) Prince William lands his helicopter in the back garden of her parents' home sparking controversy about the use of RAF equipment in April 2008.

9) In July 2008, Kate was named on Vanity Fair's international best-dressed list.

10) Formally announced by Clarence House on November 16, 2010, Kate became engaged to Prince William during a trip to Kenya.

The Prince of Wales and his bride, the Princess of Wales, make their way to Buckingham Palace in an open-top carriage after their wedding ceremony at St. Paul's Cathedral in London

Below: William with Laura Fellowes at the wedding of Prince Andrew and Sarah Ferguson (the Duke and Duchess of York) at Westminster Abbey

4 **Daily Mirror**
TUESDAY 19.10.2010
DMIST

HEIR COMES THE BRIDE

THE VENUE

THE obvious choice of wedding venue is Westminster Abbey (pictured), even though it was the scene of Diana's funeral, as well as that of the Queen Mother.

The abbey – where the Queen married in 1947 – holds around 2,000 guests.

It is believed William wants to marry in the 800-seat St George's Chapel in Windsor Castle, preferring a low-key ceremony.

But protocol demands heads of state attend so St George's is simply too small.

William is reluctant to use St Paul's Cathedral, hosting 3,500 people, because his parents married there in 1981.

A friend said: "He doesn't want it to be a re-run and endlessly compared to that wedding. He thinks similar pictures will heap more pressure on Kate."

MATES Laughs for the brothers

BEST MAN/BRIDESMAIDS

THE royals have a "supporter" rather than a best man and William's younger brother Prince Harry, 26, will undoubtedly perform the role, as Prince Andrew did for Charles in 1981.

Chief bridesmaid will most likely be Kate's younger sister Pippa, 26, helped by William's cousins Zara Phillips, 29, Prince Edward's daughter Lady Louise, six, and Lady Helen Taylor's daughter Eloise, seven.

WILLS YOU TAKE THIS WOMAN..

Couple have three summer dates in mind

EXCLUSIVE BY **RICHARD SMITH** richard.smith@mirror.co.uk

THEY have been an item for more than eight years.

Now Prince William is finally set to tie the knot with Kate Middleton – the beautiful brunette who stole his heart while they were both students.

A royal source revealed: "William realised that he couldn't keep stringing Kate along forever.

"And although he would have loved to remain single until his mid-thirties, the fact is he knows that Kate is the right girl for him."

The happy couple – both 28 – are said to be considering three possible dates in July and August next year, but will make a final decision nearer the time.

The wedding will be a perfect birthday gift for the Queen, who turns 85, and Prince Philip, who reaches 90 next year. Our source said 2012 had been ruled out because it presents such a hectic schedule.

He explained: "There are the Euro football championships in Poland and Ukraine – and William will be there as FA President.

"It's also the Queen's Diamond Jubilee and, of course, the London Olympics."

The wedding day will be declared a national holiday – with up to two million people expected to turn out to cheer the couple.

On the morning of the big day the Queen is likely to announce new titles for Wills and Kate – possibly the Duke and Duchess of Cambridge. Speculation over the wedding has been mounting for months. It was revealed at the weekend that the Royal Mint is making preparations for a coin to mark the occasion. Bookie William Hill stopped taking bets on a 2011 wedding and will now only give odds on which month.

It was also reported that senior courtiers have made overtures to Westminster Abbey about a possible ceremony in the second week of August.

William still has three years to serve as an RAF search and rescue helicopter pilot in North Wales.

He will also step up his royal duties as he sets out on the long road towards becoming King.

Our source said: "William has always said he wanted to get married when he was between 28 and 30 and so this is slap bang in the middle as he'll be 29 next year.

"A royal wedding takes months of planning. The first steps have been taken and it's all systems go, although they won't want to admit it just yet."

Many close to William – including brother Harry – believe he would change the date of a wedding if it was leaked before an official announcement.

"That's very true," said the source. "But he can't keep putting it off forever, and 2011 has now been earmarked.

"There is so much work and organisation to do that you can't just change the arrangements on a whim."

William and Kate met at St Andrews University in 2001. They have been together ever since, apart from a brief break in 2007.

Clarence House was sticking to the official line last night. A spokesman insisted: "Only Prince William and Kate Middleton know what their plans are and anything else is just speculation."

> **Wills has said he wanted to get married between 28 and 30. He'll be 29 next year**
> **ROYAL SOURCE**

THE GUEST LIST

THE congregation will include royalty from across the world, including kings and queens, and princes and princesses from the ancient European dynasties such as Sweden, Spain, Norway, Holland and Denmark.

Presidents and prime ministers will be there, although US President Barack Obama will probably be represented by wife Michelle, who has struck up a lasting rapport with the Queen.

Celebrities will include singers who have performed for the Prince's Trust, such as Phil Collins, Sir Elton John, Sir Paul McCartney and Bryan Adams.

School friends and university mates will mingle with stars such as Joan Rivers and Stephen Fry.

Kate's immediate family will sit in the front row on the other side of the church to the royals.

Dad Michael, 61, a former pilot, and mum Carole, 56, run a firm together called Party Pieces, selling children's party accessories. Kate worked for them.

As well as sister Pippa, Kate has a brother James, 24, who runs a cake business.

▲ **LEADING LADIES** Zara and Kate's sister Pippa, right, may be bridesmaids

▲ **DYNASTY** Sweden's King and Queen

▲ **ON LIST** Sir Paul

▲ **IN** Sir Elton

▲ **INVITES** Obama and Michelle

For breaking news go to: | RELATED
www.mirror.co.uk | LINKS

KATE AND WILLIAM

HAPPY COUPLE William and Kate at friend's wedding. Plans for their own are in hand

▲ **SWANKY** William lives at St James's Palace

THE MARITAL HOME

WILLIAM and Kate will continue to live at their cottage near the prince's RAF base in North Wales. The precise location is being kept a secret.

But they will also stay in London at his apartment in St James's Palace.

In the longer term, it is believed a house will be built for the couple at Harewood Park, a Duchy of Cornwall estate in Herefordshire, just an hour's drive from Prince Charles's Highgrove home.

After nine years together, the couple, both approaching 30, will want to start a family as soon as possible, producing the so-called "heir and spare" to ensure the royal succession.

81

▲ **DESIGNER** Bruce Oldfield has royal touch

THE FLOWERS

money is on rity florist an Helden, has previprovided ns for John's es. ince es may insist ccasion s for rs from beloved grove, Glos, en that has favourite, lilies.

▲ **FAVOURITE** White lilies

THE RINGS

WILLIAM inherited some of Diana's favourite jewellery, so Kate could wear a piece from her collection.

For the wedding ring itself, the royals traditionally use gold from the Clogau St David's mine and the Mawdach river in Bontddu, North West Wales.

▲ **PRICELESS** Diana's jewels may go to Kate

HAIR & MAKE-UP

KATE'S hair will be done by crimper Richard Ward, who is based in Chelsea.

He will get the best out of her rich chestnut tresses, while make-up artist Komal Singh could be called in to oversee her appearance.

Dentist Dr Didier Fillion could be asked to ensure there is no last-minute hitch with that perfect smile.

◀ **LOVELY LOCKS** Kate has her hair styled by Richard Ward

THE DRESS

KATE favours many international dress designers, but her choice would be limited to a British one as she is expected to fly the flag on her special day.

Bruce Oldfield would be an obvious candidate – he was a friend of Diana and designed wedding dresses for Queen Rania of Jordan and Jemima Khan.

London-based Jenny Packham and Amanda Wakeley are other possibilities, as well as Vivienne Westwood.

The dress is unlikely to copy Diana's 1981 gown, which, with its 25ft train, was very much in keeping with the time but would now look over the top.

Contents

Revise
A2

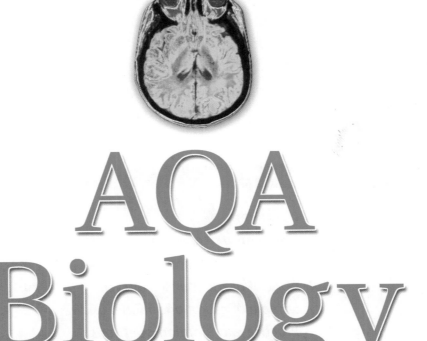

AQA
Biology

John Parker & Ian Honeysett

Contents

Specification list

The specification labels on each page refer directly to the units in the exam board specification, i.e. AQA 4.1 refers to Unit 4, section 1.

AQA Biology

UNIT	SPECIFICATION TOPIC	CHAPTER REFERENCE	STUDIED IN CLASS	REVISED	PRACTICE QUESTIONS
Unit 4	Populations	7.1, 7.2			
	ATP	1.1			
	Photosynthesis	1.2			
	Respiration	1.3			
	Energy transfer	8.1, 8.2			
	Nutrient cycles	8.3, 8.4			
	Succession	7.1, 7.2, 7.3			
	Inheritance	4.1, 4.2			
	Selection and speciation	5.2			
Unit 5	Stimuli	2.1, 2.3, 2.4, 2.5			
	Coordination	2.2, 2.5, 3.1			
	Muscles	2.4			
	Homeostasis	3.1, 3.2, 3.3			✓
	Protein synthesis	3.1, 3.4, 4.1, 5.1			
	Gene expression	4.1, 5.1			
	Gene technology	6.1			

Examination analysis

Unit 4
Examination paper (100 UMS) (75 raw marks)
6-9 short answer questions plus 2 longer questions (a short comprehension and a short structured essay)
$1\frac{1}{2}$ hours
16.67% of the total A level marks

Unit 5
Examination paper (140 UMS) (100 raw marks)
8–10 short answer questions plus 2 longer questions (a data-handling question and a synoptic essay – choice of 1 out of 2)
$2\frac{1}{4}$ hours
23.33% of the total A level marks

Unit 6
A2 Centre Assessed Unit (60 UMS) (50 raw marks)
Practical Skills Assessment (PSA) 6 marks
Investigative Skills Assignment (ISA) 44 marks
10% of the total A level marks

The AS/A2 Level Biology course

AS and A2

All Biology GCE A level courses currently studied are in two parts: AS and A2, with three separate units in each.

Some of the units are assessed by written papers, externally marked by the Awarding Body. Some units involve internal assessment of practical skills (subject to moderation).

Each Awarding Body has a common core of subject content in AS and A2. Beyond the common core material, the Awarding Bodies have included more varied content. This study guide contains the common core material and the additional material that is relevant to the AQA A2 specification.

In using this study guide, some students may have already completed the AS part of the course. Knowledge of AS is assumed in the A2 part of the course. It is therefore important to revisit the AS information when preparing for the A2 examinations.

What are the differences between AS and A2?

There are three main differences:

(i)   A2 includes the more demanding concepts. (Understanding will be easier if you have completed the AS Biology course as a 'stepping stone'.)

(ii) There is a much greater emphasis on the skills of application and analysis than in AS. (Using knowledge and understanding acquired from AS is essential.)

(iii) A2 includes a substantial amount of synoptic material. (This is the drawing together of knowledge and skills across the modules of AS and A2. Synoptic investigative tasks and questions involving concepts across the specification are included.)

How will you be tested?

Assessment units

A2 Biology comprises three units. The first two units are assessed by examinations.

The third component involves either centre assessed practical work or AQA assessed practical work. This tests practical skills. If it is marked by your teacher, the marks can be adjusted by moderators appointed by AQA.

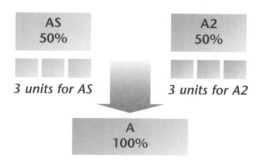

Tests are taken at two specific times of the year, January/February and June. If you are disappointed with a unit result, you can resit each unit any number of times. It can be an advantage to you to take a unit test at the earlier optional time because you can re-sit the test. The best mark from each unit will be credited and the lower marks ignored.

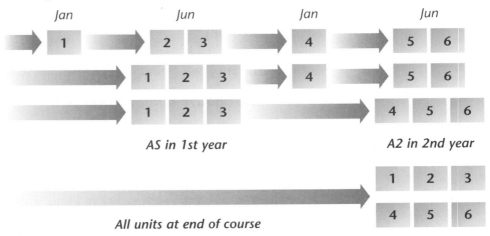

A2 and synoptic assessment

Most students who study A2 have already studied to AS Level. There are three further units to be studied.

Every A Level specification includes synoptic assessment at the end of A2. Synoptic questions draw on the ideas and concepts of earlier units, bringing them together in holistic contexts. Examiners will test your ability to inter-relate topics through the complete course from AS to A2. (See the synoptic chapter page 101).

What skills will I need?

For A2 Biology, you will be tested by assessment objectives: these are the skills and abilities that you should have acquired by studying the course. The assessment objectives are shown below.

Knowledge with understanding

- recall of facts, terminology and relationships
- understanding of principles and concepts
- drawing on existing knowledge to show understanding of the responsible use of biological applications in society
- selecting, organising and presenting information clearly and logically

Application of knowledge and understanding, and evaluation

- explaining and interpreting principles and concepts
- interpreting and translating, from one to another, data presented as continuous prose or in tables, diagrams and graphs
- carrying out relevant calculations
- applying knowledge and understanding to familiar and unfamiliar situations
- assessing the validity of biological information, experiments, inferences and statements

You must also present arguments and ideas clearly and logically, using specialist vocabulary where appropriate. Remember to balance your argument!

Investigative and practical skills

One of the three A2 units (and one of the AS units) is designed to test your investigative and practical skills. Each unit is made up of two parts:
- Practical Skills Assessment (PSA)
- Investigative Skills Assessment (ISA)

The PSA involves your teacher marking you on a scale of 0 to 6 based on your practical work throughout the course. They will be looking to see if you can...
- Follow instructions
- Select and use equipment
- Carry out practical work in an organised and safe way.

The ISA carries 44 marks and is made up of three tasks:
- First you collect some practical data.
- Then you process the data.
- This is followed by a written paper relating to the experiment.

These ISA tasks are provided by AQA and you will carry them out under controlled conditions, being supervised by your teacher. Your teacher then marks them using a mark scheme provided by AQA. A task cannot be repeated but you may be given the opportunity to do more than one type of each task. Your best mark on each will count. (There is an alternative to the ISA, which is provided and marked by AQA. Only one of these is provided each year.)

Different types of questions in A2 examinations

Questions in AS and A2 Biology are designed to assess a number of assessment objectives. For the written papers in Biology the main objectives being assessed are:

- recall of facts, terminology and inter-relationships
- understanding of principles and concepts and their social and technological applications and implications
- explanation and interpretation of principles and concepts
- interpreting information given as diagrams, photomicrographs, electron micrographs tables, data, graphs and passages
- application of knowledge and understanding to familiar and unfamiliar situations.

In order to assess these abilities and skills a number of different types of question are used.

In A2 Level Biology unit tests these include short-answer questions and structured questions requiring both short answers and more extended answers, together with free-response and open-ended questions.

Short-answer questions

A short-answer question will normally begin with a brief amount of stimulus material. This may be in the form of a diagram, data or graph. A short-answer question may begin by testing recall. Usually this is followed up by questions which test understanding. Often you will be required to analyse data. Short-answer questions normally have a space for your responses on the printed paper. The number of lines is a guide as to the number of words you will need to answer the question. The number of marks indicated on the right side of the papers shows the number of marks you can score for each question part. Here are some examples. (The answers are shown in blue).

The diagram below shows a gastric pit.

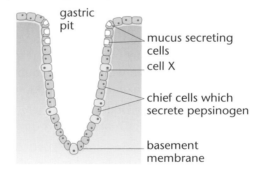

(a) (i)   Label cell X   (1)
           oxyntic cell

    (ii) What is secreted by cell X?   (1)
           hydrochloric acid

(b) (i)   Protein enters the stomach. What must take place before the
           hydrolysis of the protein begins?   (2)
           Hydrochloric acid acts on pepsinogen, to produce pepsin

    (ii) After the protein has been hydrolysed, what is produced?   (1)
           polypeptides

Structured questions

Structured questions are in several parts. The parts are usually about a common context and they often progress in difficulty as you work through each of the parts. They may start with simple recall, then test understanding of a familiar or unfamiliar situation. If the context seems unfamiliar the material will still be centred around concepts and skills from the Biology specification. (If a student can answer questions about unfamiliar situations then they display understanding rather than simple recall.)

The most difficult part of a structured question is usually at the end. Ascending in difficulty, a question allows a candidate to build in confidence. Right at the end technological and social applications of biological principles give a more demanding challenge. Most of the questions in this book are structured questions. This is the main type of question used in the assessment of both AS and A2 Biology.

The questions set at A2 Level are generally more difficult than those experienced at AS Level. A2 includes a number of higher-level concepts, so can be expected to be more difficult. The key advice given by this author is:

- Give your answers in greater detail:

  Example: Why does blood glucose rise after a period without food?

  Answer: The hormone glucagon is produced ✗ (this is not enough for credit!)

  The hormone glucagon is produced which results in glycogen breakdown to glucose. ✓

- Look out for questions with a 'sting in the tail'. A2 structured questions are less straightforward, so look for a 'twist'.

When answering structured questions, do not feel that you have to complete one question before starting the next. Answering a part that you are sure of will build your confidence. If you run out of ideas go on to the next question. This will be more profitable than staying with a very difficult question which slows down progress. You can return at the end when you have more time.

Extended answers

In A2 and AS Biology, questions requiring more extended answers will usually form part of structured questions. They will normally appear at the end of a structured question and will typically have a value of 4 to 10 marks. Longer questions are allocated more lines, so you can use this as a guide as to how many points you need to make in your response. Often for an answer worth 10 marks the mark scheme would have around 12 to 14 creditable answers. You are awarded up to the maximum, 10 marks, in this instance.

On the Unit 5 paper, there is a synoptic essay question. This is worth 25 marks. This includes marks for the quality of communication.

Candidates are assessed on their ability to use a suitable style of writing, and organise relevant material, both logically and clearly. The use of specialist biological terms in context is also assessed. Spelling, punctuation and grammar are also taken into consideration.

Question

Explain how an action potential is transmitted across a synapse.

(Total 13 marks)

The action potential depolarises the synaptic knob. ✓ This causes the calcium channels to open. ✓ There is an inflow of Ca++ into the synaptic bouton. ✓ This causes the synaptic vesicles to move towards the pre-synaptic membrane. ✓ The vesicles then fuse with the pre-synaptic membrane. ✓ They then release the neurotransmitter into the synaptic cleft, ✓ by exocytosis. ✓ The neurotransmitter diffuses across the synaptic cleft and attaches to receptors on the post synaptic membrane. ✓ This results in a change in the permeability of post-synaptic membrane/Na+ gates opened. ✓ Sodium ions enter the post synaptic cell. ✓ This will depolarise the membrane ✓ and an action potential is initiated. ✓ Cholinesterase is released into the cleft to remove the transmitter. ✓

Communication mark ✓

Remember that mark schemes for extended questions often exceed the question total, but you can only be awarded credit up to the maximum. In response to this question the candidate would be awarded the maximum of 13 marks which included one communication mark. The candidate gave one more creditable response which was on the mark scheme, but had already scored a maximum. Try to give more detail in your answers to longer questions. This is the key to A2 success.

Stretch and Challenge

Stretch and Challenge is a concept that is applied to the structured questions in Unit 4 and 5 of the exam papers in A2. In principle, it means that sub-questions become progressively harder so as to challenge more able students and help differentiate between A and A* students.

Stretch and Challenge questions are designed to test a variety of different skills and your understanding of the material. They are likely to test your ability to make appropriate connections between different areas and apply your knowledge in unfamiliar contexts (as opposed to basic recall).

Exam technique

A2 builds from the skills and concepts acquired during the AS course. It will help you cope as the A2 concepts ascend in difficulty. The chapters explain the ideas in small steps so that understanding takes place gradually. The final aim, of complete understanding of major topics, is more likely.

Can I use the AS Biology Study Guide for A2?

YES! This will be particularly useful in answering synoptic questions that require direct knowledge of the AS topics.

What are examiners looking for?

Whatever type of question you are answering, it is important to respond in a suitable way. Examiners use instructions to help you to decide the length and depth of your answer. The most common words used are given below, together with a brief description of what each word is asking for.

Define

This requires a formal statement. Some definitions are easy to recall.

Define the term transport.

This is the movement of molecules from where they are in lower concentration to where they are in higher concentration. The process requires energy.

Other definitions are more complex. Where you have problems it is helpful to give an example.

Define the term endemic.

This means that a disease is found regularly in a group of people, district or country.

Use of an example clarifies the meaning. Indicating that malaria is invariably found everywhere in a country confirms understanding.

Explain

This requires a reason. The amount of detail needed is shown by the number of marks allocated.

Explain the difference between resolution and magnification.

Resolution is the ability to be able to distinguish between two points whereas magnification is the number of times an image is bigger than an object itself.

State

This requires a brief answer without any reason.

State one role of blood plasma in a mammal.

Transport of hormones to their target organs.

List

This requires a sequence of points with no explanation.

List the abiotic factors which can affect the rate of photosynthesis in pondweed.

carbon dioxide concentration; amount of light; temperature; pH of water

Describe

This requires a piece of prose which gives key points. Diagrams should be used where possible.

Describe the nervous control of heart rate.

The medulla oblongata ✓ of the brain connects to the sino-atrial node in the right atrium, wall ✓ via the vagus nerve and the sympathetic nerve ✓ the sympathetic nerve speeds up the rate ✓ the vagus nerve slows it down.✓

Discuss

This requires points both for and against, together with a criticism of each point. (**Compare** is a similar command word).

Discuss the advantages and disadvantages of using systemic insecticides in agriculture.

Advantages are that the insecticides kill the pests which reduce yield ✓ they enter the sap of the plants so insects which consume sap die ✓ the insecticide lasts longer than a contact insecticide, 2 weeks is not uncommon ✓

Disadvantages are that insecticide may remain in the product and harm a consumer e.g. humans ✓ it may destroy organisms other than the target ✓ no insecticide is 100% effective and develops resistant pests. ✓

Suggest

This means that there is no single correct answer. Often you are given an unfamiliar situation to analyse. The examiners hope for logical deductions from the data given and that, usually, you apply your knowledge of biological concepts and principles.

The graph shows that the population of lynx decreased in 1980. Suggest reasons for this.

Weather conditions prevented plant growth ✓ so the snowshoe hares could not get enough food and their population remained low ✓ so the lynx did not have enough hares (prey) to predate upon. ✓ The lynx could have had a disease which reduced numbers. ✓

Calculate

This requires that you work out a numerical answer. Remember to give the units and to show your working, marks are usually available for a partially correct answer. If you work everything out in stages write down the sequence. Otherwise if you merely give the answer and it is wrong, then the working marks are not available to you.

Calculate the Rf value of spot X. (X is 25 mm from start and solvent front is 100 mm)

$$Rf = \frac{\text{distance moved by spot}}{\text{distance moved by the solvent front}}$$

$$= \frac{25 \text{ mm}}{100 \text{ mm}} = 0.25$$

Outline

This requires that you give only the main points. The marks allocated will guide you on the number of points which you need to make.

Outline the use of restriction endonuclease in genetic engineering.

The enzyme is used to cut the DNA of the donor cell. ✓

It cuts the DNA up like this $\begin{array}{l} ATGCCGAT \\ TACGGCTA \end{array} = \begin{array}{l} AT \\ TACGGC \end{array} + \begin{array}{l} GCCGAT \\ TA \end{array}$ ✓

The DNA in a bacterial plasmid is cut with the same restriction endonuclease. ✓

The donor DNA will fit onto the sticky ends of the broken plasmid. ✓

If a question does not seem to make sense, you may have misread it. Read it again!

Some dos and don'ts

Dos

Do *answer the question*

No credit can be given for good Biology that is irrelevant to the question.

Do *use the mark allocation to guide how much you write*

Two marks are awarded for two valid points – writing more will rarely gain more credit and could mean wasted time or even contradicting earlier valid points.

Do *use diagrams, equations and tables in your responses*

Even in 'essay-style' questions, these offer an excellent way of communicating Biology.

Do *write legibly*

An examiner cannot give marks if the answer cannot be read.

Do *write using correct spelling and grammar. Structure longer essays carefully*

Marks are now awarded for the quality of your language in exams.

Don'ts

Don't *fill up any blank space on a paper*

In structured questions, the number of dotted lines should guide the length of your answer.

If you write too much, you waste time and may not finish the exam paper. You also risk contradicting yourself.

Don't *write out the question again*

This wastes time. The marks are for the answer!

Don't *contradict yourself*

The examiner cannot be expected to choose which answer is intended. You could lose a hard-earned mark.

Don't *spend too much time on a part that you find difficult*

You may not have enough time to complete the exam. You can always return to a difficult calculation if you have time at the end of the exam.

What grade do you want?

Everyone would like to improve their grades but you will only manage this with a lot of hard work and determination. You should have a fair idea of your natural ability and likely grade in Biology and the hints below offer advice on improving that grade.

For a Grade A

You will need to be a very good all-rounder.

- You must go into every exam knowing the work extremely well.
- You must be able to apply your knowledge to new, unfamiliar situations.
- You need to have practised many, many exam questions so that you are ready for the type of question that will appear.

The exams test all areas of the syllabus and any weaknesses in your Biology will be found out. There must be no holes in your knowledge and understanding. For a Grade A, you must be competent in all areas.

For a Grade C

You must have a reasonable grasp of Biology but you may have weaknesses in several areas and you will be unsure of some of the reasons for the Biology.

- Many Grade C candidates are just as good at answering questions as the Grade A students but holes and weaknesses often show up in just some topics.
- To improve, you will need to master your weaknesses and you must prepare thoroughly for the exam. You must become a better all-rounder.

For a Grade E

You cannot afford to miss the easy marks. Even if you find Biology difficult to understand and would be happy with a Grade E, there are plenty of questions in which you can gain marks.

- You must memorise all definitions.
- You must practise exam questions to give yourself confidence that you do know some Biology. In exams, answer the parts of questions that you know first. You must not waste time on the difficult parts. You can always go back to these later.
- The areas of Biology that you find most difficult are going to be hard to score on in exams. Even in the difficult questions, there are still marks to be gained. Show your working in calculations because credit is given for a sound method. You can always gain some marks if you get part of the way towards the solution.

What marks do you need?

The table below shows how your average mark is transferred into a grade.

average	80%	70%	60%	50%	40%
grade	A	B	C	D	E

The A* grade

To achieve an A* grade, you will need to achieve a…

- grade A overall (80% or more on uniform mark scale) for the whole A level qualification.
- grade A* (90% or more on the uniform mark scale) across your A2 units.

A* grades are awarded for the A level qualification only and not for the AS qualification or individual units.

15

Four steps to successful revision

Step 1: Understand

- Study the topic to be learned slowly. Make sure you understand the logic or important concepts.
- Mark up the text if necessary – underline, highlight and make notes.
- Re-read each paragraph slowly.

GO TO STEP 2

Step 2: Summarise

- Now make your own revision note summary:
  What is the main idea, theme or concept to be learned?
  What are the main points? How does the logic develop?
  Ask questions: Why? How? What next?
- Use bullet points, mind maps, patterned notes.
- Link ideas with mnemonics, mind maps, crazy stories.
- Note the title and date of the revision notes
  (e.g. Biology: Homeostasis, 3rd March).
- Organise your notes carefully and keep them in a file.

This is now in **short-term memory**. You will forget 80% of it if you do not go to Step 3.
GO TO STEP 3, but first take a 10 minute break.

Step 3: Memorise

- Take 25 minute learning 'bites' with 5 minute breaks.
- After each 5 minute break test yourself:
  Cover the original revision note summary.
  Write down the main points.
  Speak out loud (record on tape).
  Tell someone else.
  Repeat many times.

The material is well on its way to **long-term memory**.
You will forget 40% if you do not do step 4. *GO TO STEP 4*

Step 4: Track/Review

- Create a Revision Diary (one A4 page per day).
- Make a revision plan for the topic, e.g. 1 day later, 1 week later, 1 month later.
- Record your revision in your Revision Diary, e.g.
  Biology: Homeostasis, 3rd March 25 minutes
  Biology: Homeostasis, 5th March 15 minutes
  Biology: Homeostasis, 3rd April 15 minutes
  ... and then at monthly intervals.

Chapter 1
Energy for life

The following topics are covered in this chapter:

- *Metabolism and ATP*
- *Respiration*
- *Autotrophic nutrition*

1.1 Metabolism and ATP

After studying this section you should be able to:

- *understand the principles of metabolic pathways*
- *understand the importance of ATP*

LEARNING SUMMARY

Metabolic pathways

AQA 4.2

Inside a living organism there are many chemical reactions occurring at the same time. They may be occurring in the same place, in different parts of the cell or in different cells. Each reaction is controlled by a different enzyme.

> **KEY POINT**
>
> All the chemical reactions occurring in an organism are called **metabolism**.

Often a number of chemical reactions are linked together. The product of one reaction acts as the substrate for the next reaction. This is called a **metabolic pathway** and each of the chemicals in the pathway are called **intermediates**.

> A is the substrate for this pathway, B, C and D are intermediates and E is the product. The enzymes a, b, c and d each control a different step.

$$A \xrightarrow{a} B \xrightarrow{b} C \xrightarrow{c} D \xrightarrow{d} E$$

Metabolic reactions can be classed as one of two types. Reactions that break down complex molecules are called **catabolic reactions** or catabolism. Other reactions build up complex molecules from simple molecules. They are **anabolic reactions** or anabolism.

Anabolic reactions tend to require energy, whereas catabolic reactions release energy. The link between these two types of reactions is a molecule called **ATP**.

Adenosine triphosphate (ATP)

The breakdown of many organic molecules can release large amounts of energy. Similarly, making complex molecules such as proteins requires energy. These reactions must be coupled together. This is achieved by using **adenosine triphosphate (ATP)** molecules.

ATP is a **phosphorylated nucleotide**. (Recall the structure of DNA which consists of nucleotides.) Each nucleotide consists of an organic base, ribose sugar and phosphate group. ATP is a nucleotide with two extra phosphate groups. This is the reason for the term 'phosphorylated nucleotide'.

adenine —— ribose —— phosphate —— phosphate —— phosphate

ATP is produced from adenosine diphosphate and a phosphate group. This requires energy. The energy is trapped in the ATP molecule. An enzyme called ATPase catalyses this reaction.

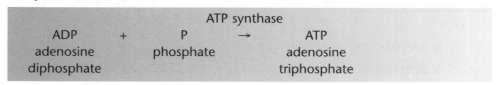

The hydrolysis of the terminal phosphate group liberates the energy. This can then be used in a number of different ways.

ATPase is a hydrolysing enzyme so that a water molecule is needed, but this is not normally shown in the equation.

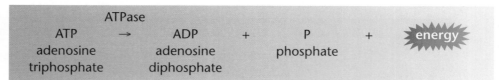

> **KEY POINT**
>
> ATP is the cell's energy currency. A cell does not store large amounts of ATP but it uses it to transfer small packets of energy from one set of reactions to another.

Uses of ATP

- muscle contraction
- active transport
- synthesis of macromolecules
- stimulating the breakdown of substrates to make even more ATP for other uses

1.2 Autotrophic nutrition

After studying this section you should be able to:

- *describe the part played by chloroplasts in photosynthesis*
- *recall and explain the biochemical processes of photosynthesis*
- *relate the properties of chlorophyll to the absorption and action spectra*
- *understand how the law of limiting factors is linked to productivity*
- *understand that glucose can be converted into a number of useful chemicals*

LEARNING SUMMARY

Synthesising food

 AQA 4.3

Autotrophic nutrition is very important. Autotrophic nutrition means that simple inorganic substances are taken in and used to synthesise organic molecules. Energy is needed to achieve this. In **photo-autotrophic nutrition** light is the energy source. In most instances, the light source is **solar energy**, the process being **photosynthesis**. Carbon dioxide and water are taken in by organisms and used to synthesise glucose, which can be broken down later during respiration to release the energy needed for life. Glucose molecules can be polymerised into starch, a storage substance. By far the greatest energy supply to support food chains and webs is obtained from photo-autotrophic nutrition. Most producers use this nutritional method.

The chloroplast

AQA 4.3

Chloroplasts are organelles in plant cells which photosynthesise. In a leaf, they are strategically positioned to absorb the maximum amount of light energy. Most are located in the palisade mesophyll of leaves, but they are also found in both spongy mesophyll and guard cells. There is a greater amount of light entering the upper surface of a leaf so the palisade tissues benefit from a greater chloroplast density.

The diagram below shows the structure of a chloroplast.

Remember that not all light reaching a leaf may hit a chloroplast. Photons of light can be reflected or even absorbed by other parts of the cell. Around 4% of light entering an ecosystem is actually utilised in photosynthesis!

Even when light reaches the green leaf, not all energy is fixed in the carbohydrate product. Just one quarter becomes chemical energy in carbohydrate.

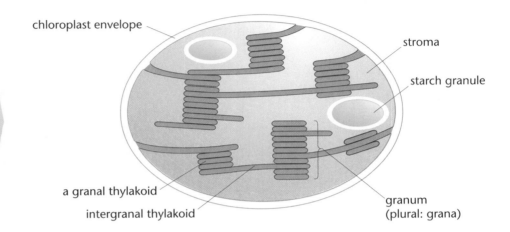

chloroplast envelope

stroma

starch granule

a granal thylakoid

intergranal thylakoid

granum
(plural: grana)

Structure and function

A system of **thylakoid membranes** is located throughout the chloroplast. These are flattened membranous vesicles which are surrounded by a liquid-based matrix, the **stroma**.

Along the thylakoid membranes are key substances:

* chlorophyll molecules
* other pigments
* enzymes
* electron acceptor proteins.

Throughout the chloroplasts, circular thylakoid membranes stack on top of each other to form **grana**. Grana are linked by longer **intergranal thylakoids**. Granal thylakoids and intergranal thylakoids have different pigments and proteins. Each type has a different role in photosynthesis.

The key substances in the thylakoids occur in specific groups comprising pigment, enzyme and electron acceptor proteins. There are two specific groups known as **photosystem I** and **photosystem II**.

Do not be confused by the photosystems. They are groups of chemicals which harness light and pass on energy. Remember this information to understand the biochemistry of photosynthesis.

The photosystems

Each photosystem contains a large number of chlorophyll molecules. As light energy is received at the chlorophyll, electrons from the chlorophyll are boosted to a higher level and energy is passed to pigment molecules known as the **reaction centre**.

> The reaction centre of photosystem I absorbs energy of wavelength 700 nanometres. The reaction centre of photosystem II absorbs energy of wavelength 680–690 nanometres. In this way, light of different wavelengths can be absorbed.

KEY POINT

The process of photosynthesis

AQA   4.3

The process of photosynthesis is summarised by the flow diagram below.

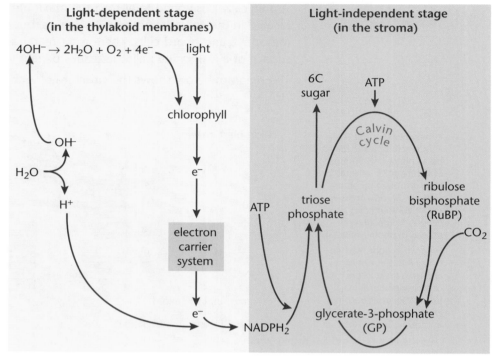

In examinations, look out for parts of this diagram. There may be a few empty boxes where a key substance is missing. Will you be able to recall it?

- Photosynthesis harnesses solar energy.
- Photosynthesis involves light-dependent and light-independent reactions.
- Photosynthesis results in the flow of energy through an ecosystem.

No ATP and NADPH$_2$ in a chloroplast would result in no glucose being made. Once supplies of ATP and NADPH$_2$ are exhausted then photosynthesis is ended. In examinations look out for the 'lights out' questions where the light-independent reaction continues for a while until stores of ATP, NADPH$_2$ and GP are used up. These questions are likely to be graph based.

Light-dependent reaction

- Light energy results in the excitation of electrons in the chlorophyll.
- These electrons are passed along a series of electron acceptors in the thylakoid membranes, collectively known as the electron carrier system.
- Energy from excited electrons funds the production of ATP (adenosine triphosphate).
- The final electron acceptor is NADP$^+$.
- Electron loss from chlorophyll causes the splitting of water (photolysis):

$$H_2O \rightarrow H^+ + OH^- \quad then \quad 4OH^- \rightarrow 2H_2O + O_2 + 4e^-$$

- Oxygen is produced, water to re-use, and electrons stream back to replace those lost in the chlorophyll.
- Hydrogen ions (H$^+$) from photolysis, together with NADP$^+$ form NADPH$_2$.

Light-independent reaction

- Two useful substances are produced by the light-dependent stage, ATP and NADPH$_2$. These are needed to drive the light-independent stage.
- They react with glycerate-3-phosphate (GP) to produce a triose sugar – triose phosphate.
- Triose phosphate is used *either* to produce a 6C sugar *or* to form ribulose bisphosphate (RuBP).
- The conversion of triose phosphate (3C) to RuBP occurs in the Calvin cycle and utilises ATP, which supplies the energy required.
- A RuBP molecule (5C) together with a carbon dioxide molecule (1C) forms two GP molecules (2 × 3C) to complete the Calvin cycle.
- The GP is then available to react with ATP and NADPH$_2$ to synthesise more triose sugar or RuBP.

How do the photosystems contribute to photosynthesis?

This can be explained in terms of the Z scheme shown below.

The **Z scheme**, so called because the paths of electrons shown in the diagram are in a 'Z' shape.

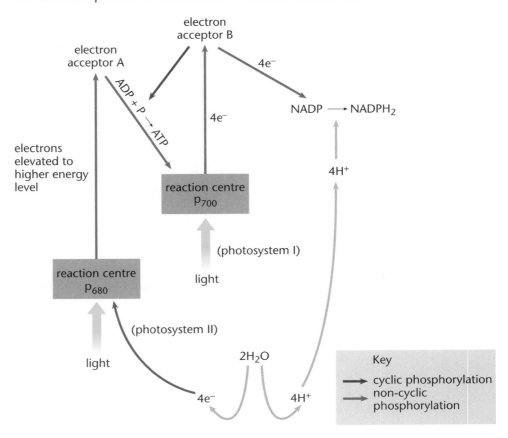

Non-cyclic photophosphorylation

- Light reaches the chlorophyll of both photosystems (P_{680} and P_{700}) which results in the excitation of electrons.
- Electron acceptors receive these electrons (**accepting** electrons is **reduction**).
- P_{680} and P_{700} have become oxidised (**loss** of electrons is **oxidation**).
- P_{680} receives electrons from the **lysis** (splitting) of water molecules and becomes neutral again (referred to as 'hydro lysis').
- Lysis of water molecules releases oxygen which is given off.
- Electrons are elevated to a higher energy level by P_{680} to electron acceptor A and are passed along a series of electron carriers to P_{700}.
- Passage along the electron carrier system funds the production of ATP.
- The electrons pass along a further chain of electron carriers to NADP, which becomes reduced, and at the same time this combines with H^+ ions to form $NADPH_2$.

After analysing this information you will be aware that in cyclic photophosphorylation P_{700} donates electrons then some are recycled back, hence 'cyclic'. In non-cyclic photophosphorylation P_{680} electrons ultimately reach NADP never to return! Neutrality of the chlorophyll of P_{680} is achieved utilising electrons donated from the splitting of water. Different electron sources hence non-cyclic.

Cyclic photophosphorylation

- Electrons from acceptor B move along an electron carrier chain to P_{700}.
- Electron passage along the electron carrier system funds the production of ATP.

Which factors affect photosynthesis?

AQA   4.3

If any process is to take place, then correct components and conditions are required. In the case of photosynthesis these are:

- light
- water
- carbon dioxide
- suitable temperature.

Additionally, it is most important that the chloroplasts have been able to develop their photosynthetic pigments in the thylakoid membranes. Without an adequate supply of magnesium and iron, a plant suffers from chlorosis due to chlorophyll not developing. The leaf colour becomes yellow-green and photosynthesis is reduced.

Limiting factors

If a component is in low supply then productivity is prevented from reaching maximum. In photosynthesis, carbon dioxide is a key limiting factor. The usual atmospheric level of carbon dioxide is 0.04%. In perfect conditions of water availability, light and temperature, this low carbon dioxide level holds back the photosynthetic potential.

Clearly light energy is vital to the process of photosynthesis. It is severely limiting at times of partial light conditions, e.g. dawn or dusk.

Water is vital as a photosynthetic component. It is used in many other processes and has a lesser effect as a limiting factor of photosynthesis. In times of water shortage, a plant suffers from a range of problems associated with other processes before a major effect is observed in photosynthesis.

A range of enzymes are involved in photosynthesis; therefore the process has an optimum temperature above and below which the rate reduces (so the temperature of the plant's environment can be limiting).

The rate of photosynthesis is limited by light intensity from points A to B. After this, a maximum rate is achieved – the graph levels off.

The rate of photosynthesis is limited by light intensity until each graph levels off. The 30°C graph shows that at 20°C, the temperature was also a limiting factor.

The lower level of CO_2 is also a limiting factor here. The fact that it holds back the process is shown by comparing both graph lines.

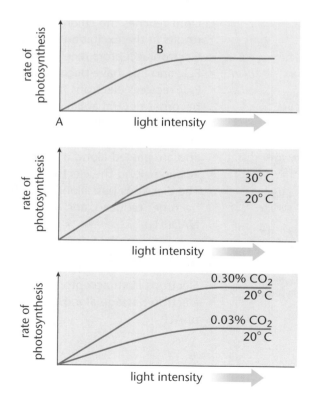

Compensation point

Another way of stating at compensation point is: 'when the rate of respiration equals the rate of photosynthesis'.

It is usual for a plant growing outside in warm conditions to have **two** compensation points every day.

Photosynthesis utilises carbon dioxide whereas respiration results in its production. At night time during darkness, a plant respires and gives out carbon dioxide. Photosynthesis only commences when light becomes available at dawn, if all other conditions are met. At one point, the amount of carbon dioxide released by respiration is totally re-used in photosynthesis. This is the compensation point.

Beyond this compensation point, the plant may increasingly photosynthesise as conditions of temperature and light improve. The plant at this stage still respires producing carbon dioxide in its cells and all of this carbon dioxide is utilised. However, much more carbon dioxide is needed which diffuses in from the air.

In the evening when dusk arrives, a point is reached when the rate of photosynthesis falls due to the decrease in light and the onset of darkness. The amount of carbon dioxide produced at one point is totally utilised in photosynthesis. Another compensation point has arrived.

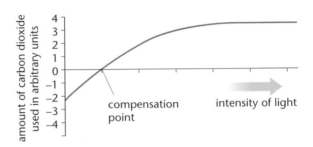

How useful is photosynthesis?

Many more substances are synthesised as a result of photosynthesis. Just a few are highlighted in this section.

Without doubt, photosynthesis is a most important process because it supplies carbohydrates and gives off oxygen. There are many more benefits in that glucose is a 'starter' chemical for the synthesis of many other substances. Cellulose, amino acids and lipids are among the large number of chemicals which can be produced as a result of the initial process of photosynthesis.

The work of the Royal Mint produces the money to run the economy; photosynthesis supplies the energy currency for the living world.

The table shows some examples of where and how some carbohydrates are used.

Carbohydrate	Use
deoxyribose (monosaccharide)	DNA 'backbone'
glucose (monosaccharide)	leaves, nectar, blood as energy supply
sucrose (disaccharide)	sugar beet as energy store
lactose (disaccharide)	milk as energy supply
cellulose (disaccharide)	protective cover around all plant cells
starch (polysaccharide)	energy store in plant cells
glycogen (polysaccharide)	energy store in muscle and liver

Progress check

1 In a chloroplast, where do the following take place:
   (a) light-dependent reaction
   (b) light-independent reaction?

2 (a) Which features do photosystems I and II share in a chloroplast?
   (b) Which photosystem is responsible for:
       (i) the elevation of electrons to their highest level
       (ii) acceptance of electrons from the lysis (splitting) of water?

3 (a) Complete the sentence by writing in the correct words.
       The compensation point of a plant is when the rate of .... equals the rate of ....

   (b) During a cloudless day in ideal conditions for photosynthesis, how many compensation points does a plant have? Give a reason for your answer.

4 List the three main factors which limit the rate of photosynthesis.

5 During the light-independent stage of photosynthesis, which substances are needed to continue the production of RuBP? Underline the substances in your answer which are directly supplied from the light-dependent stage of photosynthesis.

1 (a) thylakoid membranes (b) stroma.
2 (a) Each photosystem contains a large number of chlorophyll molecules. Light energy is received at the chlorophyll where electrons are boosted to a higher level. Energy is passed to pigment molecules known as the **reaction centre**. The reaction centre of each photosystem absorbs energy (but of different wavelengths).
(b) (i) photosystem I (ii) photosystem II.
3 (a) respiration; photosynthesis (b) Two. Around dawn and dusk there will come a time when the CO_2 produced as a result of respiration is totally used up in photosynthesis.
4 CO_2; light; temperature.
5 Triose phosphate NADPH$_2$, ATP and CO_2.

1.3 Respiration

LEARNING SUMMARY

After studying this section you should be able to:

- *recall the structure of mitochondria and relate structure to function*
- *understand that respiration liberates energy from organic molecules*
- *explain the stages of glycolysis and Krebs cycle*
- *explain the stages in the hydrogen carrier system*
- *explain the differences between anaerobic and aerobic respiration*

The site of respiration

 AQA ▸ 4.4

Respiration is vital to the activities of every living cell. Like photosynthesis it is a complicated metabolic pathway. The aim of respiration is to break down **respiratory substrates** such as glucose to produce **ATP**.

Respiration consists of a number of different stages. These occur in different parts of the cell. Some stages require oxygen and some do not.

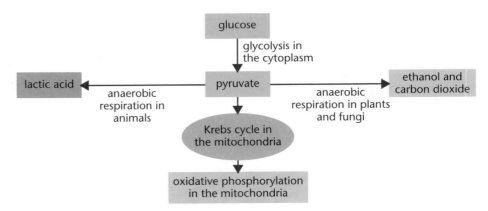

Glycolysis occurs in the cytoplasm of the cell. The pyruvate produced then enters the mitochondria. The Krebs cycle then occurs in the matrix of the mitochondria followed by oxidative phosphorylation which occurs on the inner membrane of the cristae.

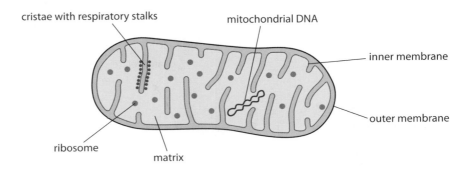

The biochemistry of respiration

 4.4

Glycolysis and the Krebs cycle

Both processes produce ATP from substrates but the Krebs cycle produces **many more** ATP molecules than glycolysis. Every stage in each process is catalysed by a specific enzyme. In aerobic respiration, **both** glycolysis and the Krebs cycle are involved, whereas in anaerobic respiration only glycolysis takes place.

The flow diagram on the following page shows stages in the breakdown of glucose in glycolysis and the Krebs cycle. The flow diagram shows only the main stages of each process.

The two molecules of ATP are needed to begin the process. Each stage is catalysed by an enzyme, e.g. a decarboxylase removes CO_2 from a molecule.

The production of hydrogen atoms during the process can be monitored using DCPIP (dichlorophenol indophenol). It is a hydrogen acceptor and becomes colourless when fully reduced.

The maximum ATP yield per glucose molecule is:

GLYCOLYSIS	2
KREBS CYCLE	2
OXIDATIVE PHOSPHORYLATION	34
	= 38 ATP

Oxygen is needed at the end of the carrier chain as a hydrogen acceptor. This is why we need oxygen to live. Without it, the generation of ATP along this route would be stopped.

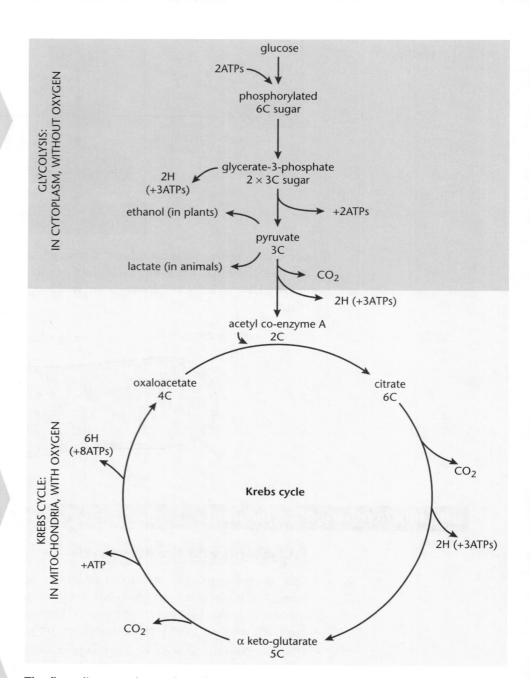

GLYCOLYSIS: IN CYTOPLASM, WITHOUT OXYGEN

glucose

2ATPs

phosphorylated 6C sugar

glycerate-3-phosphate 2 × 3C sugar

2H (+3ATPs)

ethanol (in plants) +2ATPs

pyruvate 3C

lactate (in animals) CO_2

2H (+3ATPs)

acetyl co-enzyme A 2C

KREBS CYCLE: IN MITOCHONDRIA, WITH OXYGEN

oxaloacetate 4C

citrate 6C

6H (+8ATPs)

CO_2

Krebs cycle

2H (+3ATPs)

+ATP

CO_2

α keto-glutarate 5C

The flow diagram shows that glycolysis produces 2 × 2ATP molecules but uses 2ATP so the net production is 2ATP. The Krebs cycle makes 2ATP directly. All the rest of the ATP molecules that are made (shown in brackets) are produced in oxidative phosphorylation.

Oxidative phosphorylation

The main feature of this process is the electron carrier or electron transport system. The hydrogen that is given off by glycolysis and the Krebs cycle is picked up by acceptor molecules such as NAD. These hydrogen atoms are passed along a series of carriers on the inner membrane of the mitochondrion.

Oxidation	Reduction
gain of oxygen	loss of oxygen
loss of hydrogen	gain of hydrogen
loss of electrons	gain of electrons

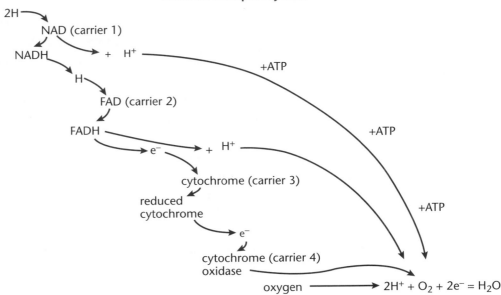

Electron transport system

This is sometimes known as the hydrogen carrier system.

The carrier, NAD, is nicotinamide adenine dinucleotide. Similarly, FAD is flavine adenine dinucleotide.

Hydrogen is not transferred to cytochrome. Instead, the 2H atoms ionise into $2H^+ + 2e^-$. H is passed via an intermediate co-enzyme Q to cytochrome.

Only the electrons are carried via the cytochromes.

e^- is an electron.
H^+ is a hydrogen ion or proton.

An enzyme can be both an oxidoreductase and a dehydrogenase at the same time!

When oxidation takes place then so does reduction, simultaneously, e.g. $NADH_2$ passes H to FAD. The NAD loses hydrogen and as a result becomes oxidised. FAD gains hydrogen and becomes $FADH_2$, and is therefore reduced. The generic term for an enzyme which catalyses this is **oxidoreductase**. Additionally an enzyme which removes hydrogen from a molecule is a **dehydrogenase**. The result is that three ATPs are produced every time 2H atoms are transported.

The chemiosmotic theory

This theory also explains ATP production in photophosphorylation in the chloroplast. The only difference is that the ions are moved in the opposite direction.

It has now been shown that the carrier molecules are arranged on the membrane of the cristae in a specific way. This means that hydrogen ions are moved out of the matrix and into the space between the two membranes. This sets up a pH gradient. The hydrogen ions can re-enter the matrix through the respiratory stalks. This movement is linked to ATP production and this process is called the **chemiosmotic theory**.

Anaerobic respiration

AQA ▶ 4.4

If oxygen is in short supply then the final hydrogen acceptor for the hydrogen atoms is missing. This means that oxidative phosphorylation will stop and NAD will not be regenerated. This will result in the Krebs cycle being unable to function.

Glycolysis can continue and produce 2ATP molecules but it would soon run out of NAD as well. A small amount of NAD can be regenerated by converting the pyruvate to lactate or ethanol. This allows glycolsis to continue in the absence of oxygen. This is **anaerobic respiration**.

Ethanol is produced in plants and yeast, lactate is made in animals.

> **KEY POINT**
> Anaerobic respiration will make 2ATP molecules from one glucose molecule compared to a possible 38ATP in aerobic respiration.

Progress check

1 Explain how hydrogen atom production in cells during aerobic respiration results in the release of energy for cell activity.

2 Give **three** similarities between respiration and photosynthesis.

3 (a) Name the **four** carriers in the electron transport system in a mitochondrion. Give them in the correct sequence.

   (b) Name the waste product which results from the final stage of the electron transport system.

4 For each of the following statements indicate whether a molecule would be oxidised or reduced.

   (a) (i)   loss of oxygen
       (ii) gain of hydrogen
       (iii) loss of electrons

   (b) Which type of enzyme enables hydrogen to be transferred from one molecule to another?

2 The stages of each process are catalysed by enzymes; both processes involve ATP; respiration involves GP in glycolysis and photosynthesis involves GP in the light-independent stage

1 Used in the electron transport system to produce ATP; 3ATP molecules produced for every 2H atoms produced; ATP → ADP + P + energy released

3 (a) NAD → FAD → cytochrome → cytochrome oxidase
   (b) water

4 (a) (i) reduced (ii) reduced (iii) oxidised
   (b) Oxidoreductase

Sample question and model answer

Radioactivity is used to label molecules. They can then be tracked with a Geiger-Müller counter.

In an experiment, pondweed was immersed in water which was saturated with radioactive carbon dioxide ($^{14}CO_2$). It was illuminated for a time so that photosynthesis took place, the light was then switched off. The graph below shows the relative levels of some substances.

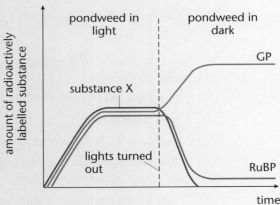

Always be ready to link the rise in one graph line with the dip of another. The relationship holds true here as substance X and RuBP are used up in the production of GP via the Calvin cycle. It is likely that some GP would have been used with substance X to make triose sugar. This is not shown on this graph.

Use the graph and your knowledge to answer the following questions.

(a) (i) Substance X is produced after a substance becomes reduced during the light-dependent stage of photosynthesis. Name substance X. [1]

       NADPH$_2$, reduced nicotinamide adenine dinucleotide phosphate

   (ii) Explain why substance X cannot be produced without light energy. [3]

       • Light energy removes electrons from chlorophyll.
       • The electrons are passed along the electron carrier chain.
       • The electrons are needed to reduce NADP.

(b) Explain the levels of substance X, GP and RuBP after the lights were turned off. [6]

       • It seems that substance X is used to make the other two substances because it becomes used up.
       • Supply of substance X cannot be produced without light energy.
       • GP is made from RuBP.
       • GP levels out because more NADPH$_2$ is needed to make triose sugar or RuBP, the supply being exhausted.
       • RuBP levels out at a low level because more NADPH$_2$ is needed to make GP.
       • ATP is needed to make RuBP, ATP is needed to make GP.

ATP is not shown on the graph. Always be ready to consider substances involved in a process but not shown. Here it is worth a mark to remember that ATP is needed to continue the light-independent system of photosynthesis.

(c) After the lights were switched off glucose was found to decrease rapidly. Explain this decrease. [1]

       • Glucose is used up in respiration to release energy for the cell.

(d) Give the specific sites of each of the following stages of photosynthesis in a chloroplast: [2]

   (i) light-dependent stage   thylakoid membranes
   (ii) light-independent stage.   stroma

Practice examination questions

1 The flow diagram below shows stages in the process of glycolysis.

> 2ATPs
>
> glucose → phosphorylated → GP → substance X → lactate
> 6C sugar   6C sugar   glycerate-   3C
>   3-phosphate
>   (2 × 3C)
>   2ATPs

Use the information in the diagram and your knowledge to answer the questions below.

(a) Where in a cell does the above process take place?   [1]

(b) Name substance X.   [1]

(c) How many ATPs are *produced* during the above process?   [1]

(d) Is the above process from an animal or plant?
    Give a reason for your answer.   [1]

(e) Under which condition could lactate be metabolised?   [1]

                                                                   [Total: 5]

2 The graph shows the relative amount of carbon dioxide taken in or evolved by a plant at different times during a day when the sun rose at 5 a.m.

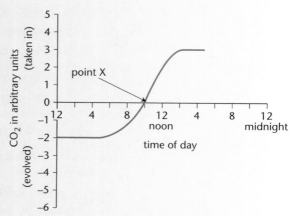

(a) Explain the significance of point X.   [2]

(b) What name is given to point X?   [1]

(c) Complete the graph between 4.00 p.m. and 12.00 midnight.   [2]

                                                                   [Total: 5]

3 The flow diagram below shows part of the electron carrier system in an animal cell.

> FADH → FAD + H^+ + e^-

(a) Where in a cell does this process take place?   [1]

(b) From which molecule did FAD receive H to become FADH?   [1]

(c) Which molecule receives the electron produced by the breakdown of FADH?   [1]

(d) As FADH becomes oxidised a useful substance is produced.
    Name the substance.   [1]

                                                                   [Total: 4]

Practice examination questions (continued)

4 The graph below shows the effect of increasing light intensity on the rate of photosynthesis of a plant where the concentration of carbon dioxide in the atmosphere was 0.03%.

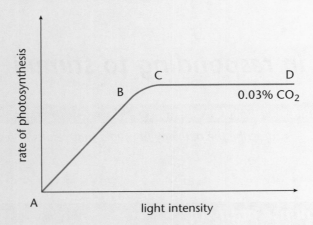

(a) Explain the effect of light intensity on the rate of photosynthesis between the following points on the graph:

   (i) A and B

   (ii) B and C

   (iii) C and D.   [3]

(b) Draw the shape of the graph which would result from a CO_2 concentration of 0.3%.   [1]

                                                [Total: 4]

Chapter 2

Response to stimuli

The following topics are covered in this chapter:

- Stages in responding to stimuli
- Receptors
- Plant sensitivity

- Neurone structure and function
- Response

2.1 Stages in responding to stimuli

After studying this section you should be able to:

- describe the pathway of events that results in response to stimuli

LEARNING SUMMARY

The stimulus/response pathway

The ability of plants and animals to respond to changes in their external environment is called **sensitivity**. This is a characteristic of all living organisms and is necessary for their survival. Organisms also respond to changes in their internal environment and this is covered in the next chapter.

The events involved in a response follow a similar pattern:

The responses shown by plants are often less obvious than animal responses because they are usually slower. They still involve a similar pathway of events.

In animals the communication between the receptors, the coordinating centre and the effectors is usually by neurones.

2.2 Neurone structure and function

After studying this section you should be able to:

- describe the structure of a motor neurone, a sensory neurone and a relay neurone.
- understand the function of sensory, motor and relay neurones
- understand nervous transmission by action potential
- describe the mechanisms of synaptic transmission

LEARNING SUMMARY

The structure and function of neurones

Neurones are **nerve cells** which help to coordinate the activity of an organism by transmitting **electrical impulses**. Many neurones are usually gathered together, enclosed in connective tissue to form **nerves**.

Important features of neurones.

1 Each has a **cell body** which contains a nucleus.
2 Each communicates via processes **from the cell body**.
3 Processes that carry impulses away from the cell body are known as **axons**.
4 Processes that carry impulses towards the cell body are known as **dendrons**.
5 All neurones transmit **electrical impulses**.

The nervous system consists of a range of different neurones which work in a network through the organs. The diagrams show three types of neurone.

Notice the direction of the impulse and that motor neurones have long axons and short dendrons. This is the other way round for sensory neurones.

Key points from AS

- **The cell surface membrane**
  Revise AS pages 50–51
- **The movement of molecules in and out of cells**
  Revise AS pages 52–53
- **The specialisation of cells**
  Revise AS pages 35–36

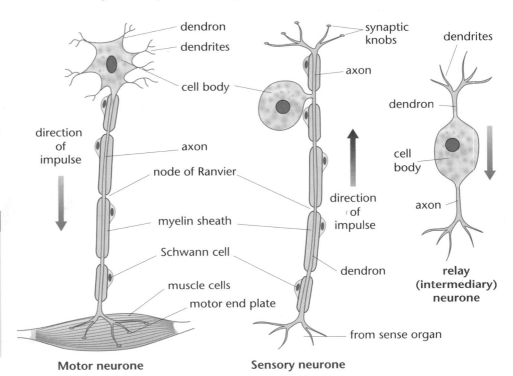

direction of impulse

dendron
dendrites
cell body
axon
node of Ranvier
myelin sheath
Schwann cell
muscle cells
motor end plate

Motor neurone

synaptic knobs
axon
direction of impulse
dendron
from sense organ

Sensory neurone

dendrites
dendron
cell body
axon

relay (intermediary) neurone

Myelinated neurones

Sensory and motor neurones are examples of myelinated neurones. This enables them to transmit an impulse at a greater velocity. Myelinated neurones have the following characteristics:

- The axon or dendron is insulated by a **myelin sheath**.
- The myelin sheath is formed by a **Schwann cell** wrapping around the axon many times. This forms many layers of cell membrane surrounding the axon.
- At intervals there are gaps in the sheath, between each Schwann cell, called **nodes of Ranvier**.

Cross-section of axon

The myelin sheath is often called a 'fatty' sheath because it is made of many layers of cell membrane which are composed largely of phospholipids.

Schwann cell nucleus
Schwann cell
axon

What are the roles of the sensory and motor neurones?

There are many similarities between the structure of sensory and motor neurones but they have different functions:

- The sensory neurones transmit impulses towards the central nervous system (CNS) from the receptors.
- The motor neurones transmit impulses from the CNS to effectors, such as muscles, to bring about a response.
- Relay neurones may form connections between sensory and motor neurones in the CNS.

Transmission of an action potential along a neurone

AQA   5.2

Neurones can 'transmit an electrical message' along an axon. However, you must never write this in your answers. Instead of nerve impulse, you must now use the term **action potential**.

The diagrams below show the sequence of events which take place along an axon as an action potential passes.

Resting potential

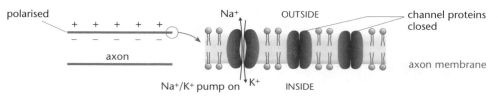

- There are 30 times more Na$^+$ ions on the outside of an axon during a resting potential.
- If any Na$^+$ ions diffuse in, then they are expelled by the '**sodium–potassium pump**'.
- The 'sodium–potassium pump' is an active transport mechanism by which a carrier protein, with ATP, expels Na$^+$ ions against a concentration gradient and allows K$^+$ ions into the axon.
- This creates a **polarisation**, i.e. there is a +ve charge on the outside of the membrane and a –ve charge on the inside.
- The potential difference is called the **resting potential** and can be measured at around –70 millivolts.

> Under resting conditions, the membrane of the axon is fairly impermeable to sodium ions.

Action potential – depolarisation

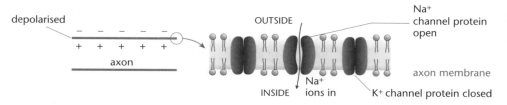

- During an action potential sodium channel proteins open to allow Na$^+$ ions into the axon.
- There is now a –ve charge on the outside and a +ve charge on the inside known as **depolarisation**.
- The potential difference changes to around +50 millivolts.
- The profile of the action potential, shown by an oscilloscope, is always the same.

Action potential – repolarisation

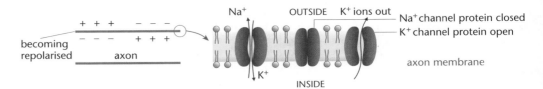

- A K$^+$ channel opens so K$^+$ ions leave the axon.
- This results in the membrane becoming polarised again.
- Any Na$^+$ ions that have entered during the action potential will be removed by the 'sodium–potassium pump'.

Measuring an action potential

- The speed and profile of action potentials can be measured with the help of an oscilloscope.
- The profile of the action potential for an organism always shows the same pattern, like the one shown.
- The changes in potential difference are tracked via a time base.
- Using the time base you can work out the speed at which action potentials pass along an axon as well as how long one lasts.

The diagram shows the typical profile of an action potential.

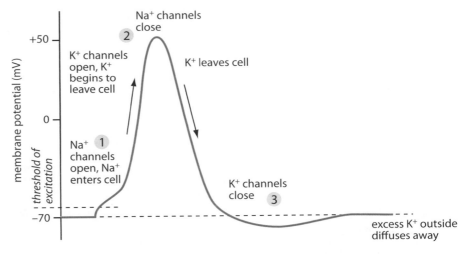

- The front of the action potential is marked by the Na$^+$ channels in the membrane opening.
- The potential difference increases to around +50 millivolts as the Na$^+$ ions stream into the axon.
- The Na$^+$ channels then close and K$^+$ channels in the membrane open.
- K$^+$ ions leave the axon and the membrane repolarises.
- During the **refractory period** no other action potential can pass along the axon, which makes each action potential separate or discrete.

Saltatory conduction

The reason why myelinated neurones are faster than non-myelinated neurones is that the action potential 'jumps' from one node of Ranvier to the next. This is because this is the only place where Na$^+$ ions can pass across the membrane. This is called **saltatory conduction**.

The velocity of the action potential also depends on temperature and the diameter of the axon. Wider axons and higher temperatures (up to a limit) give faster velocities.

Progress check

What is the function of each of the following?

(a) receptor
(b) axon
(c) myelin sheath
(d) terminal dendrites

(a) Receptors respond to stimulus by producing an action potential.
(b) Transmit action potential with the help of mitochondria.
(c) Myelin sheath is a membrane enclosing fat which acts as an insulator.
(d) Terminal dendrites have motor end plates which can stimulate muscle tissue to contract.

How do neurones communicate with each other?

AQA 5.2

The key to links between neurones are structures known as **synapses**. Terminal dendrites branch out from neurones and terminate in **synaptic knobs**. The diagram below shows a synaptic knob separated from an interlinking neurone by a synapse.

Remember an impulse can 'cross' a synapse by chemical means and the route is in ONE direction only. They cannot go back!

A synapse which conducts using acetylcholine is known as a cholinergic synapse.

There are **two** types of synapse:
- **excitatory** which can stimulate an action potential in a linked neurone
- **inhibitory** which can prevent an action potential being generated.

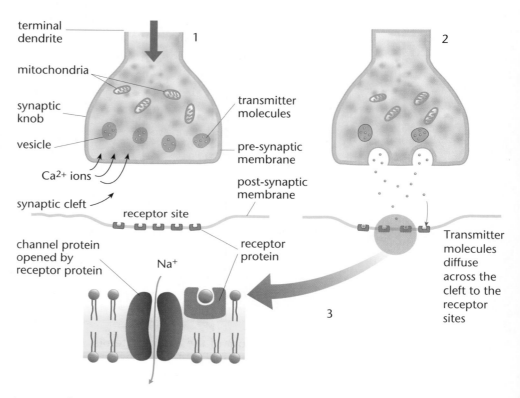

As an action potential arrives at a synaptic knob, the following sequence takes place.

- **Channel proteins** in the **pre-synaptic membrane** open to allow Ca^{2+} ions from the synaptic cleft into the synaptic knob.
- **Vesicles** then merge with the pre-synaptic membrane, so that **transmitter molecules** such as **acetylcholine** are **secreted** into the gap.
- The transmitter molecules diffuse across the cleft and bind with specific **sites** in **receptor proteins** in the **post-synaptic membrane**.
- Every receptor protein then opens a **channel protein** so that ions such as Na^+ pass through the post-synaptic membrane into the cell.
- The Na^+ ions **depolarise** the post-synaptic membrane.
- If enough Na^+ ions enter then depolarisation reaches a **threshold level** and an **action potential** is generated in the cell.

Remember that the generation of an action potential is ALL OR NOTHING. Either enough Na⁺ ions pass through the post-synaptic membrane and an action potential is generated OR not enough reach the other side, and there is no effect.

- Enzymes in the cleft then remove the transmitter substance from the binding sites, e.g. **acetylcholine esterase** removes **acetylcholine** by hydrolysing it into choline and ethanoic acid.
- Breakdown products of transmitter substances are absorbed into the synaptic knob for re-synthesis of transmitter.

Summation

A single action potential may arrive at a synaptic knob and result in some transmitter molecules being secreted into a cleft. However, there may not be enough to cause an action potential to be generated. If a series of action potentials arrive at the synaptic knob then the build up of transmitter substances may reach the threshold and the neurone will now send an action potential. We say that the neurone has 'fired' as the action potential is produced.

Progress check

1 Explain the importance of summation at a synapse.

2 The diagram shows a synaptic knob.

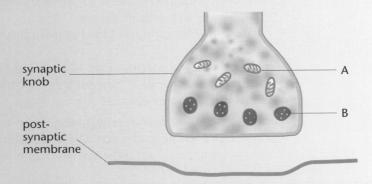

synaptic knob

A

B

post-synaptic membrane

(a) Name A and B

(b) Describe the events which take place after an action potential reaches a synaptic knob and a further action potential is generated as a result.

2 (a) A – mitochondria; B – vesicle

(b) Ca^{2+} ions flow into the synaptic knob; transmitter molecules such as acetylcholine are secreted into the gap; the transmitter molecules bind with sites in receptor proteins in the post-synaptic membrane; this opens channel proteins so that ions such as Na⁺ pass through the post-synaptic membrane into the cell; the post-synaptic membrane is depolarised; *if enough* Na⁺ ions enter a threshold level is reached and an action potential is generated in the cell.

1 A single action potential may arrive at a synaptic knob; there may not be enough transmitter molecules being secreted into a cleft to cause an action potential to be generated; a series of action potentials arrive at the synapse to build up transmitter substances to reach the threshold; the neurone will now send an action potential.

2.3 Receptors

After studying this section you should be able to:

- list the different types of receptors
- explain how receptors trigger nerve impulses
- describe how rods and cones respond to light

LEARNING SUMMARY

Types of receptors

 5.1

The more receptors there are in a position, the more sensitive it is, e.g. the fingers have many more touch receptors than the upper arm.

The function of receptors is to convert the energy from different stimuli into nerve impulses in sensory neurones.

There are a range of different types of sensory cell around the body. Each type responds to different stimuli. Receptors are classified according to these different stimuli:

- **Photoreceptors**, respond to light, e.g. rods and cones in the retina.
- **Chemoreceptors**, respond to chemicals, e.g. taste buds on the tongue.
- **Thermoreceptors**, respond to temperature, e.g. skin thermoreceptors.
- **Mechanoreceptors**, respond to physical deformation, e.g. Pacinian corpuscles in the skin or hair cells in the ear.
- **Proprioreceptors**, respond to change in position in some organs, e.g. in muscles.

Did you know?

The umbilical cord has no receptors. It can be cut without any pain.

Stimulation of a receptor usually causes it to depolarise. This is called a **generator potential**. If this change is beyond a certain magnitude, it will trigger an action potential in a sensory neurone.

Some receptors are found individually in the body such as **Pacinian corpuscles** which detect pressure in the skin. Other receptors are gathered together into sense organs. An example of this is the eye which contains receptors called rods and cones.

How do the cells of the eye respond to light?

 5.1

The retina in the eye contains two types of cell which are **photosensitive**, the rod cells and the cone cells. They each have different properties.

Rod cells

- They are very sensitive to the **intensity of light**, but are not sensitive to colour.
- They can respond to even dim light.
- They respond by the following reaction:
  rhodopsin → opsin + retinal
- They have low visual acuity in dim conditions.
- Opsin opens **ion channels** in the cell surface membrane which can result in the generation of an action potential.
- Rhodopsin can be re-generated during an absence of light.

[colour spectrum diagram: violet | blue | green | yellow | orange | red, 400 – 500 – 600 – 700, wavelength/nm]

The colour vision mechanism appears to require three types of cone: RED, GREEN, and BLUE and gives the *trichromatic* theory.

Cone cells

- Cone cells require **high light intensities** to be responsive – high visual acuity.
- They respond by the following reaction:
  iodopsin → photopsin + retinal
- They exist in three different types: red, green and blue, each having a different form of iodopsin:
  - **red** cones are stimulated by wavelengths of red light
  - **green** cones are stimulated by wavelengths of green light

– **blue** cones are stimulated by wavelengths of blue light
– all three cones are stimulated by white light
- Opsin again opens **ion channels** in the membranes which can lead to the generation of an action potential.

Structure of the retina

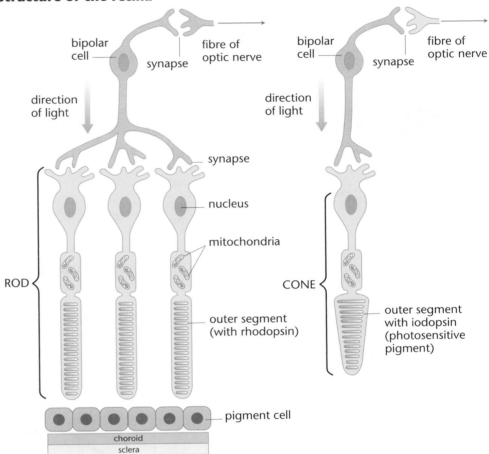

Remember that red light reaching a cone sensitive to only blue light would not stimulate the generation of an action potential. Cones are only sensitive to light of a specific range of wave-lengths.

Note the direction of light as it reaches the outer retinal surface.

Visual acuity

Did you know that the fovea consists almost entirely of cones?

What do we see with in dim conditions?

You have guessed it, rods. Their ability to detect dim light is useful but there is no colour!

Visual acuity is a measure of the detail we can see. The **cones** are responsible for high visual acuity (**high resolution**). **Large numbers** are packed **very close** to each other in the fovea. **ONE** cone cell synapses onto **ONE** bipolar cell which in turn synapses onto **ONE** ganglion cell as the information is relayed to the visual cortex. Spatially, much more clarity is perceived than for the rods. The image can be likened to a television picture with high numbers of pixels. Compare this with the rods. The rod cells are not packed close together so that visual acuity is low.

Convergence

Many rods can synapse onto one bipolar cell. A ray of light reaching one rod may not be enough to stimulate an action potential along a nerve pathway. **Several** rods link to **one** bipolar cell so that enough transmitter molecules at a synapse reach the threshold level. This depolarisation results in an action potential in the bipolar cell. This is **summation**, as a result of rod cell teamwork!

2.4 Response

After studying this section you should be able to:

- *describe different types of response*
- *understand how neurones function together in a reflex arc*
- *outline the features of the autonomic nervous system*
- *describe the structure of skeletal muscle and understand the sliding filament mechanism*

LEARNING SUMMARY

Different types of response

AQA ▶ 5.1

In order to bring about a response, nerve impulses are sent to effectors via motor neurones. Some responses do not require conscious thought. These are called reflexes or reflex actions.

The reflex arc

How can we react quickly without even thinking about making a response?

Often the brain is not involved in the response so the time taken to respond to a stimulus is reduced. This rapid, automatic response is made possible by the reflex arc.

A reflex arc

> Small organisms have simple responses called Taxes or Kineses, which enable them to spend most of their time in a favourable environment.

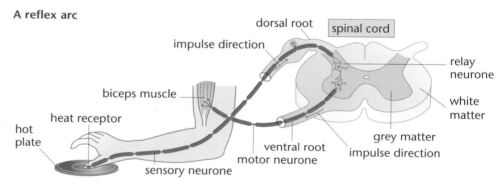

Features of a reflex arc

- The stimulus elicits a response in a **receptor**.
- As a result, an **action potential** is generated along a sensory neurone.
- The **sensory neurone** enters the spinal cord via the **dorsal root** and **synapses** onto a **relay neurone**.
- This intermediate neurone synapses onto a **motor neurone** which in turn conducts the impulse to a **muscle** via its **motor end plates**.
- The muscle contracts and the arm instantly **withdraws** from the stimulus before any harm is done.
- The complete list of events takes place so quickly because the impulses do not, initially, go to the brain! The complete pathway to the muscle conducts the impulse so rapidly, before the brain receives any sensory information.

> It is other afferent neurones which *finally* take impulses to the brain enabling us to be aware of the arc which has just taken place. These afferent neurones are NOT part of the reflex arc.

> **KEY POINT**
>
> Reflexes have a high survival value because the organism is able to respond so rapidly. Additionally, they are always automatic. There are a range of different reflexes, e.g. iris/pupil reflex, and saliva production.

Autonomic nervous system

Many reflex actions are controlled by the autonomic nervous system. This is the part of the nervous system which controls our involuntary activities, e.g. the control of the heart rate. It is divided into two parts, the sympathetic system and the parasympathetic system. Each system has a major nerve from which smaller nerves branch out into key organs. In some ways, the two systems are antagonistic to each other but in other ways, they have specific functions not counteracted by the other. The table below shows all of the main facts for each system.

This table of features shows some key points for the autonomic system. ALERT! They are difficult to learn because of the lack of logic in the 'pattern' of functions. Take time to revise this properly because many candidates mix up the features of one system with another.

| Feature | Autonomic nervous system | |
	Sympathetic	*Parasympathetic*
Nerve (example)	sympathetic nerve	vagus nerve
Transmitter substance at synapses	noradrenaline	acetylcholine
Heart rate	speeds up	slows down
Iris control	dilates	constricts
Saliva	_____	flow stimulated
Gut movements	slows down	speeds up
Sweating	sweat production stimulated	_____
Erector pili muscles	contracts erector pili muscles	_____

KEY POINT

Remember that all of the above functions take place without thought. The system is truly involuntary.

One of the main functions of the autonomic nervous system is to regulate the heart rate. Under normal conditions stretch receptors called baroreceptors in the carotid artery, the aorta and the atria detect the pressure of the blood. If it is too high then the cardiovascular centre in the medulla of the brain will reduce the heart rate via the vagus nerve. The accelerator nerve is used to increase the heart rate if the blood pressure is too low.

During exercise, increased carbon dioxide levels are detected by chemoreceptors. This will result in an increase in heart rate and the blood pressure increase is ignored until the carbon dioxide levels return to normal.

Muscles as effectors

AQA   5.2/5.3

The body has a number of different effectors, but for most responses the effector is a muscle. There are three types of muscle in the body:

- skeletal/striated or voluntary muscle
- visceral/smooth or involuntary muscle
- cardiac muscle.

Smooth muscle is controlled by the autonomic nervous system, but skeletal muscle is controlled by motor neurones of the somatic nervous system. This is under voluntary or conscious control.

How do motor neurones control muscle tissue?

The link to muscle tissue is by **motor end plates** which have close proximity to the sarcoplasm of the muscle tissue. The motor end plates have a greater surface area than a synaptic knob, but their action is very similar to the synaptic transmission described on page 36. Action potentials result in muscle contraction.

No contraction would take place without the acetylcholine transmitter being released from the motor end plate. When the sarcolemma (membrane) reaches the threshold level, then the action potential is conducted throughout the sarcolemma. Contraction is initiated!

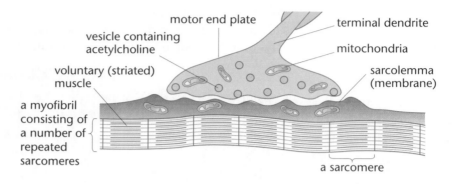

Skeletal muscle is also known as striated or striped muscle. The structure of a single muscle unit, the sarcomere, shows the striped nature of the muscle.

The sarcomere

A sarcomere showing bands

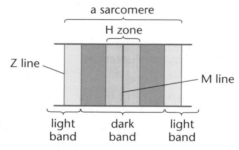

A sarcomere showing filaments

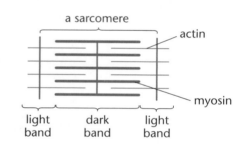

- The sarcomere consists of different filaments, thin ones (**actin**) and thick ones (**myosin**).
- These filaments form bands of different shades:
  – light band (I bands) – just actin filaments
  – dark band (A bands) – just myosin filaments or myosin plus actin.
- During contraction, the filaments slide together to form a shorter sarcomere.
- As this pattern of contraction is repeated through 1000s of sarcomeres, the whole muscle contracts.
- Actin and myosin filaments slide together because of the formation of cross bridges which alternatively build and break during contraction.
- Cross bridge formation is known as the 'ratchet mechanism'.

How does the 'ratchet mechanism' work?

To answer this question, the properties of actin and myosin need to be considered. The diagram below represents an actin filament next to a myosin filament. Many 'bulbous heads' are located along the myosin filaments (just one is shown). Each points towards an actin filament.

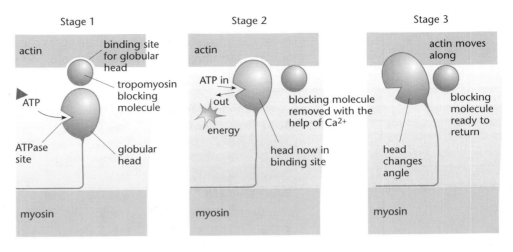

The sequence of the ratchet mechanism

Very little ATP is held in the muscles at any moment. It can be regenerated for a molecule called phosphocreatine.

- Once an action potential is generated in the muscle tissue then Ca^{2+} ions are released from the reticulum, a structure in the sarcoplasm.
- Part of the globular head of the myosin has an ATPase (enzyme) site.
- Ca^{2+} ions activate the myosin head so that this ATPase site hydrolyses an ATP molecule, releasing energy.
- Ca^{2+} ions also bind to troponin in the actin filaments, this in turn removes blocking molecules (tropomyosin) from the actin filament.
- This exposes the binding sites on the actin filaments.
- The globular heads of the myosin then bind to the newly exposed sites forming actin–myosin cross bridges.
- At the stage of energy release the myosin heads change angle.
- This change of angle moves the actin filaments towards the centre of each sarcomere and is termed the power stroke.
- More ATP binds to the myosin head, effectively causing the cross bridge to become straight and the tropomyosin molecules once again block the actin binding sites.
- The myosin is now 'cocked' and ready to repeat the above process.
- Repeated cross bridge formation and breakage results in a rowing action shortening the sarcomere as the filaments slide past each other.

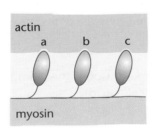
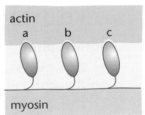
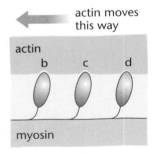

Types of skeletal muscle fibres

Under the microscope skeletal muscle fibres can be divided into two types. They are slow and fast fibres. They do different jobs and so are found in different muscles.

Fibre type	Slow fibres	Fast fibres
Speed of contraction	Slow / tonic	Fast / twitch
Size of motor neurone	Small	Large
Activity used for	Responses such as maintaining posture	Quick responses such as jumping
Duration of use	Hours	Less than 5 minutes
Power produced	Low	High
Number of mitochondria	Many	Few
Found	In muscles such as the buttocks	In muscles such as the biceps
Myoglobin content	High so red	Low so white

2.5 Plant sensitivity

After studying this section you should be able to:

- understand the range of tropisms which affect plant growth
- understand how auxins, gibberellins and cytokinins control plant growth
- understand how phytochromes control the onset of flowering in plants

LEARNING SUMMARY

Plant growth regulators

AQA   S.1-2

External stimuli such as light can affect the direction of plant growth. A **tropism** is a **growth response** to an external stimulus. It is important that a plant grows in a direction which will enable it to obtain maximum supplies. Plant regulators are substances produced in minute quantities and tend to interact in their effects.

> Growth response to light is **phototropism**
> Growth response to gravity is **geotropism**
> Growth response to water is **hydrotropism**
> Growth response to contact is **thigmotropism**
> Tropisms can be positive (towards) or negative (away from).
>
> **KEY POINT**

Phototropism

This response is dependent upon the stimulus – light affecting the growth regulator, **auxin** (indoleacetic acid).

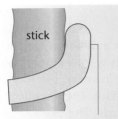

stick

auxin high
concentration here
so cells elongate

Thigmotropism helps a
climbing plant like the
runner bean to grow in
a twisting pattern
around a stick. Auxin is
redistributed away from
the contact point so the
outer cells elongate
giving a stronger outer
growth.

The diagrams show
tropic responses to light
and auxin.

Auxin and growing shoots

Auxin is produced by cells undergoing mitosis, e.g. growing tips. If a plant shoot
is illuminated from one side then the auxin is redistributed to the side furthest from
the light. This side grows more strongly, owing to the elongation of the cells,
resulting in a bend towards the light. The plant benefits from increased light for
photosynthesis. Up to a certain concentration, the degree of bending is
proportional to auxin concentration.

**Tropisms in response to light
from different directions**

Tropism in response to auxin

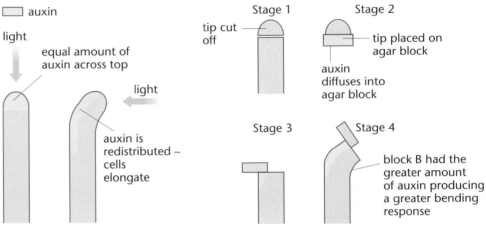

Auxin research

Many investigations of auxins have taken place using the growing tips (coleoptiles)
of grasses. Where a growing tip is removed and placed on an agar block, auxin will
diffuse into the agar. Returning the block to the mitotic area stimulates increased
cell elongation to the cells receiving a greater supply of auxin.

Is the concentration of auxin important?

It is important to consider the implications of the concentration of auxin in a tissue.
The graph below shows that at different concentrations, auxin affects the shoot
and the root in different ways.

Analyse this graph
carefully. It shows how
the same substance can
both stimulate or inhibit,
depending on
concentration.

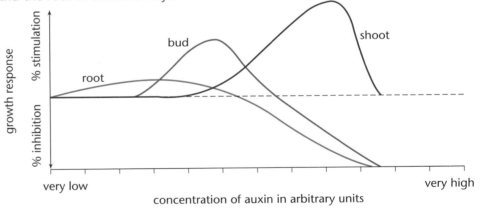

The graph shows:

- auxin has no effect on a shoot at very low concentration
- at these very low concentrations root cell elongation is stimulated
- at higher concentrations the elongation of shoot cells is stimulated
- at these higher concentrations auxin inhibits the elongation of root cells.

Auxin and root growth

The graph above shows that auxin affects root cells in a different way at different concentrations. At the root tip, auxin accumulates at a lower point because of gravity. This inhibits the lower cells from elongating. However, the higher cells at the tip have a low concentration of auxin and do elongate. The net effect is for the stronger upper cell growth to bend the root downwards. The plant therefore has more chance of obtaining more water and mineral ions.

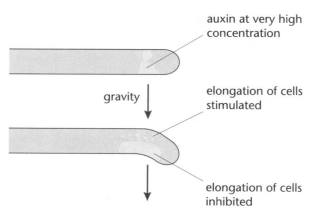

auxin at very high concentration

gravity

elongation of cells stimulated

elongation of cells inhibited

Plant growth regulators

In your examination, look out for data which will be supplied, e.g. the growth regulator gibberellin may be linked to falling starch levels in a seed endosperm and increase in maltose. Gibberellin has stimulated the enzymic activity.

Hormone	Some key functions
auxin	increased cell elongation, suppression of lateral bud development
gibberellin	cell elongation, ends dormancy in buds, promotes germination of seeds by activating hydrolytic enzymes such as amylase (food stores are mobilised!)
cytokinin	increased cell division, increased cell enlargement in leaves
ethene	promotes ripening of food

Sample question and model answer

(a) The diagram shows a neurone.

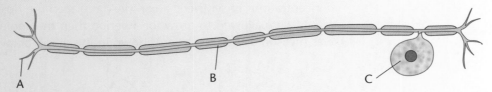

(i) What type of neurone is shown in the diagram? [1]

> sensory neurone

(ii) What structure would be found at A? [1]

> a receptor

(iii) Where precisely in the body is structure C found? [1]

> in the dorsal root ganglion

(iv) Structure B is covered by a myelin sheath.
Explain the function of the myelin sheath. [3]

> The myelin sheath insulates the neurone;
>
> Ions can only pass into the neurone at the nodes of Ranvier;
>
> This speeds up the transmission of the nerve impulse.

(b) The diagram shows a cone from the retina.

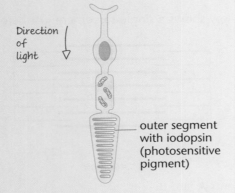

Direction of light

outer segment with iodopsin (photosensitive pigment)

(i) Place an arrow on the diagram to show the direction in which light reaches the cone. [1]

(ii) What is the function of the iodopsin in the outer segment? [4]

> when stimulated by light of the correct wavelength – breaks down to release opsin; opsin opens ion channels in the membranes; this can lead to the generation of an action potential in a bipolar cell.

(iii) How do cones contribute to high visual acuity? [3]

> cones are tightly packed giving a high surface area; each cone synapses onto a single bipolar neurone; so the greater detail gives higher resolution.

Practice examination questions

1 The growing tips were removed from oat stems. Agar blocks containing different concentrations of synthetic auxin (IAA) replaced the tips on the oat stems. The plants were allowed to grow for a period then the angle of curvature of the stems was measured. The results are shown in the graph below.

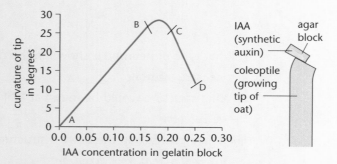

(a) What is the relationship between IAA concentration and curvature of the stem between points:

   (i) A and B   [1]

   (ii) C and D?   [1]

(b) Explain how IAA causes a curvature in the oat stems.   [2]

(c) Explain the effect a much higher concentration of IAA would have on the curvature of oat stems.   [2]

[Total: 6]

2 The diagram below shows a single sarcomere just before contraction.

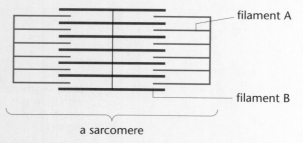

(a) Name filaments A and B.   [2]

(b) What stimulus causes the immediate contraction of a sarcomere?   [1]

(c) What happens to each type of filament during contraction?   [2]

[Total: 5]

3 The diagram below shows the profile of an action potential.

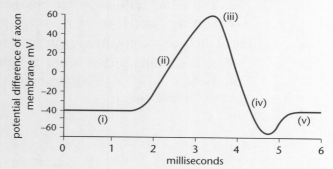

Explain what happens in the axon at each stage shown on the diagram.   [10]

[Total: 10]

Chapter 3

Homeostasis

The following topics are covered in this chapter:

- Hormones
- Regulation of blood sugar level
- Temperature control in a mammal
- Control of the menstrual cycle

3.1 Hormones

After studying this section you should be able to:

- *define homeostasis*
- *describe the route of hormones from source to target organ*
- *understand how hormones contribute to homeostasis*
- *recall the roles of a range of hormones*

LEARNING SUMMARY

The endocrine system

AQA   5.2/4/5

The endocrine system secretes a number of chemicals known as hormones. Each hormone is a substance produced by an endocrine gland, e.g. adrenal glands produce the hormone adrenaline. Each hormone is transported in the blood and has a target organ. Once the target organ is reached, the hormone triggers a response in the organ. Many hormones do this by activating enzymes. Others activate genes, e.g. steroids.

> The great advantage of homeostasis is that the conditions in the environment fluctuate but conditions in the organism remain stable.

> **KEY POINT**
>
> The endocrine and nervous systems both contribute to **coordination** in animals. They help to regulate internal processes. **Homeostasis** is the maintenance of a **constant internal environment**. Nerves and hormones have key roles in the maintenance of this **steady internal state**. Levels of pH, blood glucose, oxygen, carbon dioxide and temperature all need to be controlled.

Parts of the human endocrine system (both male and female organs shown!)

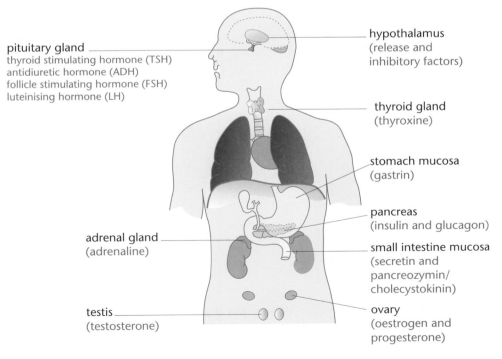

pituitary gland
thyroid stimulating hormone (TSH)
antidiuretic hormone (ADH)
follicle stimulating hormone (FSH)
luteinising hormone (LH)

hypothalamus
(release and inhibitory factors)

thyroid gland
(thyroxine)

stomach mucosa
(gastrin)

pancreas
(insulin and glucagon)

adrenal gland
(adrenaline)

small intestine mucosa
(secretin and pancreozymin/cholecystokinin)

testis
(testosterone)

ovary
(oestrogen and progesterone)

Some important mammalian hormones

The table shows the sources and some functions of a range of mammalian hormones. The pituitary gland is the key control gland. It affects many areas of the body and even stimulates, by the production of tropic hormones, other hormones, e.g. follicle stimulating hormone.

Hormone	Source	Effect
TSH	pituitary	stimulates the thyroid to secrete thyroxine
thyroxine	thyroid	increases metabolic rate
insulin	pancreas	reduces blood sugar
glucagon	pancreas	stimulates conversion of glycogen to glucose in the liver
ADH	pituitary	increased water reabsorption by kidney
gastrin	stomach mucosa	stimulates HCl production in stomach
secretin	intestinal mucosa	stimulates the pancreas to secrete fluid + alkali
pancreozymin	intestinal mucosa	stimulates the pancreas to secrete enzymes
FSH	pituitary	stimulates primary (Graafian) follicle to develop or testis to make sperms
LH	pituitary	stimulates ovulation or testis to make testosterone
oestrogen	ovary	stimulates development of endometrium stimulates secondary sexual characteristics
progesterone	ovary	maintains endometrium

Scientists are discovering a number of 'local hormones', such as histamine and prostaglandins. They do not travel far in the blood but only affect cells in the area.

How does a hormone trigger a cell in a target organ?

Hormones are much slower in eliciting a response than the nervous system. Rather than having an effect in milliseconds like nerves, hormones take longer. However, effects in response to hormones are often long lasting.

The diagram below shows one mechanism by which hormones activate target cells.

Did you know?
Each enzyme shown is constantly re-used as an active site is left free.

Look carefully at this mechanism! Just ONE hormone molecule arriving at the cell releases an enzyme which can be used many times. In turn, another enzyme is produced which can be used many times. One hormone molecule leads to amplification. This is a cascade effect.

Hormones that are proteins work in this way because they are unable to enter the cell. Steroid hormones, (e.g. oestrogen) can pass through the cell membrane as they are lipid soluble.

3.2 Temperature control in a mammal

After studying this section you should be able to:

- *outline the processes which contribute to temperature regulation in a mammal*
- *understand how nervous and endocrine systems work together to regulate body temperature*
- *understand how internal processes are regulated by negative feedback*

LEARNING SUMMARY

What are the advantages of controlling body temperature?

 AQA 5.4

It is advantageous to maintain a constant body temperature so that the enzymes which drive the processes of life can function at an optimum level.

- **Endothermic** (warm blooded) animals can maintain their core temperature at an optimal level. This allows internal processes to be consistent. The level of activity of an endotherm is likely to fluctuate less than an ectotherm.

- **Ectothermic** (cold blooded) animals have a body temperature which fluctuates with the environmental temperature. As a result there are times when an animal may be vulnerable due to the enzyme-driven reactions being slow. When a crocodile (ectotherm) is in cold conditions, its speed of attack would be slow. When in warm conditions, the attack would be rapid.

How is temperature controlled in a mammal?

Once the blood temperature decreases, the heat gain centre of the hypothalamus is stimulated. This leads to a rise in blood temperature which, in turn, results in the heat loss centre being stimulated. This is negative feedback! The combination of the two, in both directions, contributes to homeostasis.

The **hypothalamus** has **many functions**. It controls thirst, hunger, sleep and it stimulates the production of many hormones other than those required for temperature regulation.

The key structure in homeostatic control of all body processes is the **hypothalamus**. The regulation of temperature involves thermoreceptors in the skin, body core and blood vessels supplying the brain, which link to the hypothalamus.

The diagram below shows how the peripheral nerves, hypothalamus and pituitary gland integrate nervous and endocrine glands to regulate temperature.

Temperature regulation model

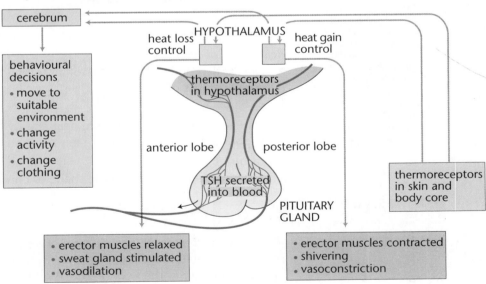

If there is an increase in core temperature then the hypothalamus stimulates greater heat loss by:

- vasodilation (dilation of the skin arterioles)
- relaxing of erector-pili muscles so that hairs lie flat
- more sweating
- behavioural response in humans to change to thinner clothing.

When the hypothalamus receives sensory information **heat loss** or **heat gain** control results.

A capillary bed

arteriole
(a sphincter
muscle)

venule

shunt vessel

artery

vein

A **fall** in temperature results in the following control responses.

Vasoconstriction
- Arteriole control is initiated by the hypothalamus which results in efferent neurones stimulating constriction of the arteriole sphincters of skin capillary beds.
- This deviates blood to the core of the body, so less heat energy is lost from the skin.

Contraction of the erector-pili muscles
- Erector-pili muscle contraction is initiated in the hypothalamus being controlled via efferent neurones.
- Hairs on skin stand on end and trap an insulating layer of air, so less heat energy is lost from the skin.

Sweat reduction
- The sweat glands control is also initiated in the hypothalamus, and is controlled via efferent neurones.
- Less heat energy is lost from the skin by evaporation of sweat.

Shivering
- Increased muscular contraction is accompanied by heat energy release.

Behavioural response
- A link from the hypothalamus to the cerebrum elicits this voluntary response.
- This could be to switch on the heating, put on warmer clothes, etc.

Increased metabolic rate
- The hypothalamus produces a release factor substance.
- This stimulates the anterior part of the pituitary gland to secrete TSH (thyroid stimulating hormone).
- TSH reaches the thyroid via the blood.
- Thyroid gland is stimulated to secrete thyroxine.
- Thyroxine increases respiration in the tissues increasing the body temperature.

Once a higher thyroxine level is detected in the blood the release factor in hypothalamus is inhibited so TSH release by the pituitary gland is prevented. This is **negative feedback**.

An **increase** in body temperature results in almost the **opposite** of each response described for a fall of temperature.

Vasodilation
- Arterioles of capillary beds dilate allowing more blood to skin capillary beds.

Relaxation of erector-pili muscles
- Hairs lie flat, no insulating layer of air trapped.
- More heat loss of skin.

Sweat increase
- More sweat is excreted so more heat energy from the body is needed to evaporate the sweat, so the organism cools down.

Behavioural response
- This could be to move into the shade or consume a cold drink.

Note
(a) the outline for heat loss methods does not show the nerve connections. Efferent neurones are again coordinated via the hypothalamus!
(b) heat is lost from the skin via a combination of **conduction**, **convection** and **radiation**.

Progress check

Hormone X stimulates the production of a substance in a cell of a target organ. The following statements outline events which result in the production of the substance but are in the wrong order. Write the correct order of letters.

A Hormone X is transported in the blood.
B Hormone X binds with a receptor protein in the cell surface membrane.
C The enzyme catalyses a reaction, forming a product.
D Hormone X is secreted by a gland.
E This releases an enzyme from the cell surface membrane.

D, A, B, E, C.

3.3 Regulation of blood sugar level

After studying this section you should be able to:

- *understand the control of blood glucose levels in a person*
- *describe the sites of insulin and glucagon secretion*
- *explain the functions of insulin and glucagon*

LEARNING SUMMARY

Why is it necessary to control the amount of glucose in the blood?

AQA   5.4

Glucose molecules are needed to supply energy for every living cell. The level in the blood must be high enough to meet this need (90 mg per 100 cm^3 blood). This level needs to be maintained at a constant level, even though a person may or may not have eaten. High levels of glucose in the blood would cause great problems. Hypertonic blood plasma would result in water leaving the tissues by osmosis. Dehydration of organs would result in a number of symptoms.

Blood glucose regulation

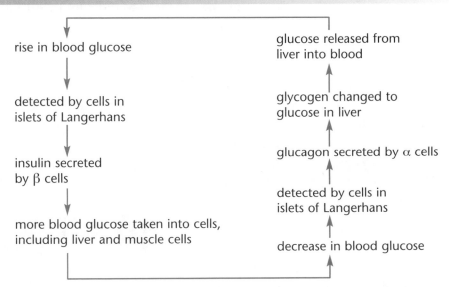

rise in blood glucose

↓

detected by cells in islets of Langerhans

↓

insulin secreted by β cells

↓

more blood glucose taken into cells, including liver and muscle cells

glucose released from liver into blood

↑

glycogen changed to glucose in liver

↑

glucagon secreted by α cells

↑

detected by cells in islets of Langerhans

↑

decrease in blood glucose

Positive feedback is rare in living organisms because any change brings about a response that increases the danger.

Negative feedback

Blood glucose regulation is an example of negative feedback. Any change in glucose level initiates changes which will result in the return of the original level – **balance is achieved.**

KEY POINT

Insulin

- Is secreted into the blood due to stimulation of pancreatic cells by a **high concentration** of glucose in the blood.
- Is produced by the **β cells** of the **islets of Langerhans** in the pancreas.
- Binds to receptor proteins in cell surface membranes activating carrier proteins to **allow glucose entry** to cells.
- Allows **excess glucose** molecules into the liver and muscles where they are converted into **glycogen** (a storage product), and some fat.

Never state that insulin changes glucose to glycogen. It allows glucose into the liver where the enzyme glycogen synthase catalyses the conversion.

Glucagon

- Is secreted into the blood due to stimulation of pancreatic cells by a **low concentration** of glucose in the blood.
- Is produced by the **α cells** of the **islets of Langerhans** in the pancreas.
- Stimulates the conversion of glycogen to **glucose.**

Diabetes

There are two types of this condition.

Type 1

- The pancreas fails to produce enough insulin.
- After a meal when blood glucose level increases dramatically, the level remains high.
- High blood glucose causes hyperglycaemia.
- Kidneys, even though they are healthy, cannot reabsorb the glucose, resulting in glucose being in the urine.
- Symptoms include dehydration, loss of weight and lethargy.

What is the answer?

- Insulin injections and a carbohydrate controlled diet.

Type 2

- This form of diabetes usually occurs in later life.
- Insulin is still produced but the receptor proteins on the cell surface membranes may not work correctly.
- Glucose uptake by the cells is erratic.
- Symptoms are similar to those for type 1 but are mild in comparison.

What is the answer?

- Dietary control including low carbohydrate intake.

More liver functions

The role of the liver in its production of bile, as well as the storage and break down of glycogen has been highlighted. The liver does so much more!

Transamination

> Children need 10 essential amino acids (adults need 8). From these they can make different ones by transamination in the liver.

This is the way an R group of a keto acid is transferred to an amino acid. It replaces the existing R group with another and a new amino acid is formed.

CH_3 amino acid + C_2H_5 keto acid → C_2H_5 amino acid + CH_3 keto acid

Note the changes in the 'R' group of each acid.

Deamination

> The liver has many functions including:
> - detoxification of poisonous substances
> - heat production.

This process is necessary to lower the level of **excess amino acids**. They are produced when proteins are digested. Nitrogenous materials have a high degree of toxicity, so the level in the blood must be limited.

$$2NH_2-\underset{\underset{H}{|}}{\overset{\overset{R}{|}}{C}}-COOH + O_2 \rightarrow 2\underset{\underset{O}{\|}}{\overset{\overset{R}{|}}{C}}-COOH + 2NH_3$$

amino acid   oxygen   keto acid   ammonia

Ornithine cycle

> Both deamination and the ornithine cycle are needed to process excess amino acids. Remember that urea is a less toxic substance. The **liver makes** it but the **kidneys** help to **excrete** it.

Ammonia is immediately taken up by ornithine to help make a less toxic substance, urea.

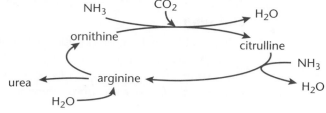

3.4 Control of the menstrual cycle

After studying this section you should be able to:

- *recall the hormones that control the menstrual cycle*
- *describe how these hormones produce cyclical changes*

What controls the menstrual cycle?

AQA ▸ 5.5

Events which take place within a female, such as ovulation and menstruation, need to be coordinated. Menstruation, the break down and loss of the lining of the uterus, would have a devastating consequence if a woman was pregnant. The foetus would be miscarried.

The menstrual cycle is controlled by the secretion of **hormones** by the **endocrine system**. The flow diagram below shows how the process achieves coordination.

> Note that at the start of the menstrual cycle FSH is supported by a smaller quantity of LH to stimulate the development of a follicle. Later the proportion reverses so that a larger amount of LH is aided by a smaller amount of FSH resulting in ovulation.

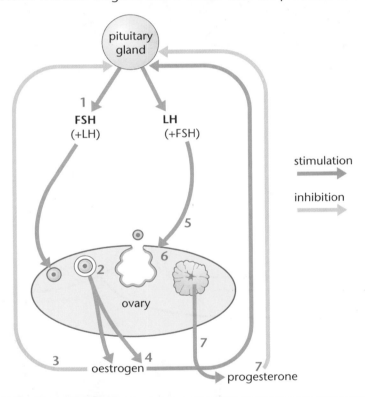

Stages of the menstrual cycle

1 (a) FSH (follicle stimulating hormone) is secreted into the bloodstream by the pituitary gland. It stimulates the development of a Graafian follicle and so triggers the development of an ovum.

   (b) At the same time a small amount of LH (luteinising hormone) is secreted by the pituitary gland which reinforces the effect of the FSH.

2 As a follicle develops, its wall (**theca**) begins to secrete oestrogen which stimulates the building of the endometrium (lining of uterus).

3 The oestrogen inhibits the secretion of FSH *temporarily* but LH hormone secretion continues.

4 A peak of oestrogen is reached which results in a surge of LH with some FSH which is no longer inhibited.

5 When LH peaks it causes ovulation – the follicle ruptures releasing the ovum.

6 The empty follicle now changes role and becomes a corpus luteum which begins to secrete progesterone.

7 (a) Progesterone keeps the endometrium in position, as it will be needed if a foetus is to develop in the uterus.

(b) Progesterone also inhibits the secretion of any FSH or LH by the pituitary gland. Ovulation is ultimately prevented by high concentrations of progesterone.

8 If no sperm fertilises an ovum during the cycle, then the corpus luteum degenerates and a drop in progesterone takes place. Low progesterone does not inhibit the FSH and LH so that they are both able to be secreted again.

The cycle is now complete – *GO BACK TO STAGE 1!*

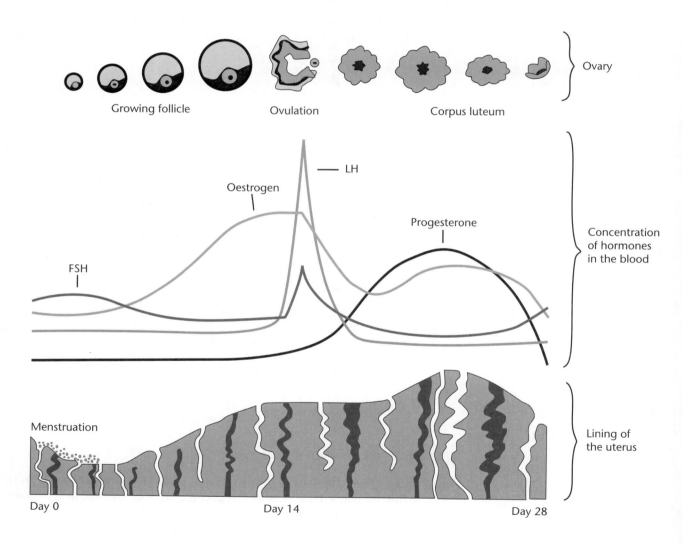

Sample question and model answer

The graph shows changes in the concentration of progesterone in the blood during the menstrual cycle.

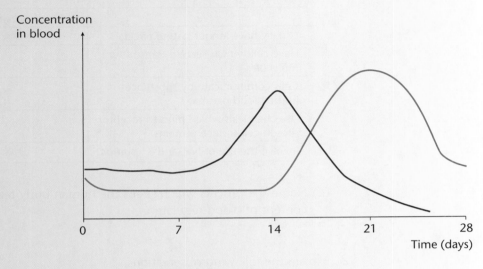

(a) Write down precisely where progesterone is produced. [1]

In the corpus luteum in the ovary.

(b) How does progesterone reach the uterus? [1]

It is carried in the plasma of the blood.

(c) On the graph, draw a line to show the concentration of oestrogen changes from day 0 to day 28. [2]

(d) Was the woman pregnant? Give a reason for your answer. [1]

No. The levels of progesterone fall after 21 days.

(e) State one effect of progesterone. [1]

Maintains the lining of the uterus. / Makes the muscle of the uterus contract less. / Inhibits the release of LH.

Practice examination questions

1 (a) Complete the table below to compare the nervous and endocrine systems. Put a tick in each correct box for the features shown.

	Nervous system	*Endocrine system*
Usually have longer lasting effects		
Have cells which secrete transmitter molecules		
Cells communicate by substances in the blood plasma		
Use chemicals which bind to receptor sites in cell surface proteins		
Involve the use of Na⁺ and K⁺ pumps		

[2]

(b) Name the process which keeps the human body temperature and water content of blood regulated. [1]

[Total: 3]

2 Explain the following observations.

(a) Dogs pant in hot weather. [2]

(b) The human skin looks pale in cold weather.

[2]

(c) It feels more uncomfortable in humid conditions compared to dry conditions. [2]

3 The graph below shows the relative levels of glucose in the blood of two people: A and B. One is healthy and the other one is diabetic.

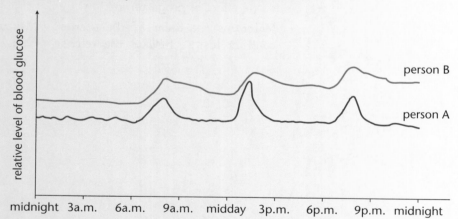

(a) Which person is diabetic? Give evidence from the graph for your answer. [1]

(b) What is the evidence that both people produce insulin? [1]

(c) Where in the body is insulin produced? [2]

[Total: 4]

Chapter 4

Further genetics

The following topics are covered in this chapter:

- Genes, alleles and protein synthesis
- Inheritance

4.1 Genes, alleles and protein synthesis

After studying this section you should be able to:

- explain how proteins are produced in cells
- describe various methods by which gene expression is controlled
- define a range of important genetic terms

LEARNING SUMMARY

Genes, alleles and protein synthesis

 AQA 5.6

A gene is a section of DNA which controls the production of a polypeptide in an organism. The total effects of all of the genes of an organism are responsible for the characteristics of that organism. Each protein contributes to these characteristics whatever its role, e.g. structural, enzymic or hormonal.

The order of bases in the gene is called the genetic code and will code for the order of amino acids in the polypeptide. The order of amino acids is called the primary structure of the protein and will determine how the protein folds up to form the secondary and tertiary structures. The formation of a protein molecule is called protein synthesis.

Protein synthesis

The process of protein synthesis involves the DNA and several other molecules.

- **Messenger RNA:** This is a single-stranded nucleotide chain that is made in the nucleus. It carries the complementary DNA code out of the nucleus to the ribosomes in the cytoplasm.
- **mRNA polymerase:** This is the enzyme that joins the mRNA nucleotides together to form a chain.
- **ATP:** This is needed to provide the energy to make the mRNA molecule and to join the amino acids together.
- **tRNA:** This is a short length of RNA that is shaped rather like a clover leaf. There is one type of tRNA molecule for every different amino acid. The tRNA molecule has three unpaired bases that can bind with mRNA on one end and a binding site for a specific amino acid on the other end.

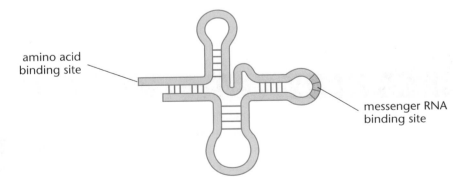

amino acid
binding site

messenger RNA
binding site

Key points from AS

- **The genetic code**
  Revise AS pages 73–75

The following diagrams show protein synthesis.

1 In the nucleus **RNA polymerase** links to a start code along a DNA strand.

2 RNA polymerase moves along the DNA. For every organic base it meets along the DNA a complementary base is linked to form mRNA (**messenger RNA**).

> There is no thymine in mRNA. Instead there is another base, uracil.

Pairing of organic bases				
DNA	G	C	T	A
mRNA	C	G	A	U

3 RNA polymerase links to a stop code along the DNA and finally the mRNA **moves** to a **ribosome**. The DNA stays in the nucleus for the next time it is needed.

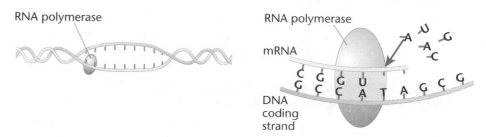

The transfer of the code from DNA to mRNA is called transcription.

4 Every three bases along the mRNA make up one **codon** which codes for a specific amino acid. Three complementary bases form an **anticodon** attached to one end of tRNA (**transfer RNA**). At the other end of the RNA is a specific amino acid.

5 All along the mRNA the tRNA 'partner' molecules enable each amino acid to bond to the next. A chain of amino acids (**polypeptide**) is made, ready for release into the cell.

> Note the link between each pair of amino acids along a polypeptide – the peptide link.

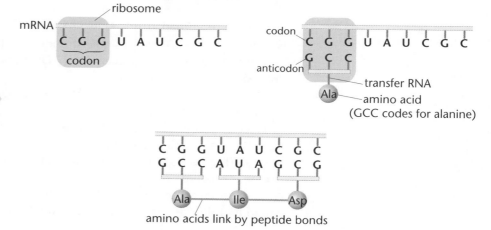

amino acids link by peptide bonds

The conversion of the mRNA code to a sequence of amino acids is called translation.

Control of protein synthesis

AQA 5.7

In a multicellular organism every cell contains all the genetic material needed to make every protein that the organism requires. However, as they develop, cells become specialised. This means that they do not need to use every protein and so it would be a waste to make every protein all the time. Genes must be switched on and switched off.

Most of the early work on gene regulation was carried out of bacteria which are prokaryotic. During the 1950s, Jacob and Monod found that the bacterium E.Coli would only produce the enzyme lactase if lactose was present in the growth medium. The production of lactose was controlled by three different genes:

- A structural gene which codes for the enzyme.
- An operator gene which turns the structural gene on.
- A regulator gene that produces a chemical that usually stops the action of the operator gene.

If lactose is present the action of the chemical inhibitor is blocked and lactase is made.

In eukaryotic cells, gene regulation seems to be much more complicated. Cells in the early embryo are called **totipotent**. This means that they can develop into any type of cell.

In mature plants many cells remain totipotent but in mature animals these totipotent or **stem cells** are harder to find. There is much interest in the possibility of using stem cells to cure certain degenerative diseases.

These cells produce all the cells of a multicellular organism and the specialised cells have to be produced in the correct place. Scientists are trying to work out how this is done and have found genes called **homeobox genes**. These genes seem to produce proteins that act as transcription factors turning on other genes. Similar homeobox genes have been found in animals, plants and fungi.

Other factors from the cytoplasm can also affect transcription. **Steroid hormones** such as oestrogen can bind with **receptors** in the cytoplasm and then move into the nucleus causing genes to be transcribed.

There is much interest at present in the possible use of siRNA to treat various genetic conditions.

Scientists have recently found a different type of RNA. This is a small double stranded molecule called siRNA (small interfering RNA). This seems to silence the action of certain genes.

Essential genetic terms

AQA   5.7

Check out all of these genetic terms.

- Look carefully at the technique of giving an example with each definition. Often examples help to clarify your answer and are usually accepted by the examiners.
- In examination papers you will need to apply your understanding to **new** situations.
- Genetics has a specialist language which you will need to use.

It is necessary to understand the following range of specialist terms used in genetics.

Allele – an alternative form of a gene, always located on the same position along a chromosome. This position is called a locus.

    E.g. an allele coding for the white colour of petals

Dominant allele – if an organism has two different alleles then this is the one which is expressed, often represented by a capital letter.

    E.g. an allele coding for the red colour pigment of petals, **R**

Recessive allele – if an organism has two different alleles then this is the one which is **not** expressed, often represented by a lower case letter. Recessive alleles are only expressed when they are not masked by the presence of a dominant allele.

    E.g. an allele coding for the white colour pigment of petals, **r**.

Homozygous – refers to the fact that in a diploid organism both alleles for a particular gene are the same.

    E.g. **R R** or **r r**.

Heterozygous – refers to the fact that in a diploid organism both alleles for a particular gene are different.

    E.g. **R r** (petal colour would be expressed as red).

A number of inherited alleles of a range of genes often exhibit continuous variation, e.g. height. Each allele contributes small incremental differences. That is why there are smooth changes in height across a population.

Co-dominance – refers to the fact that occasionally two alleles for a gene are expressed equally in the organism.

E.g. **A**, **B** alleles = **AB** (blood group with antigens A and B).

Polygenic inheritance – where an inherited feature is controlled by two or more genes, along different loci along a chromosome. This results in continuous variation.

E.g. the height of a person is controlled by a number of different genes.

Remember that both sperms and ova are haploid.

Haploid – refers to a cell which has a single set of chromosomes.

E.g. a nucleus in a human sperm has 23 single chromosomes.

Diploid – refers to a cell which has two sets of chromosomes.

E.g. a nucleus in a human liver cell has 23 pairs of chromosomes.

In diploid cells one set of chromosomes is from the male parent and one from the female.

Homologous chromosomes – refers to the pairs of chromosomes seen during cell division. These chromosomes lie side by side, each gene at each locus being the same.

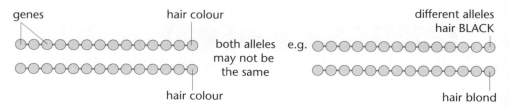

Often polyploid organisms cannot reproduce sexually but asexually they are successful.

Polyploid – refers to the fact that a cell has three or more sets of chromosomes. This can increase yield.

E.g. cultivated potato plants are tetraploid, that is four sets of chromosomes in a cell. (Tetraploidy is a form of polyploidy.)

Genotype – refers to all of the genes found in the nuclei of an organism, including both dominant and recessive alleles.

    dominant

E.g. A B c d E F g H i   (all alleles are included in a genotype)

      a B C D e f g h I

 recessive

phenotype = genotype + environment

Phenotype includes all alleles which are expressed in an organism. The environment supplies resources and conditions for development. Varying conditions result in an organism developing differently. Identical twins fed different diets will show some differences, e.g. weight.

Environment has considerable effect.

Linkage – refers to two or more genes which are located on the same chromosome.

E.g. linked X------------------Y-- not linked X-------------------- ← different

same chromosomes ⟋   -------------------Y-- ← chromosomes

Somatic cell – refers to any body cell which is not involved in reproduction.

E.g. liver cell

Autosome – refers to every chromosome apart from the sex chromosomes, X and Y.

4.2 Inheritance

After studying this section you should be able to:

- *understand Mendel's laws of inheritance*
- *understand the principles of monohybrid inheritance*
- *describe the principle of sex determination*
- *use the Hardy–Weinberg principle to predict the numbers of future genotypes*

Mendel and the laws of inheritance

AQA   4.8

Gregor Mendel was the monk who gave us our understanding of genetics. He worked with pea plants to work out genetic relationships.

> **KEY POINT**
>
> Mendel's first law indicates that:
> - each character of a diploid organism is controlled by a pair of alleles
> - from this pair of alleles only one can be represented in a gamete.

Monohybrid inheritance

> Always show your working out of a genetical relationship in a logical way, just like solving a mathematics problem.

Mendel found that when homozygous pea plants were crossed, a predictable ratio resulted. The cross below shows Mendel's principle.

pea plants   pea plants
T = TALL (dominant)   t = dwarf (recessive)

A homozygous TALL plant was crossed with a homozygous recessive plant

$$TT \quad \times \quad tt$$

gametes   (T)   (T)   (t)   (t)

F_1 generation   Tt

All offspring 100% TALL, and heterozygous.

> If you have to choose the symbols to explain genetics, then use something like **N** and **n**. Here the upper and lower cases are very different. **S** and **s** are corrupted as you write quickly and may be confused by the examiner awarding your marks.

Heterozygous plants were crossed

$$Tt \quad \times \quad Tt$$

gametes   (T)   (t)   (T)   (t)

	(T)	(t)
(T)	TT	Tt
(t)	Tt	tt

2 × 2 Punnet square to work out different genotypes

> In examinations you may have to work out a probability. 3:1 is the same as a 1 in 4 chance. Remember only large numbers would confirm the ratio.

F_2 generation   3 TALL : 1 DWARF

In making this cross Mendel investigated **one** gene only. The height differences of the plants were due to the different alleles. Mendel kept all environmental conditions the same for all seedlings as they developed. The 3:1 ratio of tall to short plants only holds true for large numbers of offspring.

Sex determination and sex linkage

AQA   4.8

The genetic information for gender is carried on specific chromosomes. In humans there are 22 pairs of autosomes plus the special sex determining pair, either **XY** (**male**) or **XX** (**female**). In some organisms such as birds this is reversed.

Some genes for sex determination are on autosomes but are activated by genes on the sex chromosomes.

Sperm can carry an X or Y chromosome, whereas an egg carries only an X chromosome.

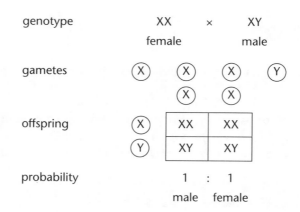

genotype   XX   ×   XY
          female   male

probability   1   :   1
         male   female

> The genetic cross shown should not give you any problems at A2 Level. However, look out for the combination of another factor which will increase difficulty.

This shows how 50:50 males to females are produced.

Sex linkage

Look more closely at the structure of the X and Y chromosomes.

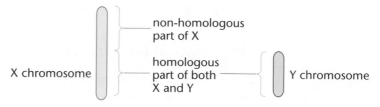

> Why do they not look like X and Y? Only when the cells are dividing, do they take the XY shape, after chromatid formation.

Homologous part of the sex chromosomes

- Has the same genes in both sexes.
- Each gene can be represented by the same or different alleles at each locus.

Non-homologous part of the sex chromosomes

- This means that the X chromosome has genes in this area, whereas the Y chromosome, being shorter, has no corresponding genes.
- Genes in this area of the X chromosome are always expressed, because there is no potential of a dominant allele to mask them.
- There are some notable genes found on the non-homologous part, e.g. haemophilia trait, and colour blindness trait.

The sex chromosomes, X and Y, carry genes other than those involved in sex determination. Examples of such genes are:

- a gene which controls blood clotting, i.e. is responsible for the production of factor VIII vital in the clotting process
- a gene which controls the ability to detect red and green colours.

The loci of both genes are on the non-homologous part of chromosome X.

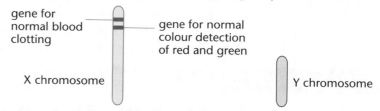

What is the effect of sex linked genes?

The fact that these genes are linked to the X chromosome has no significant effect when the **genes perform their functions correctly**. There are consequences, however, if the genes fail. This can be illustrated by a consideration of **red–green colour blindness**. When a gene is carried on a sex chromosome, the usual way to show this is by X^R.

R = normal colour vision (dominant)   r = red–green colour blindness (recessive)

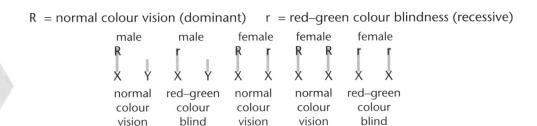

	male	male	female	female	female
	R	r	R r	R R	r r
	X Y	X Y	X X	X X	X X
	normal colour vision	red–green colour blind	normal colour vision (carrier)	normal colour vision	red–green colour blind

You can see the four possible genotypes. A female needs two r alleles, a male just needs one.

The genetic diagram shows that a female needs two recessive alleles (one from each parent) to be colour blind. A male has only one gene at this locus, so one recessive allele is enough to give colour blindness. The colour blindness gene is rare, so the chances of being a colour blind female are very low.

Consider these crosses.

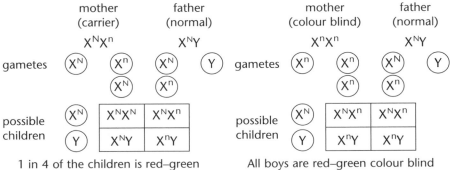

	mother (carrier) $X^N X^n$	father (normal) $X^N Y$
gametes	X^N X^n	X^N Y
	X^N X^n	

possible children	X^N	Y
X^N	$X^N X^N$	$X^N X^n$
X^n	$X^N Y$	$X^n Y$

1 in 4 of the children is red–green colour blind. 50% of boys are colour blind, but no girls.

	mother (colour blind) $X^n X^n$	father (normal) $X^N Y$
gametes	X^n X^n	X^N Y
	X^n X^n	

possible children	X^N	Y
X^n	$X^N X^n$	$X^N X^n$
X^n	$X^n Y$	$X^n Y$

All boys are red–green colour blind. No girls are colour blind.

Progress check

What is the probability of a colour blind male and carrier female producing:
(a) a boy with normal colour vision
(b) a colour blind girl?
Show your working.

(a) 1 in 4 (b) 1 in 4

	mother (carrier)	father (colour blind)
	$X^N X^n$	$X^n Y$
X^N	$X^N X^n$	$X^N Y$
X^n	$X^n X^n$	$X^n Y$

Co-dominance

 AQA 4.8

This term is given when each of two *different* alleles of a gene are expressed in the phenotype of an organism. In humans there are two co-dominant alleles that determine our blood groups. These alleles produce the antigens in blood which are responsible for our blood groups.

Remember that for co-dominance there is no dominance. Both alleles are equally expressed.

Consider these crosses

Blood group	Genotypes
A	$I^A I^A$, $I^A I^O$
B	$I^B I^B$, $I^B I^O$
AB	$I^A I^B$
O	$I^O I^O$

The allele for production of:

A antigen in blood = I^A
B antigen in blood = I^B
No antigen in blood = I^O

Look out for more examples of co-dominance in examination questions, e.g. in shorthorn cattle, R = red and W = white. Where they occur in the phenotype together they produce a dappled intermediary colour known as roan.

	Mother × Father
	$I^B I^O$ $I^A I^O$
gametes	I^B I^O I^A I^O

children	I^B	I^O
I^A	$I^A I^B$	$I^A I^O$
I^O	$I^B I^O$	$I^O I^O$

All blood groups produced by this cross.

	Mother × Father
	$I^A I^B$ $I^A I^O$
gametes	I^A I^B I^A I^O

children	I^A	I^B
I^A	$I^A I^A$	$I^A I^B$
I^O	$I^A I^O$	$I^B I^O$

There must be a I^O from both parents to produce an O blood group.

In this instance, there are two co-dominant alleles, I^A and I^B. When inherited together they are both expressed in the phenotype. Group O blood does not have any antigen. I^A and I^B are both dominant over I^O.

The gene that controls our blood group is also said to show multiple alleles. This means that there are more than two possible alleles that can be found in the gene (I^A, I^O and I^B).

Remember, however, that one person can only have two copies of the alleles.

Hardy–Weinberg principle

AQA   4.8

The application of this principle allows us to **predict numbers of expected genotypes** in a population in the future. The principle tracks the proportion of two different alleles in the population.

Before applying the Hardy–Weinberg principle, the following criteria must be satisfied.

- There must be no immigration and no emigration.
- There must be no mutations.
- There must be no selection (natural or artificial).
- There must be true random mating.
- All genotypes must be equally fertile.

Once the above criteria are satisfied then **gene frequencies remain constant**.

> A **gene pool** consists of all genes and their alleles, which are part of the reproductive cells of an organism. Only genes that are in cells that **can be passed on** are part of the gene pool.

Hardy–Weinberg principle: the terms identified

p   = the frequency of the dominant allele in the population

q   = the frequency of the recessive allele in the population

p^2 = the frequency of homozygous dominant individuals

q^2 = the frequency of homozygous recessive individuals

2pq = the frequency of heterozygous individuals

The principle is based on two equations:

(i) $p + q = 1$ (gene pool)
(ii) $p^2 + 2pq + q^2 = 1$ (total population)

KEY POINT

Applying the Hardy–Weinberg principle

A population of *Cepaea nemoralis* (land snail) lived in a field. In a survey there were 1400 pink-shelled snails and 600 were yellow. There were two alleles for shell colour.

Y = pink shell (dominant)   y = yellow shell (recessive). Snails with pink shells can be YY or Yy. Snails with yellow shells can be yy only.

phenotype   pink   yellow
genotype   YY   Yy   yy

This part of the calculation is to find the frequency of the recessive and dominant alleles in the population.

$$q^2 = \frac{600}{2000}$$
$$= 0.3$$
$$q = \sqrt{0.30} = 0.55$$

But: $p + q = 1$
$p = 1 - 0.55$
$= 0.45$

This part of the calculation is to find the frequency of homozygous and heterozygous snails in the population.

So: $p^2 = 0.20$

But: $p^2 + 2pq + q^2 = 1$
$0.20 + 0.50 + 0.30 = 1$
YY   Yy   yy

Always use the $p + q = 1$ equation to calculate the frequency of alleles if you are given suitable data, e.g. 'out of 400 diploid organisms in a population there were 40 homozygous recessive individuals'. 40 organisms have 80 recessive alleles.

$$q = \frac{80}{800}$$
$$= 0.1$$

From this figure you can calculate the others.

Points to note

- These proportions can be applied to the snail populations in say, 10 years in the future.
- If there were 24 000 snails in the population, then the relative numbers would be:
  YY $0.2 \times 24\,000 = 4800$
  Yy $0.5 \times 24\,000 = 12\,000$
  yy $0.3 \times 24\,000 = 7200$
- Remember that the five criteria must be satisfied if the relationship is to hold true.
- It is not possible to see which snails are homozygous dominant and which are heterozygous. They all look the same, pink! Hardy–Weinberg informs us, statistically, of those proportions.

It is also possible to apply the Hardy–Weinberg principle to a co-dominant pair of alleles. P and q are calculated by exactly the same method.

Sample question and model answer

(a) Explain the difference between sex linkage and autosomal linkage. [2]

sex linkage – genes are located on a sex chromosome

autosomal linkage – genes are located on one of the other 44 chromosomes

(b) The diagram below shows part of a family tree where some of the people have haemophilia.

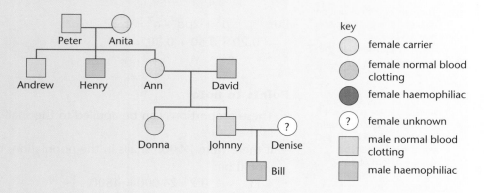

This type of question is a challenge! Note the key for the symbols and then apply them to the family tree. Think logically and work up and down the diagram. In your 'live' examination write on the diagram to help you work out each individual genotype asked in the question. If there are a range of possible genotypes they may be helpful.

Show the possible genotypes of Denise. Give evidence from the genetic diagram to support your answer. [3]

Let H = normal blood clotting

Let h = haemophiliac trait

The genotype can be X^HX^h or X^hX^h

Reason – Johnny is X^HY so he is responsible for Bill's Y chromosome (Y chromosomes do not carry a blood clotting gene)

Working backwards, Bill is haemophiliac so Denise must have at least one X^h

She can, therefore, be X^hX^h or X^HX^h

(c) Peter and Anita had three children. Andrew was born first, then Henry and finally Ann. Use the information in the diagram to answer the questions.

(i) When could genetic counselling have been given to help Peter and Anita? [1]

After the birth of Henry.

(ii) Explain the useful information which they could have been given. [3]

Since Henry is haemophiliac his genotype is X^hY.

His father, Peter, has normal clotting blood so is X^HY and passes on a Y to his son, Henry.

His mother is not haemophiliac but must be a carrier, X^HX^h because mother passes on X^h.

We can predict 2 in 4 children will have normal clotting of blood,

1 in 4 will be female and a carrier and 1 in 4 will be haemophiliac male.

Practice examination questions

1 (a) List the criteria which must be satisfied before applying the Hardy–Weinberg principle. [4]

(b) In a population of 160 small mammals, some had a dark brown coat and the others had a light brown coat. Dark brown (B) is dominant over light brown (b). In the population there were 48 light brown individuals. Using the Hardy–Weinberg equations calculate:

(i) the frequency of homozygous dominant and heterozygous individuals in the population [3]

(ii) how many of each of the genotypes (BB, Bb, bb) there would be in a future population of 10 000 individuals. [2]

[Total: 9]

2 Match each term with its correct definition.

A co-dominance
B polygenic inheritance
C genotype
D polyploid
E somatic

(i) a cell which is not involved in reproduction [1]

(ii) a nucleus which has three or more sets of chromosomes [1]

(iii) a feature which is controlled by two or more genes, along different loci along a chromosome [1]

(iv) two alleles which are equally expressed in the organism [1]

(v) all of the genes found in a nucleus, including both dominant and recessive alleles [1]

[Total: 5]

3 The letters below represent the organic bases along the coding strand of a DNA molecule.

CCG ATT CGA TAG

(a) What term is given to each group of three bases? [1]

(b) Give **two** functions of a group of three organic bases. [2]

[Total: 3]

Chapter 5

Variation and selection

The following topics are covered in this chapter:

- Variation
- Selection and speciation

5.1 Variation

After studying this section you should be able to:

- explain the different sources of variation in organisms
- describe different types of mutation

LEARNING SUMMARY

Variation and mutations

AQA   5.6

Meiosis and sexual reproduction can produce variation in a number of ways. These include:

- segregation or independent assortment of homologous chromosomes
- chiasmata formation leading to crossing over
- random fusion of gametes.

All these processes will combine alleles in different combinations.

The environment will also contribute to variation. The combination of environmental variation and a number of genes controlling a characteristic (polygenic inheritance) will often result in a wide range of phenotypes and continuous variation. However, the only way that new alleles can be made is by mutation.

Mutation is a change in the DNA of a cell. If the cell affected by mutation is a somatic cell, then its effect is restricted to the organism itself. If, however, the mutation affects gametes, then the genetic change will be inherited by the future population.

Gene mutations

A gene mutation involves a change in a single gene. This is often a point mutation.

Bases can change along DNA and this may cause mutation. One changed base along the coding strand of DNA may have a sequential effect of changing most amino acids along a polypeptide.

before mutation
TTA CCG GCC ATC

after mutation
ATT ACC GGC CAT C

This is addition!

> DNA codes for the sequence of amino acids along polypeptides and ultimately the characteristics of an organism. Each amino acid is coded for by a triplet of bases along the coding strand of DNA, e.g. TTA codes for threonine. The change in a triplet base code can result in a new amino acid, e.g. ATT codes for serine. This type of DNA change along a chromosome is known as a point mutation. A point mutation involves a change in a single base along a chromosome by addition, insertion, deletion or inversion.
>
> KEY POINT

An example of a gene mutation is a change in the DNA coding for the protein haemoglobin. This can cause sickle-cell anaemia.

Sometimes a point mutation may not cause a change in the phenotype. This is because the genetic code is degenerate. Often one amino acid has more than one triplet coding for it. Therefore a change in a base may not change the amino acid.

Key points from AS

- **Variation**
  Revise AS pages 83–84

More mutations are shown below. Each section of DNA along the chromosomes is shown by organic bases.

Addition

before

TTA CCG GCC ATC

after

CCG TTA CCG GCC ATC

A new triplet has been added. If a triplet is repeated it is also duplication.

Deletion

before

TTA CCG GCC ATC

after

TTA CCG GCC

Inversion

before

TTA CCG GCC ATC

after

TTA CCG GCC **CTA**

CTA codes for a new amino acid.

Translocation

before

TTA CCG GCC ATC

after

TTA CCG GCC ATC **CAT**

CAT broke away from another chromosome.

Chromosome mutations

If a complete chromosome is added or deleted, this is a chromosomal mutation. Sometimes something goes wrong during meiosis and both members of a homologous pair of chromosomes move to the same pole. This produces a gamete with an extra chromosome and, after fertilisation, the zygote has an extra chromosome. This is called aneuploidy. A example is Down's syndrome where a person has an additional chromosome, totalling 47 in each nucleus rather than the usual 46.

If the spindle fails altogether, then an individual can be produced with whole extra sets of chromosomes. This is called polyploidy and is important in plant evolution.

What causes mutations?

All organisms tend to mutate randomly, so different sections of DNA can appear to alter by chance. The appearance of such a random mutation is usually very rare, typically one mutation in many thousands of individuals in a population. The rate can be increased by mutagens such as:

- **Ionising radiation** – including ultra violet light, X-rays and α(alpha), β(beta) and γ (gamma) rays and neutrons. These forms of radiation tend to dislodge the electrons of atoms and so disrupt the bonding of the DNA which may re-bond in different combinations.
- **Chemicals** – including asbestos, tobacco, nitrous oxide, mustard gas and many substances used in industrial processes such as vinyl chloride. Many pesticides are suspected mutagens. Dichlorvos, an insecticide, is a proven mutagen. Additionally, colchicine is a chemical derived from the Autumn crocus, *Colchicium*, which stimulates the development of extra sets of chromosomes.

Are mutations harmful or helpful?

An individual mutation may be either harmful or helpful. When tobacco is smoked, it can increase the rate of mutation in some somatic cells. The DNA disruption can result in the formation of a cell which divides uncontrollably and causes the disruption of normal body processes. This is cancer, and can be lethal. The presence of certain genes called oncogenes is thought to increase the rate of cell division and lead to cancer.

Chrysanthemum plants have a high rate of mutation. A chrysanthemum grower will often see a new colour flower on a plant, e.g. a plant with red flowers could develop a side shoot which has a different colour, such as bronze. Most modern chrysanthemums appeared in this way, production being by asexual techniques.

Some mutated human genes have, through evolution, been successful. Many successful mutations contributed to the size of the cerebrum which is proportionally greater in humans than in other primates.

5.2 Selection and speciation

After studying this section you should be able to:

- *understand the process of natural selection*
- *predict population changes in terms of selective pressures*
- *understand a range of isolating mechanisms and how a new species can be formed*
- *understand the difference between allopatric and sympatric speciation*

Natural selection

 AQA ▸ 4.8

Throughout the biosphere, communities of organisms interact in a range of ecosystems. Darwin travelled across the world in his ship, the *Beagle*, observing organisms in their habitats. In 1858 Darwin published *On the Origin of Species*. In this book he gave his theory of **natural selection**.

The key features of this theory are that as organisms interact with their environment:

- individual organisms of populations are not identical, and can **vary in both genotypes and phenotypes**
- **some organisms survive** in their environment other organisms **die** before reproducing, effectively being **deleted from the gene pool**
- surviving organisms **go on to breed** and **pass on their genes** to their offspring
- this **increases the frequency of the advantageous genes** in the population.

> Learn this theory carefully then apply it to the scenarios given in your examination. Candidates often identify that some organisms die and others survive, but few go on to predict the inheritance of advantageous genes and the consequence to the species.

Consider these factors

- Adverse conditions in the environment could make a species extinct, but a range of genotypes increases the chances of the species surviving.
- Different genotypes may be suited to a changing environment, say, as a result of global warming.
- A variant of different genotype, previously low in numbers, may thrive in a changed environment and increase in numbers.
- Where organisms are well suited to their environment they have adaptations which give this advantage.
- If other organisms have been selected against, then more resources are available for survivors.
- Breeding usually produces many more offspring than the mere replacement of parents.
- Resources are limited so that competition for food, shelter and breeding areas takes place. Only the fittest survive!

What is selective pressure?

Selective pressure is the term given to a factor which has a direct effect on the numbers of individuals in a population of organisms, for example:

> 'It is late summer and the days without rainfall have caused the grassland to be parched. There is little food this year.'

> In this example, the fact that the numbers of herbivores decrease is *another* selective pressure. This time numbers of predators may decrease.

Here the **selective pressure** is a **lack of food** for the herbivores. Species which are **best adapted** to this habitat **compete** well for the limited resources and go on to survive. Within a species there is a further application of the selective pressure as weaker organisms perish and the strongest survive.

Mutations are random

New genes can appear in a species for the first time, due to a form of mutation. Over thousands of years, repeated natural selection takes place, resulting in superb adaptations to the environment.

- The Venus fly trap with its intricate leaf structures captures insects. The insects decompose, supplying minerals to the mineral deficient soil.
- Crown Imperial lilies (*Fritillaria*) produce colourful flowers, and a scent of stinking, decomposing flesh. Flies are attracted and help pollination.
- The bee orchid flower is so like a queen bee that a male will attempt mating.

Considering these examples, it is no wonder that candidates seem to consider that the organisms actively adapt to develop in these ways. They suggest that the organisms themselves have control to make active changes. **This is not so! There is no control, no active adaptation.**

> *New genes appear by CHANCE!*

KEY POINT

Selective pressures and populations

To find out more about the effects that selective pressures can have, the **normal distribution** must be considered. The distribution below is illustrated with an example.

The mean value is at the peak. There are fewer tall and short individuals in this example. A taller plant intercepts light better than a shorter one.

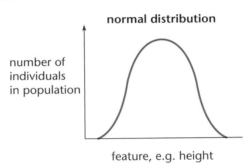

normal distribution

number of individuals in population

feature, e.g. height

The further distributions below show effects of selective pressures (shown by the blue arrows). Each is illustrated with an example.

Selective pressure at both ends of the distribution causes the extreme genotypes to die. This maintains the distribution around the mean value. Mean wing length is better for flight, better for prey capture.

Selective pressure results in death of slower animals. Many die out due to predators. Faster ones (with longer legs) pass on advantageous genes. Distribution moves to the right as the average individual is now faster.

Selective pressure results in the death of organisms around the mean value. In time this can lead to two distributions. Long fur is adapted to a cold temperature and short fur to a warm temperature. The mean is suited to neither extreme.

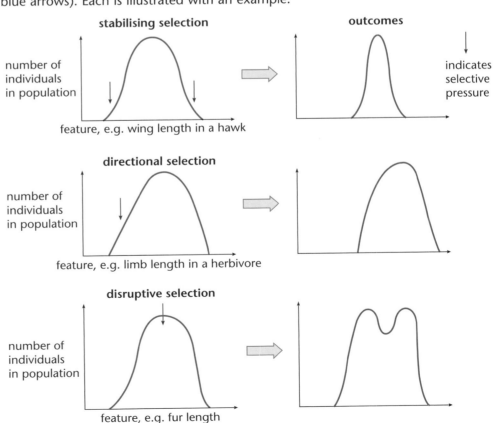

stabilising selection

number of individuals in population

feature, e.g. wing length in a hawk

outcomes

indicates selective pressure

directional selection

number of individuals in population

feature, e.g. limb length in a herbivore

disruptive selection

number of individuals in population

feature, e.g. fur length

Speciation

AQA 4.8

The previous example of disruptive selection showed how two extreme genotypes can be selected. Continued selection against individuals around the former mean genotype finally results in two discrete distributions. This division into two groups may be followed by, for example, advantageous mutations. There is a probability that, in time, the two groups will become incompatible and unable to breed successfully. They have become a new species. The development of new species is called speciation.

To enable enough genetic differences to build up between the two groups, they must be isolated to stop them breeding. This can happen in a number of ways.

Geographical isolation

This takes place when a population becomes divided as a result of a physical barrier appearing. For example, a land mass may become divided by a natural disaster like an earthquake or a rise in sea level. Geographical isolation followed by mutations can result in the formation of new species. This can be illustrated with the finches of the Galapagos islands. There are many different species in the Galapagos islands, ultimately from a common ancestral species. Clearly new species do form after many years of geographical isolation. This is allopatric speciation.

Reproductive isolation

This is a type of genetic isolation. Here the formation of a new species can take place in the same geographical area, e.g. mutation(s) may result in reproductive incompatibility. A new gene producing, for example, a hormone, may lead an animal to be rejected from the mainstream group, but breeding may be possible within its own group of variants. The production of a new species by this mechanism is known as sympatric speciation.

This will help you. Different finches evolved on different islands, but they did have a common ancestor.

A new pheromone is produced by several antelopes as a result of a mutation. The mainstream individuals refuse to mate as a result of this scent. An isolated few do mate. This is reproductive isolation.

Sample question and model answer

The graphs below show the height of two pure breeding varieties of pea plant, Sutton First and Cava Late.

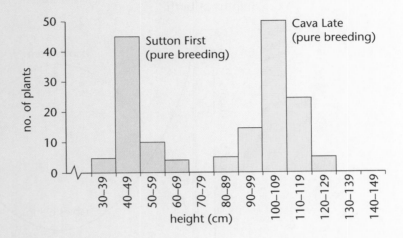

Continuous variation can confuse you sometimes when examiners display the data in categories as histograms. **This is not discontinuous!**

(a) (i) Which types of variation are shown by the pea variety, Sutton First? Give evidence from the bar graph to support your answer. [4]

Continuous variation – this is shown by the increase across the distribution (even though the peas are pure breeding).

Environmental variation – shown by the range of different heights.

(ii) Which type of variation is shown **between** varieties Sutton First and Cava Late? Give evidence from the bar graphs to support your answer. [2]

Discontinuous variation – the two distributions are separate and do not intersect.

(iii) Both Sutton First and Cava Late have compatible pollen for cross-breeding. Suggest why they do **not** cross breed. [1]

As implied by the names, Sutton First flowers before Cava Late, so that the flowers are not ready at the same time.

When you are asked to 'suggest', then a range of different plausible answers are usually acceptable.

(b) Plant geneticists considered that many years ago the two varieties of pea had the same ancestor.

(i) Suggest what, in the ancestor, resulted in the difference in height of the two varieties? [1]

mutation

(ii) Suggest what caused this change. [1]

radiation/random processes

(c) (i) Define polygenic inheritance. [1]

The inheritance of a feature controlled by a number of genes (not just a gene at one locus).

(ii) Which type of variation is a consequence of polygenic inheritance? [1]

continuous variation

Practice examination questions

1 The graph shows the birth weight of babies born in a London hospital between 1935 and 1946. It also shows the chance of the babies dying within two months of birth.

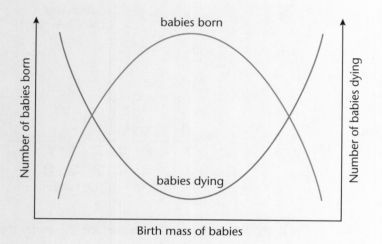

(a) What type of variation is shown by the birth weight of the babies? [1]

(b) What factors decide the birth weight of a baby? [2]

(c) Scientists argue that the information in the graphs shows that stabilising selection acts on the birth weight of babies. Explain why they think this. [3]

(d) The data was collected between 1935 and 1946. Modern medical techniques may have altered the selection pressure on the birth weight of babies. Explain why. [2]

[Total: 8]

2 (a) Explain the difference between allopatric and sympatric speciation. In each instance use an example to illustrate your answer. [6]

(b) How is it possible to find out if two female animals are from the same species? [2]

[Total: 8]

Chapter 6

Biotechnology and genes

The following topics are covered in this chapter:

- *Mapping and manipulating genes*

6.1 Mapping and manipulating genes

Identifying genes

 5.8

In order to identify the genes of an individual, a number of different processes are used.

Polymerase chain reaction

The polymerase chain reaction (PCR) is used to make numerous copies of a section of DNA. This is called **amplifying** the DNA. It uses the principle of semiconservative replication of DNA to produce new molecules that can in turn act as templates to produce more molecules. This therefore sets up a chain reaction. The enzyme DNA polymerase is used to copy the DNA.

Electrophoresis

This is used to separate sections of DNA according to their size.

Enzymes called restriction endonucleases can be used to cut up an organism's DNA.

- DNA sections are put into a well in a slab of agar gel.
- The gel and DNA are covered with buffer solution which conducts electricity.
- Electrodes apply an electrical field.
- Phosphate groups on DNA are negatively charged causing DNA to move towards the anode.
- Smaller pieces of DNA move more quickly down the agar track; larger ones move more slowly, leading to the formation of bands.

Genetic fingerprinting

PCR and electrophoresis have many applications. DNA is highly specific so the bands produced using this process can help with identification. In some crimes, DNA is left at the scene. Blood and semen both contain DNA specific to an individual. DNA evidence can be checked against samples from suspects. This is known as **genetic fingerprinting**. Genetic fingerprinting can be used in paternity disputes. Each band of the DNA of the child must correspond with a band from *either* the father or the mother.

Isolating genes

Along chromosomes are large numbers of genes. Scientists may need to identify and isolate a useful gene; one way of doing this is to use the enzyme **reverse transcriptase**. This is produced by viruses known as **retroviruses**. Reverse transcriptase has the ability to help make DNA from mRNA.

Stage 1

When a polypeptide is about to be made at a mRNA ribosome, reverse transcriptase allows a strand of its coding DNA to be made.

Stage 2

The single stranded DNA is parted from the mRNA.

Stage 3

The other strand of DNA is assembled using DNA polymerase.

Using this principle, the exact piece of DNA which codes for the production of a vital protein can be made.

Progress check

1   A length of DNA was prepared and then electrophoresis was used to separate the sections. The statements below describe the process of electrophoresis but they are in the wrong order. Write the letters in the correct sequence.

   A   electrodes apply an electrical field
   B   DNA sections are put into a well in a slab of agar gel
   C   smaller pieces of DNA move more quickly down the agar track with larger ones further behind
   D   the gel and DNA are then covered with buffer solution which conducts electricity
   E   restriction endonucleases can be used to cut up the DNA

2   Reverse transcriptase is an enzyme which enables the production of DNA from RNA. Work out the sequence of organic bases along the DNA of the following RNA sequence.

   A A U GCCCGGAUU

2   RNA AAUGCCCGGAUU   DNA₂ AATGCCCGGATT   DNA₁ TTACGGGCCTAA
1   E B D A C

The Human Genome Project

The Human Genome Project is an analysis of the complete human genetic make-up, which has mapped the organic base sequences of the nucleotides along our DNA.

A brief history

- 1977 Sanger devised DNA base sequencing.
- 1986 The Human Genome Project was initiated in the USA and the UK.
- 1996 30 000 genes were mapped.
- 1999 one billion bases were mapped including all of chromosome 22.
- 2000 chromosome 21 was mapped with the human genome almost complete.
- 2001 human genome mapping complete.

Some important points

- The genome project will sequence the complete set of over 100 000 genes.
- Only around 5% of the base pairs along the DNA actually result in the expression of characteristics. These DNA sequences are known as exons.
- 95% of DNA base sequences are not transcribed and do not appear to be involved in the expression of characteristics. These are known as introns.
- Introns do not outwardly seem to be responsible for characteristics. It is likely that they may be regulatory, perhaps in multiple gene role.

Effects of single nucleotide polymorphism

Example

5 base sequences from five people →

GTATAGCCGCAT 1

GTATAGCCGCAT 1

GTATAGCCGCAT 1

GTATAGCCGCCT 2

GTATAGCCGCCT 2

Version 1 = ●

Version 2 = ●

Proportion of the SNP in healthy members of population:

Proportion of the SNP in diseased members of population:

A greater incidence of an SNP in people with a disease may point to a cause.

Single nucleotide polymorphisms (SNPs)

Around 99.9% of human DNA is the same in all individuals. Merely 0.1% is different! The different sequences in individuals can be the result of **single nucleotide polymorphism**. One base difference from one individual to another at a site may have no difference. Up to a maximum of six different codons can code for one amino acid. An SNP will not necessarily have any effect.

Some SNPs do change a protein significantly. Such changes may result in genetic disease, resistance or susceptibility to disease.

How can the mapping of SNPs be useful?

* The mapping of SNPs along chromosomes signpost where base differences exist.
* Across the gene pool a pattern of SNP positions will be evident.
* There may be a high frequency of common SNPs found in the DNA of people with a specific disease.
* This highlights interesting sites for future research and will help to find answers to genetic problems.

Benefits obtained from the Human Genome Project

Ultimately, the human genome data will be instrumental in the development of drugs to treat genetic disease. Additionally, by analysis of parental DNA, it will be possible to give the probability of the development of a specific disease or susceptibility to it, in offspring. Fetal DNA, obtained through amniocentesis or by chorionic villi sampling, will give genetic information about an individual child.

Genetic counsellors will have more information about an individual than ever before. Companies will be able to produce 'designer drugs' to alleviate the problems which originate in our DNA molecules. Soon the race will begin to produce the first crop of drugs to treat or even cure serious genetic diseases. Look to the media for progress updates.

Manipulating DNA

 5.8

Scientists have developed methods of manipulating DNA. It can be transferred from one organism to another. Organisms which receive the DNA then have the ability to produce a new protein. This is one example of **genetic engineering**.

> The genetic code is universal. This means that it is possible to move genes from one organism to another and the recipient organism may be from a different species. The DNA will still code for the same protein.
>
> **KEY POINT**

Genes have now been transferred to and from many different types of organisms.

Here are some examples:

* From humans to bacteria: this technique produced the first commercially available genetically engineered product, insulin.
* From plants to plants: this technique has been used to produce GM crops such as Golden Rice that contain vitamin A.
* Into humans: this technique may be successful in treating genetic conditions such as cystic fibrosis (but it is not a cure).

Gene transfer to bacteria

The gene which produces human insulin was transferred from a human cell to a bacterium. The new microorganism is known as a **transgenic bacterium**. The process which follows shows how a human gene can be inserted into a bacterium.

The human gene for insulin is produced using an enzyme called **reverse transcriptase**. This converts the mRNA coding for insulin back into DNA. In this way all the introns are removed. Then the DNA can be inserted.

1 An enzyme known as **restriction endonuclease** cuts the DNA and the gene was removed. Each time a cut was made the two ends produced were known as 'sticky ends'.

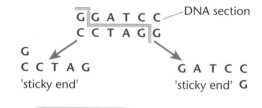

2 Circles of DNA called **plasmids** are found in bacteria.

3 A plasmid was taken from a bacterium and cut with the same restriction endonuclease.

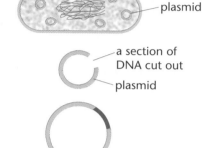

4 The human gene was inserted into the plasmid. It was made to fix into the open plasmid by another enzyme known as **ligase**.

5 The plasmid **replicated** inside the bacterium.

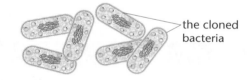

6 Large numbers of the new bacteria were produced. Each was able to secrete perfect human insulin, helping diabetics all over the world.

> Restriction endonucleases are produced by some bacteria as a defence mechanism. They cut up the DNA of invading viruses. This can be exploited during gene transfer.

> Note that **both** the donor DNA and recipient plasmid DNA are cut with the same enzyme. This allows the new gene to be a matching fit.

> Many exam candidates fail to state that the plasmids are cloned inside the bacterium.

> The bacteria themselves are also cloned. There may be two marks in a question for each cloning point!

Gene transfer to plants

Inserting genes into crop plants is becoming increasingly important in meeting the needs of a rising world population. One example of this is the production of a type of rice called Golden Rice. This contains a gene that produces vitamin A. The aim is to prevent vitamin A deficiency which can lead to blindness.

In **plants** there is an important technique which uses a **vector** to insert a novel gene. The vector is the bacterium *Agrobacterium tumefaciens*.

Agrobacterium tumefaciens
- This is a **pathogenic bacterium** which **invades** plants forming a gall (abnormal growth).
- The bacterium contains **plasmids** (circles of DNA) which carry a gene that stimulates tumour formation in the plants it attacks.
- The part of the plasmid which does this is known as the **T-DNA region** and can insert into any of the chromosomes of a host plant cell.
- Part of the T-DNA controls the production of two growth hormones, auxin and cytokinin.
- The extra quantities of these hormones stimulate rapid cell division, the cause of the tumour.

KEY POINT

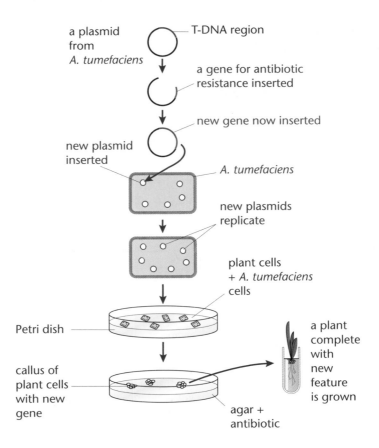

How can *Agrobacterium tumefaciens* be used in gene transfer?

The principle of using *A. tumefaciens* can be used in gene transfer to many different plants. Applications are at an early stage of development.

- Firstly, the DNA section controlling auxin and cytokinin was deleted, tumours were not formed, and cells of the plant retained their normal characteristics.
- A gene which gave the bacterial cell **resistance to a specific antibiotic** was inserted into the T-DNA position.
- The **useful gene** (e.g. the gene for vitamin A) was **inserted into a plasmid**.
- Plant cells, minus cell walls, were removed and put into a Petri dish with nutrients and *A. tumefaciens*, which contained the engineered plasmids.
- The cells were **incubated** for several days, then transferred to another Petri dish containing nutrients plus the specific antibiotic.
- **Only plant cells with antibiotic resistance and the desired gene grew.**
- Any surviving cells grew into a callus, from which an adult plant formed, complete with the transferred gene.

Inserting genes into humans

The idea of changing a person's genes in order to cure genetic disease is called **gene therapy**.

There are two main possibilities:

- **Somatic cell therapy** in which the genes are inserted into the cells of the adult where they are needed.
- **Germ line gene therapy** involves changing the genes of the gametes or early embryo. This means that all the cells of the organism will contain the new gene.

Sample question and model answer

The diagrams below show the transfer of a useful gene from a donor plant cell to the production of a transgenic crop plant. The numbers on the diagram show the stages in the process.

Look out for transgenic stories in the media. The principles are often the same. This will prepare you for potentially new ideas in your 'live' examinations. You could encounter the same account!

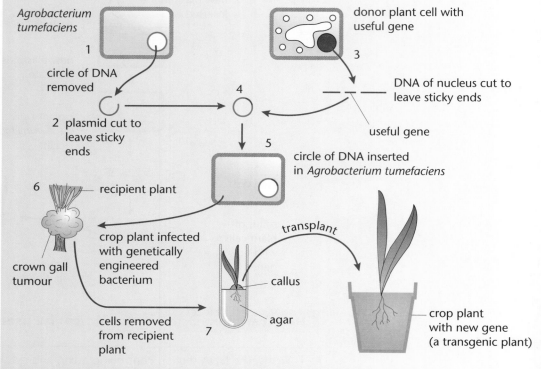

(a) Give the correct name for the circle of DNA found in the bacterium, *A. tumefaciens*.   [1]

plasmid

(b) The same enzyme was used to cut the DNA of the bacterium and of the plant cell.

(i) Name the type of enzyme used to cut the DNA.   [1]

restriction endonuclease

(ii) Explain why it is important to use exactly the same enzyme at this stage. [2]

The same enzyme produces the same sticky ends.

Complementary sticky ends on the donor gene bind with the sticky ends of the plasmid.

This question covers key techniques in gene transfer. Be prepared for your examination.

(iii) Which type of enzyme would be used to splice the new gene into the circle of DNA?   [1]

ligase

(c) How was the new gene incorporated into the DNA of the crop plant cells?   [2]

Crop plant infected by genetically engineered bacterium.

The DNA of bacterium causes a change in the DNA of the crop plant to produce the gall or tumour cells.

(d) How would you know if the gene had been transferred successfully?   [1]

The feature would be expressed in the transgenic plants.

Practice examination questions

1 A new genetically modified soya bean plant has been developed. It has a new gene which prevents it from being killed by herbicide (weed killer).

(a) Describe the stages which enable a gene to be transferred from one organism to another. [5]

(b) Suggest how the genetically modified soya plants could result in higher bean yields. [3]

[Total: 8]

Chapter 7

Ecology and populations

The following topics are covered in this chapter:

- *Investigation of ecosystems*
- *Colonisation and succession*
- *Human populations*

7.1 Investigation of ecosystems

After studying this section you should be able to:

- *use the capture, mark, recapture technique to assess animal populations*
- *use quadrats to map the distribution of organisms*
- *understand the factors that affect the distribution of organisms*
- *describe conservation techniques and methods of population control*

Measurement in an ecosystem

AQA   4.1

The study of ecology investigates the inter-relationships between organisms in an area and their environment. The area in which organisms live is called a **habitat**. The combination of the organisms that live in a habitat and the physical aspects of the habitat is called an **ecosystem**.

Estimating populations

All the individuals of one species living together in a habitat are called a **population**. The size of plant populations can be estimated by using a quadrat placed at random. Animals, however, do not tend to stay still for long enough to be sampled using a quadrat. The population size of an animal species can be estimated by using capture–recapture.

Capture, mark, release, recapture

This is a method which is used to estimate animal populations. It is an appropriate method for motile animals such as shrews or woodlice. The ecologist must always ensure minimum disturbance of the organism if results are to be truly representative and that the population will behave as normal.

The technique

- Organisms are captured, *unharmed*, using a quantitative technique.
- They are counted then discretely marked in some way, e.g. a shrew can be tagged, a woodlouse can be painted (*with non-toxic paint*).
- They are released.
- Organisms from the same population are recaptured, and another count is made, to determine the number of marked animals and the number unmarked.

Before using the technique you must be assured that:

- there is no significant migration
- there are no significant births or deaths
- marking does not have an adverse effect, e.g. the marking paint should not allow predators to see prey more easily (or vice versa)
- organisms integrate back into the population after capture.

Remember that the method is suitable for large population size only.

The calculation

S = total number of individuals in the total population.

S_1 = number captured in sample one, marked and released, e.g. 8.

S_2 = total number captured in sample two, e.g. 10.

S_3 = total marked individuals captured in sample two, e.g. 2.

$$\frac{S}{S_1} = \frac{S_2}{S_3} \quad \text{so, } S = \frac{S_1 \times S_2}{S_3} \quad \text{population} = \frac{8 \times 10}{2} = 40 \text{ individuals}$$

Remember the equation carefully. You will **not** be supplied with it in the examination, but you will be given data.

Measuring the distribution of organisms

This can be measured using another quadrat technique called a belt transect. This method should be used when there is a transition across an area, e.g. across a pond or from high to low tide on the sea shore. Use belt transects where there is change. The belt transect is a line of quadrats. In each quadrat a measurement such as density can be made. One transect is not enough! Always do a number of transects then find an average for quadrats in a similar zone.

A bar graph would be used to show the distribution of plant species across the pond. Note that there would be more than just two species. The graphs show how you could illustrate the data. Clearly flag irises occupy a different niche to water lilies.

A simplified results table

Quadrat no.	flag iris	water lily
1	10	0
2	7	0
3	1	0
4	0	5
5	0	4
6	0	0
7	0	5
8	0	3
9	0	0
10	1	0
11	8	0
12	4	0

This is just one belt transect. A number would be used and an average taken for each corresponding quadrat.

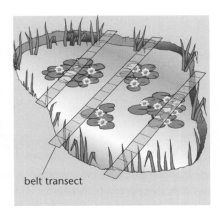

belt transect

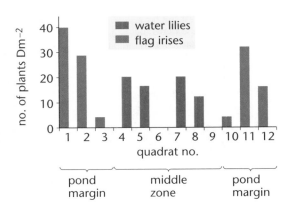

Other uses of quadrats

Quadrats can also be used to survey animal populations. It is made easier if the organisms are **sessile** (*they do not move from place to place*), e.g. barnacles on a rock. In a pond the belt transect could be coupled with a kick sampling technique. Here rocks may be disturbed and escaping animals noted. Adding a further technique can help, such as using a catch net in the quadrat positions. The principle here is that the techniques are **quantitative**.

KEY POINT

Factors that determine population size

Graphical data can show relative numbers and distribution of organisms in a habitat. The ecologist is interested in the factors that determine the size and distribution of organisms.

These factors can be **biotic** or **abiotic**.

Abiotic factors are non-living factors. They include:

- carbon dioxide level
- oxygen level
- pH
- light intensity
- mineral ion concentration
- level of organic material.

Biotic factors are living factors.

They include:

- **Competition** This occurs when organisms are trying to get the same resources. There are two types. **Interspecific competition** takes place when **different** species share the same resources. **Intraspecific competition** takes place when the **same** species share the same resources.
- **Predation** This involves feeding relationships.

Predators and prey

There can be many examples of this type of relationship in an ecosystem. **Primary consumers** rely on the **producers**, so a flush of new vegetation may give a corresponding increase in the numbers of primary consumers. Predators which eat the primary consumers may also follow with a population increase. Each population of the ecosystem may have a **sequential effect** on other populations. Ultimately, the ecosystem is in **dynamic equilibrium** and has limits as to how many of each population can survive, i.e. its **carrying capacity**.

Note that graphs are often given in predator–prey questions. A flush of spring growth is often responsible for the increase in prey. Plant biomass may not be shown on the graph! Candidates are expected to suggest this for a mark. Also remember that as prey increase, their numbers will go down when eaten by the predator. Predator numbers rise after this.

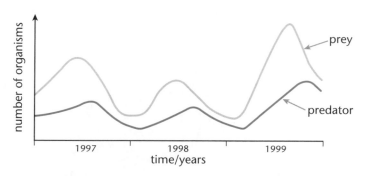

Ecological conservation

AQA   4.7

In a world where human population increase is responsible for the destruction of so many habitats, it is necessary to retain as many habitats as possible. Ecological surveys report to governments and difficult decisions are made. Fragile habitats like the bamboo woodlands of China support a variety of wildlife. Conservation areas need to be kept and maintained to prevent extinction of organisms at risk. In the UK we have **sites of special scientific interest (SSSI)** which are given government protection.

Conservation requires management

Although the word 'conservation' implies to 'keep' something as it is, much effort is needed. An area of climax vegetation, e.g. oak woodland, is less of a problem, since it will not change if merely left to its own devices. However, many of the seral stages, e.g. birch woodland along the route to climax, require much maintenance.

Animal populations need our help, especially when it is often by our own introduction that specific species have colonised an area. Deer introduced into a forest may thrive initially but due to an efficient reproductive rate exceed the carrying capacity of the habitat. **Carrying capacity** is the population of the species which can be adequately supported by the area.

Sometimes herbivores could destroy their habitat by overgrazing, and so must be **culled**. **Predators** could be introduced to reduce numbers, but they also may need culling at some stage. **Difficult decisions** need to be taken. In the aquatic habitats similar problems exist. Cod populations in the North Sea are being reduced by over-fishing. Agreements have been made by the EU to **reduce fishing quotas** and create **exclusion zones** to **allow fish stocks to recover**. Even before this agreement, smaller fish had to be returned to the sea after being caught to increase the chances of them growing to maturity and breeding successfully.

Endangered species require protection

All over the world many animals and plants are at the limits of their survival. The World Wide Fund for Nature is a charity organisation which helps. The organisation receives support from the public and artists such as David Shepherd. He gives donations from the sale of all of his wildlife paintings, helping to maintain the profile of animals so that we invest in survival projects like protected reserves.

7.2 Human populations

After studying this section you should be able to:

- understand the growth of the human population
- understand population structure

LEARNING SUMMARY

Growth of the human population

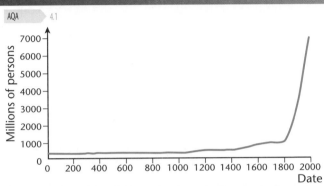

AQA 4.1

It is difficult to estimate the size of the human population thousands of years ago but most estimates produce graphs that look like the one here.

The increase was fairly slow up until about 300 years ago. Recently, a more rapid increase was brought about by improvements in medicine and healthcare, industrial productivity and food production.

There are many predictions as to how long and how fast this increase can continue.

Population structure

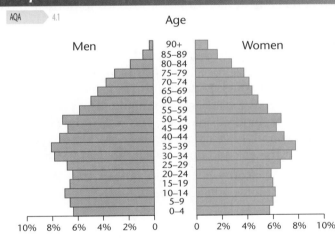

AQA 4.1

In any population there will be individuals of different ages and of different sex. A population pyramid shows how each population varies in terms of its composition.

The graph for the UK shows a number of interesting features, such as a bulge in 30 to 40 year olds. It also shows that women have a longer **life expectancy** than men.

7.3 Colonisation and succession

After studying this section you should be able to:

- understand how colonisation is followed by changes
- understand how colonisation and succession lead to a climax community

LEARNING SUMMARY

How colonisation and succession take place

AQA 4.7

Any area which has never been inhabited by organisms may be available for **primary succession**. Such areas could be a garden pond filled with tap water, lava having erupted from a volcano, or even a concrete tile on a roof. The latter may become colonised by lichens. Occasionally an ecosystem may be destroyed, e.g. fire destroying a woodland. This allows **secondary succession** to begin, and signals the reintroduction of plant and animal species to the area.

Colonisation and succession also take place in water. Even an artificial garden pond would be colonised by organisms naturally. Aquatic algae would arrive on birds' feet.

- **Pioneer species (primary colonisers)** begin to exploit a 'new' habitat. Mosses may successfully grow on newly exposed heathland soil. These are the **primary colonisers** which have adaptations to this environment. Fast germination of spores and the ability to grow in waterlogged and acid conditions aid rapid colonisation. These plants may support a specific food web. In time, as organic matter drops from these herbaceous colonisers it is decomposed, nutrients are added to the soil and acidity increases. In time, the changes caused by the primary colonisers make the habitat unsuitable.

- Conditions unsuitable for primary colonisers may be ideal for other organisms. In heathland, mosses are replaced by heathers which can thrive in acid and xerophytic (desiccating) conditions. This is **succession**, where one community of organisms is replaced by another. In this example, the secondary colonisers have replaced the primary colonisers; this is known as **seral stage 1** in the succession process. Again, a different food web is supported by the secondary colonisers.

Primary colonisers   **Secondary colonisers**

heather

moss

- At every seral stage, there are changes in the environment. The **second seral stage** takes place as the tertiary colonisers replace the previous organisms. In heathland, the new conditions would favour shrubs such as gorse and bilberry plus associated animals.

- The shrubs are replaced in time with birch woodland, the **third seral stage**. Eventually, acidic build up leads to the destruction of the dominant plant species.

- Finally, conditions become suitable for a dominant plant species, the oak. Tree saplings quickly become established. Beneath the oak trees, grasses, ferns, holly and bluebells can grow as a balanced community. This final stage is **stable** and can continue for hundreds of years. This is the **climax community**. Associated animals survive and thrive alongside these plant resources. Insects such as gall wasps exploit the oak and dormice eat the wasp larvae.

Jays are birds which eat some acorns but spread others which they store and forget. The acorns germinate; the woodland spreads.

Climax community

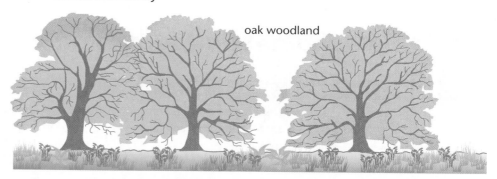

oak woodland

In Britain, an excellent example of a climax community is Sherwood Forest where the 'Major Oak' has stood for 1000 years. Agricultural areas grow crops efficiently by **deflecting succession**. Plants and animals in their natural habitat are 'more than a match' for domesticated crops. Herbicides and pesticides are used to stop the invaders!

Sometimes, conservationists have to prevent succession from occurring in order to protect habitats and species. The chalk grassland of the South Downs is an example of this. It contains some rare plant species that may disappear if deciduous woodland was to return.

Sample question and model answer

When given a passage, line numbers are often referred to. Try to understand the words in context. Do not rush in with a pre-conceived idea.

Read the passage, then answer the questions below.

line 1   Around the UK coast there are two species of barnacle, *Chthamalus stellatus* and *Balanus balanoides*. Both species are sessile, living on rocky sea shores.

The adult barnacles do not move from place to place but do reproduce
line 5   sexually. They use external fertilisation. Larvae resemble tiny crabs and are able to swim. At a later stage these larvae come to rest on a rock where they become fixed for the remainder of their lives.

The barnacles are only able to feed while submerged.

Adult *Chthamalus* are found higher on the rocks than *Balanus* in the adult
line 10 form as shown in the diagram below. Scientists have shown that the larvae of each species are found at all levels.

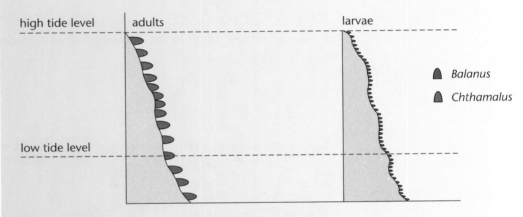

(a) Name the genus for each barnacle. [1]

    Chthamalus and Balanus

(b) What does the term sessile mean? (line 2) [1]

    is not motile, i.e. does not move from place to place

In this question are key terms, of which you will need to recall the meaning. This is only possible with effective revision. Did you already know the key terms **genus**, **sessile** and **motile**? Knowledge of these terms would enable you to access other marks, only easy when you have key word understanding. Try writing out a glossary of terms to help your long-term memory.

(c) Suggest how it is possible for neighbouring *Balanus* individuals to breed sexually (line 5) with each other even though they are sessile. [1]

    produce sperms which swim through the water

(d) Explain **one** advantage of the larvae being motile. [2]

    able to colonise new areas

    where there may be more nutrients/food

(e) Which type of competition exists between *Chthamalus* and *Balanus*? [1]

    interspecific competition

(f) Suggest an explanation for the distribution of each species of barnacle. [6]

    The larvae are found at all tide levels;

    at a lower tide level the barnacles are submerged for longer;

    Balanus may grow at a faster rate; can compete for food better;
    Chthamalus, which die out at lower levels

    near higher tide level the barnacles are exposed to open air for longer;
    Balanus may not be adapted to withstand desiccation; whereas
    Chthamalus can withstand drying out; and so survive without
    the competition from Balanus.

Practice examination questions

1 Ecologists wished to estimate the population of a species of small mammal in a nature reserve.

- They placed humane traps throughout the reserve and made their first trapping on day one, capturing 16 shrews.
- They were tagged then released.
- After day four a second trapping was carried out, capturing 12 shrews.
- Five of these shrews were seen to be tagged.

(a) The ecologists must be satisfied of a number of factors before using the 'capture, mark, release, recapture' method. List three of these factors. [3]

(b) Use the data to estimate the shrew population.
Show your working. [2]

(c) Comment on the *level* of reliability of your answer. [1]

[Total: 6]

2 The diagrams show stages in the development of a garden pond over a 10-year period.

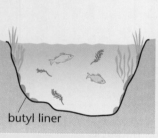

butyl liner

A hole was dug, lined with butyl liner and new plants were placed in the pond.

1990

Marginal plants grow, spread and die down in the winter. As they rot sediment falls to the bottom of the pond.

1995

After a number of years the pond has completely covered over.

2000

(a) In 1990 irises, oxygenating pondweed and a water lily were planted in the pond. Algae were not planted but arrived in the pond in some other way.

(i) What term describes an organism that grows in a new habitat that previously supported no life? [1]

(ii) After a time the algae produced a thick 'carpet' of growth on the surface of the pond. Explain the effect this may have on organisms under the water. [5]

(b) Describe the stages which took place to produce the stable grassland after 10 years. [4]

[Total: 10]

Chapter 8

Energy and ecosystems

The following topics are covered in this chapter:

- *Energy flow through ecosystems*
- *Nutrient cycles*
- *Energy transfer and agriculture*
- *Effects of human activities on the environment*

8.1 Energy flow through ecosystems

LEARNING SUMMARY

After studying this section you should be able to:

- *understand the roles of producers, consumers and decomposers in food chains*
- *understand the flow of energy through an ecosystem*

Food chains and energy flow

AQA   4.5

Before energy is available to organisms in an ecosystem, photosynthesis must take place. Sunlight energy enters the ecosystem and some is available for photosynthesis. Not all light energy reaches photosynthetic tissues. Some totally misses plants and may be absorbed or reflected by items such as water, rock or soil. Some light energy which does reach plants may be reflected by the waxy cuticle or even miss chloroplasts completely! The energy that is trapped by photosynthesis and converted into biomass is called the **gross primary productivity (GPP)**.

> **KEY POINT**
>
> Around 4% of light entering an ecosystem is actually used in photosynthesis.

The green plant uses the **carbohydrate** as a first stage substance and goes on to make **proteins** and **lipids**. Plants are a rich source of nutrients, available to the herbivores which eat the plants. Some energy is not available to the herbivores because green plants **respire** (releasing energy).

The energy that is available to herbivores is called the **net primary productivity (NPP)**. It is calculated as follows:

Net primary productivity = gross primary productivity – energy lost in respiration

Energy is also lost from the food chain as **not all parts** of plants may be **consumed**, e.g. roots.

Food chains and webs

Energy is passed along a food chain. Each food chain always begins with an **autotrophic** organism (producer), then energy is passed to a primary consumer, then a secondary consumer, then a tertiary consumer and so on.

direction of energy flow →

Producer → primary consumer → secondary consumer → tertiary consumer
         (herbivore)   (1st carnivore)   (2nd carnivore)

The following example shows three food chains linked to form a food web.

Each feeding level along a food chain can also be represented by a **trophic level**. The food chain below is taken from the food web above and illustrates trophic levels. Energy may be used by an organism in a number of different ways:

- respiration releases energy for movement or maintenance of body temperature, etc.
- production of new cells in growth and repair
- production of eggs
- released trapped in excretory products.

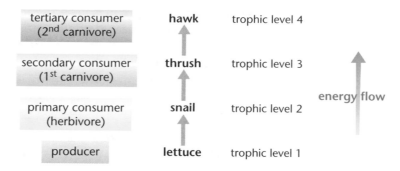

Pyramids of numbers, energy and biomass

A food chain gives limited information about feeding relationships in an area. Actual proportions of organisms in an area give more useful data. Consider a food chain from a wheat field. The pyramid of numbers sometimes does not give a suitable shape. In the example shown below, there are more aphids in the field than wheat plants. This gives the shape shown below (not a pyramid in shape!). A pyramid of biomass is more likely to be a pyramid in shape because it takes into account the size of the organism. It does not always take into account the rate of growth and so only a pyramid of energy is always the correct shape.

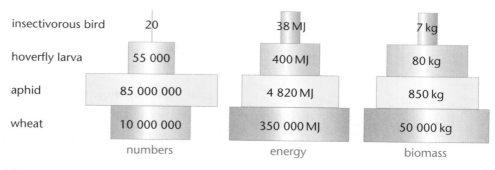

The organisms in the above food chain may die rather than be consumed. When this happens, the decomposers use extra-cellular enzymes to break down any organic debris in the environment. Corpses, faeces and parts that are not consumed are all available for decay.

8.2 Energy transfer and agriculture

After studying this section you should be able to:

- *understand a range of agricultural methods used to increase yield*

How are high yields achieved in agriculture?

AQA   4.5

The aim in agriculture is often to obtain good quality produce at maximum yield. Farmers grow crops and rear domesticated animals, like cattle, for meat and milk. Humans usually end the food chain as the top consumer. The human population is increasing constantly so **efficient** methods of agriculture have been developed.

Reduction of competition

Weeds reduce water, minerals and light reaching the crop plant; ultimately its rate of growth would be limited by the competing weeds. This is **interspecific competition** and takes place when different species need the same resources. Weeds can be removed **chemically** by use of a **herbicide** (weedkiller) or physically by an implement such as a rotavator which cuts up the weeds into tiny pieces, eventually killing them.

Intraspecific competition can also take place. This is where neighbouring plants of the same species compete for identical resources. This problem is reduced by making sure that crop plants are a suitable distance apart to achieve a maximum yield.

Use of fertilisers

It is important that crop plants have access to all the minerals they require to give a maximum yield. Farmers supply these minerals in fertilisers, usually in the form NPK (nitrogen, phosphates and potassium). By supplying them with these minerals, nitrogen is available to make protein, a key substance for growth. Phosphates help the production of DNA, RNA and ATP. Potassium helps with protein synthesis and chlorophyll production. Other minerals are also needed like iron and calcium. The more a plant grows, the more its biomass increases and usually the greater its surface area for light absorption. The amount of photosynthesis increases proportionally. If a farmer is to reach the maximum productivity of a crop, fertiliser is vital.

Increasing photosynthetic rate

As well as fertilisers helping to achieve a high productivity, other factors have a positive influence on growth:

- **irrigation** ensures that a plant has enough water for photosynthesis
- **suitable temperatures** can be achieved by use of a greenhouse to give ideal conditions for the process. If a gas heater is used then the **high concentration of carbon dioxide** excreted can be harnessed in photosynthesis.

Pest control

If pests such as aphids or caterpillars begin to damage crops then both quality and yield are reduced. Farmers combat pests in many different ways. A combination of different methods is called integrated pest management. This may include:

- **Pesticides**, sprayed onto crops, to kill pests. Chemicals used to kill insects are insecticides. **Contact insecticides** kill insects directly but **systemic insecticides** are absorbed into the cell sap. Any insect consuming part of the plant or sucking the sap then dies.
- **Biological control** which includes a range of different methods to get rid of pests.

  (a) The most commonly used method is to use **predators** to reduce pest numbers, e.g. in greenhouses infested with whitefly (*Trialeurodes vaporariorum*) the predatory wasp (*Encarsia formosa*) is introduced. The female wasp lays eggs into the scale (larva) of the whitefly. A young wasp emerges from each larva, having used the larva as a nutrient supply. The whitefly young are killed so its population decreases. Wasps increase in numbers and remain as long as some whitefly still remain.

  (b) **Pheromones** are also used. These are compounds secreted by organisms which affect the **behaviour** within the species, e.g. the apple codling moth larva spoils the fruit by tunnelling through apples. Female adult moths secrete a powerful chemical which attracts many males. This pheromone is now used in a trap. The sticky tent-shaped trap (below) shows how male moths are attracted and stick to the sides of the trap. Here they die and thousands of female moths out in the orchards are not mated and their eggs are not fertilised.

a codling moth trap

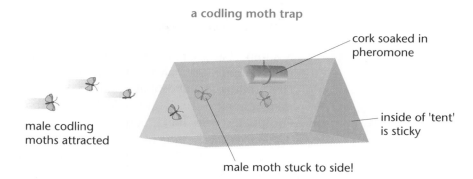

cork soaked in pheromone

male codling moths attracted

inside of 'tent' is sticky

male moth stuck to side!

  (c) **Irradiation** is used on insect pests which mate only once, e.g. the New World screw-worm fly lays eggs in cattle (and humans!). Larvae attack the internal systems having a devastating effect. Millions of screw-worm flies are bred then **irradiated**. They are subsequently released into cattle-producing regions. Irradiated males cannot produce fertile gametes. Any male mating with a female from the cattle fields results in unfertilised eggs so the population decreases. Cattle productivity is maintained.

- **Genetic engineering** can be used. A gene has been transferred to potato plants which enables them to produce a natural insecticide. This destroys 50% of aphids that attack the plants. The amount of damage is decreased.
- **Crop rotation** can be used to prevent build up of pests in the soil.

Examination questions on this topic often test knowledge of the advantages and disadvantages of each method. Chemicals may pass along food chains, and accumulate in greater quantities higher in the food chain due to the consumption of many smaller organisms, each carrying a small amount of the toxin. Biological control does not usually rely on a chemical agent so that the chemical risk is removed.

Biological control is usually much cheaper in the long term. If predators are used they go on to breed. Several repeat sprays of insecticides are needed through the growing season.

8.3 Nutrient cycles

After studying this section you should be able to:

- *recall how carbon and nitrogen are recycled*

LEARNING SUMMARY

The nitrogen cycle

AQA   4.6

Nitrogen is found in every amino acid, protein, DNA and RNA. It is an essential element! Most organisms are unable to use atmospheric nitrogen directly so the nitrogen cycle is very important.

There are three parts of the nitrogen cycle which are regularly examined:
- nitrogen fixation in leguminous plants
- nitrification
- denitrification.

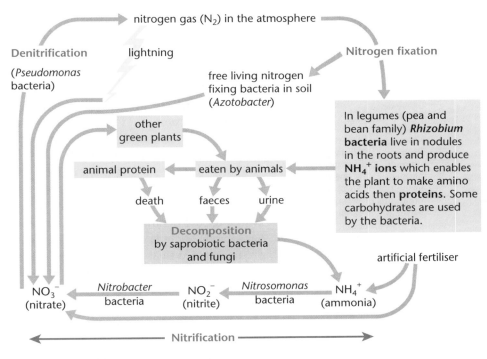

Some important points

The association of *Rhizobium* bacteria with legume plants give advantages to both organisms. This relationship is known as **mutualism**.

Saprobiotic bacteria and fungi secrete extra-cellular enzymes.

The biochemical route from ammonia to nitrate is **nitrification**. This is helped by ploughing which allows air into the soil. Nitrifying bacteria are aerobic. Draining also helps.

- **Nitrogen gas** from the atmosphere is used by *Rhizobium* bacteria. These bacteria, living in nodules of legume plants, convert nitrogen gas into **ammonia** (NH_3) then into amine ($-NH_2$) compounds. The plants transport the amines from the nodules and make amino acids then proteins. *Rhizobium* bacteria gain carbohydrates from the plant, therefore each organism benefits.
- Plants support food webs, throughout which excretion, production of faeces and death take place. These resources are of considerable benefit to the ecosystem, but first **decomposition** by **saprobiotic** bacteria takes place, a waste product of this process is **ammonia**.
- Ammonia is needed by *Nitrosomonas* bacteria for a special type of nutrition (chemo-autotrophic). As a result another waste product, **nitrite** (NO_2) is formed.
- Nitrite is needed by *Nitrobacter* bacteria, again for chemo-autotrophic nutrition. The waste product from this process is **nitrate**, vital for plant growth. Plants absorb large quantities of nitrates via their roots.
- Nitrogen gas is returned to the atmosphere by **denitrifying bacteria** such as *Pseudomonas*. Some nitrate is converted back to nitrogen gas by these bacteria. The cycle is complete!

The carbon cycle

AQA 4.6

Carbon is the key element in all organisms. The source of this carbon is atmospheric carbon dioxide which proportionally is 0.03% of the volume of the air. Most organisms cannot use carbon dioxide directly so the carbon cycle is very important.

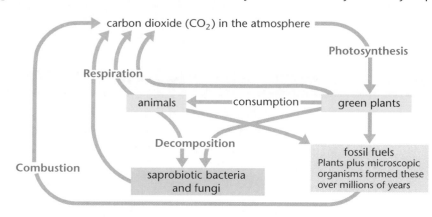

Some important points

* Producers carry out photosynthesis. This process incorporates the carbon dioxide into carbohydrates. These chemicals are used as a starting point to make lipids and proteins. Some of the carbon helps to form structures in the producers and some is released as carbon dioxide as a waste product of respiration.
* Producers are the starting point of food chains. After the plants are eaten by primary consumers carbon can be passed along to subsequent consumers. It can be incorporated into tissues, respired or excreted.
* Even after the death of a plant or animal, carbon dioxide can still be released. Saprobiotic bacteria and fungi respire using the organic chemicals in dead organisms as well as faeces and urine, etc.
* Compression of organisms millions of years ago resulted in the formation of fossil fuels. Combustion of these fuels releases carbon dioxide back into the atmosphere.
* The return of carbon dioxide to the air completes the cycle!

Other elements are also recycled. The decomposers have a major role in maintaining the availability of vital chemicals.

Examiners often give a question about what happens to the energy in the chemicals of dead organisms or organic waste. Many candidates correctly state that microorganisms rot down the materials but then go on to state that energy goes into the ground. Big mistake! Energy is released by the respiration of the decomposers to support their life.

8.4 Effects of human activities on the environment

After studying this section you should be able to:

* *understand some causes and effects of pollution*
* *understand the effects of deforestation*

LEARNING SUMMARY

How human activities affect the environment

AQA 4.6

Activities carried out by the human population to supply food, power and industrial needs have considerable effects on the environment. These effects include atmospheric and water pollution, and destroying habitats and communities.

What is the greenhouse effect?

This is caused by specific gases which form a thin layer around the atmosphere. These gases include water vapour, carbon dioxide, methane, ozone, nitrogen oxides and CFCs. CFCs (CCl_2F_2, CCl_3F) have a greenhouse factor of 25 000 based on the same amount of carbon dioxide at a factor of 1.0. The **quantity** of the greenhouse factor gas needs to be considered to work out the overall greenhouse effect, e.g.

> carbon dioxide is 0.035% of the troposphere × greenhouse factor value
>   1 = 0.035
> CCl_2F_2 is 4.8×10^{-8}% of the troposphere × greenhouse factor value
>   25 000 = 0.012
> Water vapour is 1% of the troposphere × greenhouse factor
>   0.1 = 0.1

KEY POINT

It is clear that water vapour has the greatest overall greenhouse effect!

- The greenhouse gases allow short wavelength radiation from the sun to reach the Earth's surface.
- Some of the infra-red radiation fails to pass back through the greenhouse layer resulting in **global warming**.
- Polar ice caps may melt causing the sea to rise and subsequent reduction of land mass. Some aquatic populations could increase and some terrestrial populations decrease.
- Climatic changes are expected, so rainfall changes and heat increases will have significant effects.

Do not mix up the greenhouse effect with the 'hole in the ozone layer' – that is different! The ozone layer around the Earth absorbs some ultra-violet radiation from the sun. If a lot of ultra-violet radiation reaches the Earth's surface then many people succumb to skin cancer. CFCs cause a hole to form in the ozone layer. Not using these chemicals is the answer to this problem.

greenhouse effect

Follow the numbers to remember sequence in correct order!

some radiation reflected back to Earth causing global warming

some radiation reflected back from Earth's surface. 3

4

1 solar radiation

2 some radiation reaches Earth's surface. It warms up.

Deforestation

In countries such as Brazil, forests have been burned down. Large quantities of carbon dioxide and water vapour released into the atmosphere contribute to the greenhouse effect. However, the long-term effects are highly significant. Habitats and complete food webs are lost. Biodiversity is decreased so that many fewer species are represented on the land left after deforestation. The canopy of a forest intercepts and holds rain water, so too much rain does not reach the ground and cause flooding. Instead, much water evaporates back into the atmosphere. Without the forest, flooding is a danger, and without the tree roots, soil erosion takes place. If the deforestation was to make way for agriculture then there are major problems. Top soil is lost and nutrients leach into the ground and in the long term agriculture fails.

Water pollution

'Run off', containing fertilisers, enters rivers from fields. Similarly, sewage also pollutes rivers. The diagrams below show a river before and after sewage entry.

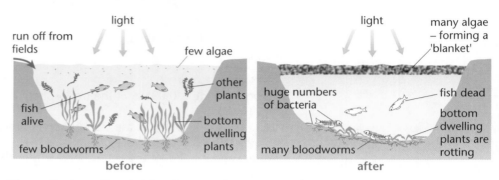

The polluting effect of fertilisers and sewage are caused by the constituent ions such as nitrates and phosphates. They result in **eutrophication**.

The sequence of stages of eutrophication are important. Take care to learn the correct sequence. Do not miss out any stage. Some candidates merely state that nitrates enter the river and fish die. Give more detail and score more marks!

- **Nitrates and phosphates** enter the river and are absorbed by plants. This promotes plant growth.
- **Algae** float near the water surface and their population increases dramatically. A 'blanket' of algae soon covers the surface.
- Bottom dwelling plants do not share the same advantage. Initially the ions promote growth but **surface algae block the sunlight**. Plants beneath the algae die.
- **Bacteria** and other decomposers begin to **break down** the **dead plants** and some short lived algae. The **bacterial population increases** and proportionally takes more oxygen from the river water.
- **Fish die** as the oxygen content becomes much too low. Rotting dead fish contribute to even lower oxygen levels; again aerobic bacteria are responsible.
- Often there is an **increase in bloodworms** (tubifex). These are mud dwellers and possess a protein similar to haemoglobin which helps them to take in enough oxygen for survival, even at low concentration. Without fish to eat them numbers of bloodworms increase even more.

How can the water pollution be measured?

There are many ways to measure both pollutants and their effects. Populations of algae, bloodworms or fish can be estimated. A key measurement is **biological oxygen demand (BOD)**. This is the amount of oxygen taken up by a sample of water at 20°C over 5 days. Clean water takes up much less oxygen than that polluted with organic material. Aerobic bacteria take up a large proportion of this oxygen. A river, heavily polluted with organic matter, has a very high BOD.

Indicator species

The presence or absence of a species in the river can be used as a sign of pollution. Mayfly larvae can only tolerate well oxygenated water. Bloodworms are only found in large numbers in water heavily polluted with organic matter. As the river flows downstream, organisms change the organic matter and eventually the oxygen content increases. A large population of mayfly larvae found in water downstream suggests that there is:

- a low BOD
- organic material further upstream which has been changed by bacteria so the water is no longer polluted.

Sample question and model answer

(a) The sequence below shows how nitrate can be produced from a supply of oak leaves.

Some questions give information that you can use to deduce the answers (a) (i) is one of them!

$$\text{dead oak leaves} \xrightarrow{\text{decomposers}} \underset{\text{(ammonia)}}{NH_3} \xrightarrow{\substack{\textit{Nitrosomonas} \\ \text{bacteria}}} \underset{\text{(nitrite)}}{NO_2} \xrightarrow{\substack{\textit{Nitrobacter} \\ \text{bacteria}}} \underset{\text{(nitrate)}}{NO_3}$$

This question targets the nitrogen cycle. Be ready to answer questions about *any part* of the cycle. Pure recall of the cycle is not enough! You need to apply your knowledge.

(i) Suggest the consequences of death of the *Nitrosomonas* bacteria. [4]

build up of ammonia; build up of dead leaves; death of Nitrobacter bacteria; no nitrite/no nitrate

(ii) Name the process by which bacteria produce nitrate from ammonia. [1]

nitrification

(iii) Name **two** populations of organisms not shown in the sequence which would be harmed by a lack of nitrate. [2]

denitrifying bacteria or Pseudomonas; plants or producers

(iv) Which organisms fix atmospheric nitrogen on the nodules of bean plants? [1]

(Rhizobium) bacteria

(b) Apart from adding fertiliser or irrigating a crop, how can a farmer make sure of producing a high yield ? [4]

In questions targeting yield in agriculture make sure that you have clarified all terms, e.g. do not confuse herbicide with pesticide.

make sure that the plants are the correct distance apart; use of pesticide or insecticide; use of herbicide or fungicide; use of biological control or named biological control; use of variety produced by selective breeding [any 4]

(c) (i) A farmer rears pigs by a factory-farming method. Pigs are kept indoors 24 hours per day in warm, confined cubicles.

How can this method result in the production of a greater yield of pork than from animals reared outside? [3]

Note that the reverse explanation for pigs reared outside can be given, e.g. more energy used for movement.

less energy is released for movement; less energy is used to maintain body temperature; more energy is used for biomass

(ii) Suggest why many consumers object to this factory-farming method. [1]

cruel or not ethical

(iii) Pigs are often given copper with their food because it promotes their growth. Suggest **one** disadvantage of using this method. [2]

it may contaminate the pork; people eat the pork and may be harmed

Practice examination questions

1 The number of species of grass and the number of leguminous plants growing in two fields was measured over a 10-year period. Field A was given nitrogenous fertiliser each year, but field B was given none. The results are shown in the graphs.

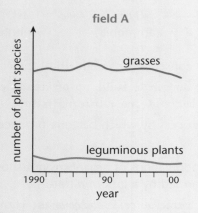

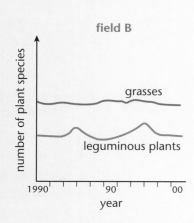

(a) (i) Suggest why there were fewer leguminous plant species in field A. [2]

    (ii) Suggest why there were more leguminous plant species in field B. [2]

(b) After the main investigation no fertiliser at all was used in either field. Cattle were allowed to graze in both fields. At the end of five years the number of legume species in each field had decreased. Suggest why the number of legume plants decreased. [1]

[Total: 5]

2 The following two gases help cause the greenhouse effect.

	Greenhouse effect factor	Relative amount in troposphere
Water vapour	0.1	1%
CFCs	25 000	4.8×10^{-8}

(a) Work out which gas has the greatest influence on the greenhouse effect. [2]

(b) Suggest **one** reason for the greenhouse effect resulting in:

    (i) an increase in the population of a species [1]

    (ii) a decrease in the population of a species. [1]

[Total: 4]

Chapter 9
Synoptic assessment

What is synoptic assessment?

You must know the answer to this question if you are to be fully prepared for your A2 examinations!

Synoptic assessment:

- involves the drawing together of knowledge, understanding and skills learned in different parts of the AS/A2 Biology courses
- requires that candidates apply their knowledge of a number of areas of the course to a variety of contexts
- is tested at the end of the A2 course both by assessment of investigative/ practical skills and by examinations
- is valued at 20% of the marks of the course total.

AQA assesses synoptic assessment in the A2 units by two types of question: structured questions carrying 15 marks and an essay question carrying 25 marks.

There is a structured question on Unit 4 requiring candidates to use subject matter and skills from Unit 4 and the AS specification. There is a structured question in Unit 5 requiring candidates to apply knowledge, understanding and skills from the AS and A2 specification. In the essay in Unit 5, candidates are required to use knowledge and understanding from across all units.

Practical investigations

You will need to apply knowledge and understanding of the concepts and principles, learned throughout the course, in the planning, execution, analysis and evaluation of each investigation.

How can I prepare for the synoptic questions?

- Check out the modules which will be examined for your specification's synoptic questions.
- Expect new contexts which draw together lots of different ideas.
- Get ready to apply your knowledge to a new situation; contexts change but the principles remain the same.
- In modular courses there is sometimes a tendency for candidates to learn for a module, achieve success, then forget the concepts. Do not allow this to happen! Transfer concepts from one lesson to another and from one module to another. Make those connections!
- Improve your powers of analysis – take a range of different factors into consideration when making conclusions; synoptic questions often involve both graphical data and comprehension passages.
- Less able candidates make limited conclusions; high ability candidates are able to consider several factors at the same time, then make a number of sound conclusions (not guesses!).
- You need to do regular revision throughout the course; this keeps the concepts 'hot' in your memory, 'simmering and distilling', ready to be retrieved and applied in the synoptic contexts.
- The bullet point style of this book will help a lot; back this up by summarising points yourself as you make notes.

Why are synoptic skills examined?

Once studying at a higher level or in employment, having a narrow view, or superficial knowledge of a problem, limits your ability to contribute. Having discrete knowledge is not sufficient. You need to have confidence in applying your skills and knowledge.

Synoptic favourites

The final modules, specified by AQA for synoptic assessment, include targeted synoptic questions. Concepts and principles from earlier modules will be tested together with those of the final modules. You can easily identify these questions, as they will be longer and span wide-ranging ideas.

> **Can we predict what may be regularly examined in synoptic questions?**
>
> 'Yes we can!' Below are the top five concepts. Look out for common processes which permeate through the other modules. An earlier module will include centrally important concepts which are important to your understanding of the rest.
>
> **KEY POINT**

Check out the synoptic charts

1 Energy release

Both aerobic and anaerobic respiration release energy for many cell processes. Any process which harnesses this energy makes a link.

Examples

- Reabsorption of glucose involves active transport in the proximal tubule of a kidney nephron. If you are given a diagram of tubule cells which show both mitochondria and cell surface membrane with transporter proteins, then this is a cue that active transport will probably be required in your answer.

- Contraction of striated (skeletal) muscle requires energy input. This is another link with energy release by mitochondria and could be integrated into a synoptic question.

- The role of the molecule ATP as an energy carrier and its use in the liberation of energy in a range of cellular activity may be regularly linked into synoptic questions. The liberation of energy by ATP hydrolysis to fund the sodium pump action in the axon of a neurone.

- The maintenance of proton gradients by proton pumps is driven by electron energy. Any process involving a proton pump can be integrated into a synoptic question.

2 Energy capture

Photosynthesis is responsible for availability of most organic substances entering ecosystems. It is not surprising that examiners may explore knowledge of this process and your ability to apply it to ecological scenarios.

Examples

- Given the data of the interacting species in an ecosystem you may be given a short question about the mechanism of photosynthesis then have to follow the energy transfer routes through food webs.

- Often both photosynthesis and respiration are examined in a synoptic type question. There are similarities in both the thylakoid membranes in chloroplasts and cristae of mitochondria.

- Many graphs in ecologically based questions show the increase in herbivore numbers, followed by a corresponding carnivore increase. Missed off the graph, your knowledge of a photosynthetic flush which stimulates herbivore numbers may be expected.

Synoptic links

Try this yourself! Think logically. Write down an important biological term such as 'cell division'. Link related words to it in a 'flow diagram' or 'mind map'. The links will become evident and could form the framework of a synoptic question.

Energy: input and output

This has to be a favourite for many synoptic questions. Energy is involved in so many processes that the frequency of examination will be high.

3 The structure and role of DNA

It is important to know the structure of DNA because it is fundamentally important to the maintenance of life processes and the transfer of characteristics from one generation of a species to the next. DNA links into many environmentally and evolutionarily based questions.

- The ultimate source of variation is the mutation of DNA. Questions may involve the mechanism of a mutation in terms of DNA change and be followed by natural selection. This can lead to extinction or the formation of a new species. Clearly there are many potential synoptic variations.

- DNA molecules carry the genetic code by which proteins are produced in cells. This links into the production of important proteins. The structure of a protein into primary, secondary, tertiary and quaternary structure may be tested. All enzymes are proteins, so a range of enzymically based question components can be expected in synoptic questions.

- The human genome project is a high-profile project. The uses of this human gene 'atlas' will lead to many developments in the coming years. The reporting of developments, radiating from the human genome project, could be the basis of many comprehension type questions, spanning diverse areas of Biology. Save newspaper cuttings, search the internet and watch documentaries. Note links with genetic diseases, ethics, drugs, etc.

4 Structure and function of the cell surface membrane

There are a range of different mechanisms by which substances can cross the cell surface membrane. These include diffusion, facilitated diffusion, osmosis, active transport, exocytosis and pinocytosis. Additionally glycoproteins have a cell recognition function and some proteins are enzymic in function. Knowledge of these concepts and processes can be tested in cross-module questions.

- In an ecologically based question the increasing salinity of a rock pool in sunny conditions could be linked to water potential changes in an aquatic plant or animal. Inter-relationships of organisms within a related food web could follow, identifying such a question as synoptic.

- In cystic fibrosis a transmembrane regulator protein is defective. A mutant gene responsible for the condition codes for a protein with a missing amino acid. This can link to the correct functioning of the protein, the mechanism of the mutation and the functioning of the DNA.

5 Transport mechanisms

This theme may unify the following into a synoptic question, transport across membranes, transport mechanisms in animal and plant organs. Additionally, they may be linked to homeostatic processes.

- The route of a substance from production in a cell, through a vessel to the consequences of a tissue which receives the substance, could expand into a synoptic question. Homeostasis and negative feedback could well be linked into these ideas.

Sample questions and model answers

A short question which cuts across the course. It refers back to AS. Do not forget those modules! See the *Letts AS Guide* for additional advice and those concepts not found in this volume.

Question 1 (a short structured question)

The kangaroo rat (*Dipodomys deserti*) is a small mammal that lives in the Californian desert. It has specialised kidneys so that it can live in these hot conditions.

(a) Name the genus that contains the kangaroo rat. [1]

Dipodomys

(b) What is the biological naming system called that gives the kangaroo rat its scientific name? [1]

binomial system

(c) Why is it important for any mammal to keep its body temperature close to 37°C? [2]

For correct enzyme action. Too hot and the enzymes will denature and too cold and the reactions will slow down.

(d) During the day the kangaroo rat spends most of the time underground. Suggest why this is. [2]

To keep cool. Otherwise too much moisture would be lost in keeping the temperature constant.

(e) The desert community that contains the kangaroo rat is the final product of succession in California. What is the name of the final, stable community that is produced by succession? [1]

a climax community

[Total: 6]

Question 2 (a longer, more open-ended question)

Plants and animals both need to exchange gases with the environment. Describe how animals and plants are adapted for efficient gaseous exchange. [10]

(Quality of written communication assessed in this answer.)

- examples of respiratory surfaces in animals:
  gills/lungs;
  tracheoles in insects;
  surface of protoctists;
  stomata in plants
- large surface area:
  way(s) in which this is achieved e.g.
  many alveoli;
  surface area/volume ratio in protoctists;
  many gill filaments;
  large surface area of leaves;
  many mesophyll cells
- maintenance of diffusion gradients
  way(s) in which this is achieved
  rich blood supply;
  ventilation mechanisms;
  sub-stomatal airspaces;
  spongy mesophyll air spaces;
  use of carbon dioxide in mesophyll cells

Sample questions and model answers *(continued)*

- small diffusion pathway
  barriers one cell thick;
  specialised cells, e.g. squamous epithelium;
  thin cell walls of palisade cells

Note, there is one mark available for legible text with accurate spelling, punctuation and grammar.

[Total: 10]

Question 3 *(a longer question of higher mark tariff)*

Different concentrations of maltose were injected in the small intestine of a mouse. The amount of glucose appearing in the blood and the small intestine after 15 minutes were measured. The results are shown in the graph.

> Prepare yourself for this type of synoptic question. It cuts across a large part of the specification. Make the links with different ideas. This fact is very important; concepts from AS are needed.

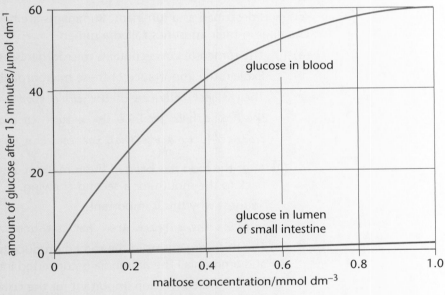

(a) (i) Describe the structure of a maltose molecule [2]

Two molecules of (alpha) glucose;

joined together by a glycosidic bond.

(ii) Maltose is converted into glucose by a hydrolysis reaction. What is a hydrolysis reaction? [1]

A reaction that breaks down a substance by the addition of water.

(b) Describe the effect of different maltose concentrations on the amount of glucose found in the lumen of the small intestine compared to the effect on the amount found in the blood. [2]

the maltose concentration has much more effect on the amount of glucose in the blood; the amount of glucose found in the blood is starting to level off but the amount in the lumen is increasing steadily.

> Even if you only cover one of these points, you can pick up a second mark by correctly using figures from the graph in your answer.

Sample questions and model answers (continued)

(c) The enzyme maltase is found on the cell surface membrane of the epithelial cells of the small intestine.

(i) How does the data on the graph indicate that the enzyme is not released into the lumen? [1]

Very little/no increase in the amount of glucose in the lumen.

This is a harder stretch and challenge question.

(ii) Explain why having the enzyme fixed to the cell surface will increase the rate of glucose absorption. [2]

Higher concentration of glucose produced close to intestinal lining;

will increase the concentration gradient between intestine and blood.

[Total: 8]

Question 4

A cow is described as a ruminant. Ruminants are herbivores that have a chamber in their intestines called a rumen.

(a) (i) The rumen of cows contains microorganisms.

Explain the importance of these microorganisms to the cow. [3]

They digest cellulose in the cow's food;

the cow cannot produce the enzyme to digest cellulose;

produce fatty acids that the cow can use.

(ii) After the food has been in the rumen for some time it is regurgitated back to the mouth for a second chewing.

Suggest why this is important. [1]

Increase the surface area for digestion.

(iii) The microorganisms in the rumen produce two waste products, methane and ammonia. The ammonia is converted into urea by the cow's liver.

Why is this conversion important for the cow? [1]

Ammonia is more toxic than urea.

(b) The table shows the amount of methane produced by different domesticated animals

Animal type	Methane production per animal in kg per animal per year	Total methane production in tonnes per year
buffaloes	50	6.2
camels	58	1.0
goats	5	2.4
sheep	6	3.4

(i) Which of the animals in the table are ruminants? Explain how you can tell this. [2]

Buffaloes and camels;

they produce much more methane per animal.

Sample questions and model answers (continued)

This is a typical synoptic question as it links two different topics, digestion in herbivores and the greenhouse effect!

(ii) Which type of animal in the table is domesticated in the highest numbers? Explain how you worked out your answer. [2]

Sheep; dividing the total methane production by the production per animal gives the highest number.

(iii) Methane is a potent greenhouse gas.
What is a greenhouse gas? [2]

A gas that prevents the escape of infra red radiation from the atmosphere; therefore causes the atmosphere to warm.

(iv) It has recently been discovered that methane is released when arctic ice melts.
Explain why people are concerned by this discovery. [2]

The release of methane would increase global warming;

which in turn would result in the release of even more methane.

[Total: 13]

Practice examination answers

Chapter 1   Energy for life

1

(a) in cytoplasm [1]

(b) pyruvate [1]

(c) 2 ATPs begin the process;
2ATPs are produced from each of the two GP
molecules, so −2 + 4 = +2 ATPs net [1]

(d) animal; animal cells produce lactate [1]

(e) oxygen or aerobic [1]

[Total: 5]

2

(a) At this point the amount of carbon dioxide given
off by the plant in *respiration*, is totally used by the
plant in *photosynthesis*. [2]

(b) compensation point [1]

(c) The continued graph line falls (as light dims); line
ends below the horizontal axis (when it's dark!). [2]

[Total: 5]

3

(a) mitochondrion [1]

(b) NADH [1]

(c) cytochrome [1]

(d) ATP [1]

[Total: 4]

4

(a) (i)   rate of photosynthesis is proportional to light
intensity; rate limited by amount of light available

(ii) as light intensity increases it results in significantly
less increase in the rate of photosynthesis

(iii) rate of photosynthesis has levelled off, no longer
limited by light (but other conditions could be
limiting!). [3]

(b) Similar shape of graph, begins at origin, but graph line
above the given plotted curve. [1]

[Total: 4]

Chapter 2   Response to stimuli

1

(a) (i)   IAA (at these lower) concentrations is *proportional*
to the angle of curvature of the stem. [1]

(ii) IAA (at these higher) concentrations is *inversely
proportional* to the angle of curvature. [1]

(b) *More* IAA causes the cells at side of stem in contact
with agar block to elongate more than other side.

So this side grows more strongly bending stem
towards the weaker side. [2]

(c) Growth is only stimulated up to a certain high IAA
concentration, after this curvature would be inhibited. [2]

[Total: 6]

2

(a) A = actin; B = myosin [2]

(b) action potential reaches sarcomere [1]

(c) both filaments slide alongside each other;
they form cross bridges;
during contraction the filaments slide together to
form a shorter sarcomere [2]

[Total: 5]

3

(i)   resting potential achieved; Na$^+$ / K$^+$ pump is on [2]

(ii) Na+ / K$^+$ pump is off; so Na$^+$ ions enter axon [2]

(iii) maximum depolarisation achieved; K$^+$ ions leave [2]

(iv) Na$^+$ ions leave due to Na$^+$/ K$^+$ pump being back on;
this is during the refractory period;

(v) at end of this resting potential re-established;
axon membrane re-polarised [4]

[Total: 10]

Chapter 3   Homeostasis

1 (a)

	Nervous system	Endocrine system
Usually have longer lasting effects		✓
Have cells which secrete transmitter molecules	✓	
Cells communicate by substances in the blood plasma		✓
Use chemicals which bind to receptor sites in cell surface proteins	✓	✓
Involve the use of Na$^+$ and K$^+$ pumps	✓	

[2]

(b) homeostasis [1]

[Total: 3]

2

(a) Moisture evaporates from the dog's mouth; takes heat
away from the body; cannot sweat from the skin
because of fur. [2]

(b) Vasoconstriction occurs; less blood flows close to the
skin's surface. [2]

Chapter 3 Homeostasis (cont.)

(c) Sweat cannot evaporate so easily; as air is saturated with water vapour; therefore, less heat is lost from the skin. [2]

[Total: 6]

3

(a) **B**, because as glucose levels rose after meals they did not decrease enough (this kept the blood glucose level too high) [1]

(b) glucose levels fell after every meal, so glucose must have entered the cells and liver [1]

(c) in the pancreas;
in the β cells of islets of Langerhans (max 2) [2]

[Total: 4]

Chapter 4 Further genetics

1

(a) no immigration and no emigration; no mutations; no natural selection; true random mating; all genotypes must be equally fertile [4]

(b) (i) $q^2 = \dfrac{48}{160}$

$= 0.3$

$q = 0.55$

but $p + q = 1$
so $p = 1 - 0.55$
$= 0.45$
but $p^2 + 2pq + q^2 = 1$
so $0.45^2 + 2 \times 0.45 \times 0.55 + 0.55^2 = 1$
$0.2 + 0.5 + 0.3 = 1$
BB = 0.2   Bb = 0.5 bb = 0.3 [3]

(ii) BB 2000   Bb 5000   bb 3000 [2]

[Total: 9]

2

A (iv), B (iii), C (v), D, (ii), E (i). [Total: 5]

3

(a) triplet [1]

(b) codes for an amino acid, codes for stop or start [2]

[Total: 3]

Chapter 5 Variation and selection

1

(a) continuous variation; [1]

(b) two from:
genetic;
the nutrition of the mother;
mother's smoking;
mother's alcohol intake;
mother's health; [2]

(c) three from:
heavy babies have higher death rate;
light babies have higher death rate;
so babies of average mass more likely to survive;
they are more likely to have babies of average mass; [3]

(d) Modern techniques can increase survival of light and heavy babies; they in turn will reproduce; [2]

[Total: 8]

2

(a) **Allopatric speciation** takes place after geographical isolation;
• the rising of sea level splits a population of animals; formerly connected by land creating two islands;
• mutations take place so that two groups result in different species.

Sympatric speciation takes place through genetic variation;
• in the same geographical area;
• mutation may result in reproductive incompatibility;
• perhaps a structure in birds may lead to a different song being produced by the new variant;
• this may lead to the new variant being rejected from the mainstream group;
• breeding may be possible within its own group of variants. [6]

(b) Mate them both with a similar male, to give them a chance to produce fertile offspring.
• If they both produce offspring, take a male and female from the offspring, mate them,
• if they produce fertile offspring then original females **are** from the same species. [2]

[Total: 8]

Chapter 6 Biotechnology and genes

1

(a) Identify the specific section of DNA which contains the gene; this can be done using reverse transcriptase; insert DNA into a vector/insert into *Agrobacterium tumefaciens*; this bacterium/this vector then passes the DNA into the recipient cell. [5]

(b) herbicide kills weeds; which reduces competition; for light or water or minerals; soya plants unharmed [3]
[Total: 8]

Chapter 7 Ecology and populations

1

(a) no significant migration;
no significant births or deaths;
marking does not have an adverse effect. [3]

(b) S = total number of individuals in the total population
S_1 = number captured in sample one, marked and released, i.e. 16
S_2 = total number captured in sample two, i.e. 12
S_3 = total marked individuals captured in sample two, i.e. 5

$$\frac{S}{S_1} = \frac{S_2}{S_3} \quad \text{so, } S = \frac{S_1 \times S_2}{S_3}$$

$S = \frac{16 \times 12}{5}$ Estimated no. of shrews is 38 [2]

(c) Not very reliable because the numbers are quite low. High population numbers are more reliable. [1]
[Total: 6]

2

(a) (i) pioneer or primary coloniser [1]
(ii)
- algae cut off light from plants underneath;
- they die as a result;
- bacteria or fungi or saprobiotics decay them;
- they use a lot of oxygen;
- fish die due to not enough oxygen;
- blood worms increase in number as they are adapted to small amounts of oxygen.

[any 5 points] [5]

(b)
- marginal plants or irises were introduced;
- they spread;
- each year the foliage died and rotted;
- this organic material or humus added to the soil or mud;
- secondary colonisers spread from other areas;
- succession took place.

[any 4 points] [4]
[Total: 10]

Chapter 8 Energy and ecosystems

1

(a) (i) When given fertiliser the grasses competed for resources better that the legumes; some legume species could not grow in these conditions. [2]
(ii) Without fertiliser the grass species did not have enough minerals so did not compete as well; the legumes fixed nitrogen in root nodules so could grow effectively. [2]

(b) Cows grazed on some species more than others/ perhaps trampling by cattle destroyed some species but others were tougher and survived/perhaps waste encouraged the growth of some species whereas others were destroyed. [1]
[Total: 5]

2

(a) greenhouse effect factor x amount
= water vapour
CFCs 25 000 x 4.8 x 10^{-8} % = 0.012
water vapour has greatest greenhouse effect [2]

(b) (i) new sea areas so more marine organisms or named organism/formerly cold area grows new warm-climate plants [1]
(ii) deserts formed which reduce food availability/ cold-adapted organisms not suited to new climate/terrestrial organisms destroyed by the rising seas [1]
[Total: 4]

Index

Contents

KU-189-418

The early atmosphere and oceans

The early atmosphere

- The early **atmosphere** of the Earth was formed from gases that escaped from volcanoes.
- We can tell that the main gases in the early atmosphere were water vapour (H_2O) and carbon dioxide (CO_2) because these gases are still produced by modern volcanoes.

Remember!
There was very little oxygen in the atmosphere when the Earth first formed.

- Rocks contain a record of the gases that were in the atmosphere at the time they formed.
- Scientists analyse rocks that formed at different times to provide evidence for the way the atmosphere has changed.
- The atmosphere of volcanic planets such as Mars provides evidence for the early atmosphere of Earth.

- Oxygen is one of the most reactive gases in the atmosphere.
- **Oxidation reactions** can be seen in rusting metals and the maintenance of fire.
- The type of iron compounds found in rocks leaves a permanent record of the oxygen content of the atmosphere at the time the rocks were formed.
- More recent rocks contain iron oxide, but in older rocks the iron is not oxidised. This provides evidence that oxygen levels in the atmosphere have increased.
- Nitrogen has also increased and carbon dioxide has dramatically decreased.

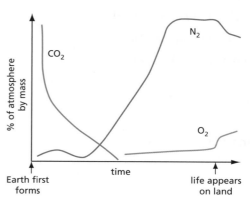
Earth's changing atmosphere.

The early oceans

- As the Earth cooled, water vapour in the atmosphere **condensed** and fell as rain to make the oceans.
- Carbon dioxide from the atmosphere **dissolved** into the oceans, causing the percentage in the atmosphere to drop.
- Early sea plants used the dissolved carbon dioxide for **photosynthesis**, and released oxygen into the atmosphere.
- Some sea animals took in carbon dioxide to make their shells. Shells from dead animals collected on the sea floor and over many years turned into **carbonate** rocks.

EXAM TIP
Use scientific terminology in your answers – condensed, dissolved, oxidised.

- The chemical symbol for water is H_2O.
- H_2O can exist in different states – solid, liquid or gas.
- When water vapour condenses, intermolecular forces hold the molecules together.

Life on Earth

- The evolution of life caused major changes to the atmosphere.
- Photosynthesis decreased the level of carbon dioxide and increased the level of oxygen in the atmosphere:

$$6CO_2 \text{ (g)} + 6H_2O \text{ (l)} \longrightarrow C_6H_{12}O_6 \text{ (aq)} + 6O_2 \text{ (g)}$$

carbon dioxide + water ⟶ glucose + oxygen

- State symbols tell us whether a chemical is a solid (s), a liquid (l), a gas (g) or dissolved in water (aq).

Improve your grade

The changing atmosphere

Foundation: Explain how the early atmosphere changed to become the atmosphere we have today.

AO1 [4 marks]

Collins
Revision

NEW GCSE

Chemistry

Foundation and Higher

for Edexcel

Author: Alison Dennis

Revision Guide +
Exam Practice Workbook

Contents

Today's atmosphere

Investigating change

- The modern atmosphere contains:
  - 78% nitrogen
  - 21% oxygen
  - 1% argon
  - 0.03% carbon dioxide
  - tiny amounts of other gases.
- Iron oxide is formed when iron reacts with oxygen in the air.
- We can measure how much iron oxide is formed from a known volume of air. This lets us calculate the percentage of oxygen in the air.
- The gases in air can be separated by fractional distillation.
- Scientific instruments can measure accurately the amount of each gas in the atmosphere. This allows any small changes to be detected.
- The gases in the atmosphere change when volcanoes erupt, when humans burn **fossil fuels** and when forests are cut down.

The changing atmosphere

- Burning fossil fuels (which are mainly **hydrocarbons**) for energy releases lots of carbon dioxide into the atmosphere.
- Additional carbon dioxide is released into the atmosphere when volcanoes erupt.
- Forests carry out more photosynthesis than fields. This means that the amount of carbon dioxide taken in by photosynthesis decreases when humans cut down large areas of trees to plant crops (**deforestation**).
- Atmospheric carbon dioxide levels have increased over the last 300 years due to human activity.
- Farming with fertilisers increases the amount of nitrogen oxides in the atmosphere, while cattle farming increases the amount of methane.

Chemical equations

- In a chemical reaction, no atoms are created or destroyed.
- Chemical equations can be shown as formulae equations or word equations.
- An example of a word equation is:

iron + oxygen $\longrightarrow$ iron oxide

- Formulae equations must be balanced – there must be the same number of atoms on the **reactant** side as on the **product** side.

> **Remember!**
> When you balance an equation, the formulae of the reactants and products doesn't change. Never change the subscripts!

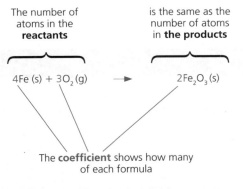

The number of atoms in the **reactants** is the same as the number of atoms in **the products**

$$4Fe\,(s) + 3O_2\,(g) \longrightarrow 2Fe_2O_3\,(s)$$

The **coefficient** shows how many of each formula

- Change the **coefficients** to balance the equation.

Improve your grade

Measuring gases

Higher: The percentage of gases in the atmosphere has remained the same for thousands of years, but recently there have been small changes.

Explain how we can tell when the atmosphere changes and suggest some reasons for the change.

AO1 [4 marks]

Types of rock

Different rocks

- Different types of rock have different properties. These properties reveal how the rocks formed.

- **Igneous rock** forms when molten **magma** or lava cools and becomes solid.
  - Igneous rock that has solidified on the surface of the Earth has small crystals. Basalt is an example.
  - Igneous rock that has solidified underground has large crystals. Granite is an example.

- **Sedimentary rock** forms when tiny particles (sediment) settle on to the ocean floor. Over a long time, more and more layers of sediment settle on top. The pressure causes the layer to harden.
  - Chalk and limestone are examples of sedimentary rock. They are made from the shells of tiny sea creatures that fell to the bottom of the ocean.

- **Metamorphic rock** is formed from sedimentary rock that has come under heat and pressure underground. This makes the arrangement of the crystals in the rock change.
  - Limestone and chalk change to marble when they come under heat and pressure.

Remember!
Magma is molten rock under the ground and lava is magma that has reached the Earth's surface.

G–E

Cooling down

- Scientists learn about how igneous rock has formed by looking at the crystals within it.

- **Intrusive** igneous rock cools slowly under the ground because it is insulated by the surrounding rock. It forms rock with large crystals.

- **Extrusive** igneous rock cools quickly above the ground. It forms rock with small crystals.

Remember!
When metamorphic rock forms, the minerals line up and crystals form, but it never becomes liquid.

D–C

Crystal formation

- The rate of cooling affects the crystal size in igneous rocks.

- Crystals are formed by atoms or molecules fitting together in rigid structures with regular lines and particle layers.

- The amount of **kinetic** energy (energy of movement) in atoms and molecules is related to their temperature.

- As molten rock cools, the particles within it have less and less kinetic energy. Eventually they bond together to form solid crystals.

- If cooling is slow, just a few crystals start to form, and gradually more particles join on to each crystal. A few large crystals are made.

- If cooling is rapid, many crystals start to form at once. Each crystal collects only a small share of the cooling particles, so many small crystals are made.

B–A*

How science works

You should be able to:

- understand how scientists use their observations to form ideas about how different igneous rocks were made.
  - They *observe* that different rocks contain different sized crystals.
  - This leads to a *hypothesis* that the crystal size depends upon the rate at which molten rock cools.
  - The hypothesis can be used to make a *prediction* – cooling molten salol slowly and quickly will produce different sized crystals.
  - An *experiment* then provides some data which will confirm or refute the prediction.

Improve your grade

Igneous rock formation

Foundation: Scientists can gain a great deal of information by looking at the properties of rocks.

What is igneous rock, and what does the appearance of igneous rock tell scientists about the way it has formed?

AO1 [5 marks]

Sedimentary rock and quarrying

Sedimentary rock formation and fossils

- Weathering breaks rocks into fragments, which are transported to the ocean by rivers. The fragments fall to the bottom of the ocean as sediments.

- The sediment particles become squashed (**compaction**) and are cemented together by minerals. After a very long time, sedimentary rock is formed.

- Sedimentary rock changes into metamorphic rock when it comes under heat and pressure. This happens because it gets buried deep underground and comes close to hot molten rock.

- The particles in **chalk** and **limestone** are rearranged to form **marble**.

- Fossils form in sedimentary rock when:
  - organisms fall into sediment
  - there is not enough oxygen to cause the organism to decay
  - the organism has hard enough parts to leave a caste in the forming rock
  - water filtering through the rock deposits minerals in the caste.

- Chalk is full of microscopic fossils because the sediment from which it is made comes from the shells of microscopic sea organisms.

Remember!
Fossils are only found in sedimentary rock, not in igneous or metamorphic rock.

Erosion

- Rocks may be **eroded** by wind and water, producing small fragments.

- The eroded rock fragments build up in layers at the bottom of oceans and eventually form layers of rock.

- After long periods of time, the layers may be uplifted and exposed to wind and water.

- The different exposed layers erode at different rates because of their varying properties, such as solubility or hardness.

Quarrying limestone

- The chemical in limestone, chalk and marble is calcium carbonate ($CaCO_3$).

- Limestone is dug up (quarried) for use in making glass, cement and concrete.

- Problems associated with quarrying limestone include:
  - the fact that it creates noise and dust, and damages animal habitats
  - transporting limestone contributes to traffic congestion and road damage.

- Advantages of quarrying limestone include:
  - it provides jobs for those near the quarry
  - the industries using limestone are important for both the local and national economy.

> ### EXAM TIP
> It is always good to give the composition of substances where relevant, for example the chemical composition of limestone – $CaCO_3$.

- Limestone is an important raw material. It is processed to make the following materials:
  - Glass is made by heating limestone, sodium carbonate and sand together.
  - Cement is made by heating limestone and clay.
  - Concrete is made by mixing together sand, gravel, cement and water.

- The negative impacts of essential quarrying can be minimised by:
  - restricting the size of quarries
  - only blasting in the quarries at specific times
  - using water sprays to reduce the amount of dust created
  - creating earth barricades to reduce the noise impact of blasting
  - factoring in the reclamation of the land once the quarry closes.

Improve your grade

Uses of limestone

Foundation: The limestone industry plays an important part in the British economy but it also causes environmental problems.

Explain what limestone is and how it is used. Discuss whether you think that the damage to the environment means we should no longer use limestone.

AO2 [4 marks]

Atoms and reactions

Fundamentals of chemistry

- **Atoms** are the smallest particles of an **element** that take part in a chemical reaction.
- All the atoms of an element are the same. Atoms from different elements have different properties.
- Atoms cannot be created or destroyed in chemical reactions.
- In a chemical reaction, the atoms of the reactants are rearranged to make the products. Reactants and products have different properties.
- The mass of all the reactants added together at the start of a reaction is the same as the mass of all the products at the end of a reaction. This is called the **conservation of matter**.

Products and reactants

- **Chemical properties** describe how something behaves in a chemical reaction. Examples are how easily something burns or the way something reacts with acid.
- The chemical properties of the reactants in a chemical reaction are always different to the chemical properties of the products.
- Examples of **physical properties** are solubility, melting point, density, colour and magnetism.
- Two dissolved chemicals reacting to form a solid is called **precipitation**.
- If a reaction takes place in a sealed container, there will be no change in mass before and after the reaction.

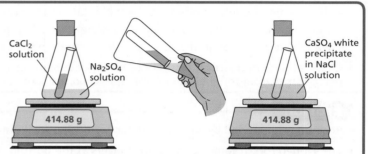

$CaCl_2$ solution

Na_2SO_4 solution

$CaSO_4$ white precipitate in NaCl solution

414.88 g

414.88 g

The conservation of matter. Note that the mass remains the same.

Remember!
In a *physical* change the *chemical* properties of the substance do not change.

Conservation of matter

- The number of each type of atom in the reactants is the same as the number of each type of atom in the products.
- Formula equations must be balanced to show this, for example:

$$4Fe\ (s) \quad + \quad 3O_2\ (g) \quad \longrightarrow \quad 2Fe_2O_3\ (s)$$

Forming iron oxide.

- The equation above shows the formation of iron oxide.
  - Four iron atoms react with six oxygen atoms.
  - They produce two iron oxide molecules, each made up of two iron atoms and three oxygen atoms.
- The law of conservation of mass can be used to calculate the amount of oxygen in iron oxide:
  - Weigh a sample of iron.
  - Heat with a known volume of air.
  - The mass of iron oxide produced minus the mass of iron reactant = mass of oxygen used as reactant.

Improve your grade

Rearranging atoms

Higher: Prakash and John are discussing where all the nitrogen gas in the atmosphere came from. Prakash thinks that the carbon dioxide in the early atmosphere was converted into nitrogen.

$$CO_2\ (g) \quad \longrightarrow \quad N_2\ (g)$$
carbon dioxide   nitrogen

John disagrees. Who do you agree with and why?

AO2 [3 marks]

Thermal decomposition and calcium

Calcium carbonate

- In a **thermal decomposition** reaction, a chemical breaks down into more than one substance when heated.
- Calcium carbonate decomposes to make calcium oxide and carbon dioxide.
- Other metal carbonate compounds follow the same pattern:

  zinc carbonate $\longrightarrow$ zinc oxide + carbon dioxide
  copper carbonate $\longrightarrow$ copper oxide + carbon dioxide

- Calcium oxide is useful for making glass, cement and **limewater**.

Remember!
metal carbonate $\longrightarrow$ metal oxide + carbon dioxide

G–E

Calcium oxide

- The reaction between calcium oxide and water produces calcium hydroxide (slaked lime). It gives off a lot of heat, causing the water to boil and spit.

  CaO (s) $\quad + \quad$ H_2O (l) $\quad \longrightarrow \quad$ $Ca(OH)_2$ (s)
  calcium oxide $\quad + \quad$ water $\quad \longrightarrow \quad$ calcium hydroxide

- Limewater is calcium hydroxide solution. When limewater reacts with carbon dioxide, a cloudy precipitate of calcium carbonate forms, because calcium carbonate is **insoluble**.

  $Ca(OH)_2$ (aq) $\quad + \quad$ CO_2 (g) $\quad \longrightarrow \quad$ $CaCO$ (s)
  calcium hydroxide $\quad + \quad$ carbon dioxide $\quad \longrightarrow \quad$ calcium carbonate

D–C

Metal carbonates

- Many metal carbonates undergo thermal decomposition to metal oxides and carbon dioxide, but some decompose more easily (at a lower temperature) than others.
- Calcium carbonate decomposes at 825 °C, zinc carbonate at 300 °C and copper carbonate at 200 °C.
- Uses of metal oxides include:
  - zinc oxide (ZnO) – rubber, concrete, medicines, cosmetics
  - copper oxide (CuO) – pigments, semiconductors.

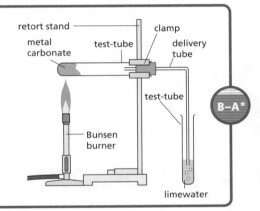

retort stand — clamp
metal carbonate — test-tube — delivery tube
test-tube
— Bunsen burner
limewater

Apparatus to carry out thermal decomposition.

B–A*

Calcium and neutralisation

- Neutral soil (**pH 7**) is best for growing crops.
- Acid soil can be made less acidic by mixing it with calcium carbonate, oxide or hydroxide.
- Burning coal produces sulfur dioxide gas. If this gets into the atmosphere it makes **acid rain**.
- Calcium compounds are used to prevent sulfur dioxide getting into the atmosphere.

G–E

- Both calcium oxide (lime) and calcium hydroxide (slaked lime) are irritants and cause severe burns.
- Three times more limestone than lime is needed to neutralise the same amount of soil.
- Lime and slaked lime neutralise soil faster, but limestone acts for longer.

D–C

- Calcium oxide neutralises acidic sulfur dioxide to produce calcium sulfate:

  CaO (aq) + SO_2 (g) $\longrightarrow$ $CaSO_3$ (s)

- When coal is burned in power stations, the sulfur dioxide gas is removed from the waste gases by passing them thorough a scrubber.
- Calcium sulfate is a useful product of calcium oxide and can be sold.
- Nitrogen oxides are also acidic gases made in power stations that can cause acid rain. They can be removed in a similar way.

B–A*

Improve your grade

Limestone reactions

Foundation: Explain the reaction that occurs when limestone is heated and why this makes it more useful.

AO2 [4 marks]

Acids, neutralisation and their salts

Neutralising acids

- A **base** is a compound that can neutralise an acid. The reaction is called **neutralisation**.
- After neutralisation there is no acid left. A neutral solution has a pH of 7.
- All acids and bases react to form the same type of products.

  acid + base ⟶ salt + water

- If you neutralise an acid using a carbonate, carbon dioxide is produced.

  acid + carbonate ⟶ salt + water + carbon dioxide

- Bases are compounds of metals – either metal oxides (e.g. calcium oxide) or metal hydroxides (e.g. potassium hydroxide) or metal carbonates (e.g. sodium carbonate).
- Not all bases will dissolve to make solutions. Bases that *are* soluble are called **alkalis** (e.g. sodium hydroxide).
- Hydrochloric acid (HCl) is made naturally in our stomachs. It is important for killing bacteria and for activating some enzymes for digestion.
- Too much stomach acid causes indigestion. **Antacids** are medicines taken to relieve indigestion. They work by neutralising excess stomach acid.

Antacids

- Antacids are indigestion remedies that contain bases.
- You can work out how effective indigestion remedies are by measuring how much acid they can neutralise.
- You can find out how acidic something is by measuring its pH. Acids have a pH less than 7 while alkalis have a pH more than 7.
- To tell when an acid is neutralised you can measure the pH. As the acid is neutralised, the pH rises. At pH 7 all the acid has been neutralised.
- **Titration** is slowly adding alkali to acid (or acid to alkali) until exactly the right amount has been added to neutralise it.
- When all the acid is neutralised, only salt and water remain.

Acids and their salts

- A salt is a compound formed when an acid is neutralised.
- The name of the salt formed depends upon the acid and base used.
- The first word of the name comes from the name of the metal in the base, e.g. *calcium* carbonate, *sodium* hydroxide, *magnesium* oxide.
- The second word in the name comes from the acid. Hydrochloric acid forms salts whose name ends in chloride, sulfuric acid forms sulfates and nitric acid forms nitrates.

Remember!
A salt is neutral, neither an acid nor a base.

Acid	Base	Salt
Hydrochloric acid	Sodium hydroxide	Sodium chloride
Hydrochloric acid	Calcium carbonate	Calcium chloride
Nitric acid	Calcium oxide	Calcium nitrate
Sulfuric acid	Calcium carbonate	Calcium sulfate

Examples of acids, bases and the salts produced.

Improve your grade

Neutralising acid spills

Higher: Commercial spill kits are available to help deal with acid spills in the workplace. They often contain sodium carbonate.

Explain how such kits would help to prevent damage from a spill of sulfuric acid. Include any reactions that occur in your answer.

AO2 [5 marks]

Electrolysis and chemical tests

Electrical energy and charged solutions

- **Electrolysis** is when a compound is split up using electrical energy. An electric current is made to pass through a solution of the compound.

- Electrolysis of water produces oxygen and hydrogen.

- Electrolysis of hydrochloric acid produces hydrogen gas at the negative **electrode** (the **cathode**) and chlorine gas at the positive electrode (the **anode**).

- Chlorine can also be produced by the electrolysis of seawater.

- Chlorine is important for the manufacture of poly(chloroethene) and of bleach.

Electrolysis of hydrochloric acid.

Remember!
Electrolysis requires a direct current (d.c.) so that one electrode remains negative and the other positive.

- The two electrodes used in electrolysis have opposite charges.

- Negative **ions** are attracted to the positive electrode and positive ions are attracted to the negative electrode. In this way the ions in the solution separate and move to opposite electrodes.

- Gases produced at the electrode are less dense than liquid and so bubble up. Gases can be captured when they displace water from an upturned container.

- Electrolysis of hydrochloric acid produces an equal volume of gas at each electrode. There are equal amounts of chlorine and hydrogen in hydrochloric acid (HCl).

- Twice as much hydrogen as oxygen is produced when water is electrolysed. This tells us that there is twice as much hydrogen as oxygen in water (H_2O).

Chemical testing

- Chemical tests help us to identify some gases:
  - A lighted splint causes a popping sound when plunged into a tube of hydrogen, but goes out in a tube of chlorine.
  - A glowing splint relights in oxygen.
  - Damp indicator paper is bleached to white when it comes into contact with chlorine.

- In chemical tests, scientists must consider all the evidence before coming to a conclusion.

- Physical and chemical properties are useful in identifying gases. For example:
  - Chlorine is pale green with a distinctive pungent smell.
  - Oxygen and hydrogen are colourless and odourless.

Gases and their uses

- Oxygen is essential for breathing. It is supplied commercially for medical use and for underwater diving tanks.

- Oxygen is essential for combustion. Many fire-fighting techniques depend on removing oxygen to put out fires.

- Hydrogen is required for ammonia manufacture, **cryogenics** and hydrogen balloons. It must be used with caution because it is very flammable.

- Chlorine is toxic, which makes it hazardous to handle but useful in destroying microorganisms. It is used in bleach and **disinfectant** manufacture.

How science works

You should be able to:
- assess the risks involved when conducting experiments with toxic substances such as chlorine
- adopt appropriate safety precautions.

Improve your grade

Creating chlorine
Foundation: Describe how you could produce a test tube full of chlorine from hydrochloric acid.
AO2 [4 marks]

Metals – sources, oxidation and reduction

Rocks, minerals and ores

- Most metals are found in the Earth as part of a chemical compound. Naturally occurring compounds are called **minerals**.
- Rocks are mixtures of different minerals. Some rocks are metal **ores**.
- Very unreactive metals like gold can be found in the Earth as elements.

- Metal ores contain metal compounds and unwanted rock. The metal must be extracted from the ore.
- The cost of the metal is higher if:
  - the ore is difficult to obtain
  - the method of extraction is expensive
  - the ore contains a low percentage of the metal.
- Iron is cheap because iron ore (haematite) is plentiful and inexpensive to extract. Gold has a high price because the ore is rare. Aluminium ore (bauxite) is plentiful but aluminium is expensive because it costs a lot to extract.
- Some metals can be extracted by heating with carbon, e.g. extracting iron.

  iron oxide + carbon ⟶ carbon dioxide + iron
- Other metals must be extracted by **electrolysis**, e.g. extracting aluminium.

  aluminium oxide $\xrightarrow{\text{electricity}}$ aluminium + oxygen
- Electrolysis is expensive because of the high cost of the electricity.

Methods of extraction

- Metal ores often contain metal oxides. To extract the metal, oxygen must be removed from the oxide.
- The method of extraction chosen depends on how reactive the metal is.
- The **reactivity series** shows which metals are more reactive than carbon and must be extracted by electrolysis, and which are less reactive and can be extracted with carbon.

> **Remember!**
> The method of extraction of a metal depends on the properties of the metal.

Oxidation and reduction

- Metals can gain oxygen atoms and become oxides. This is called **oxidation**, e.g. iron + oxygen ⟶ iron oxide. This is what happens when iron rusts.
- Oxidation of metals is called corrosion.
- Metal oxides can lose oxygen and become metals. This is called **reduction**. Reduction takes place when iron is extracted from its ore.

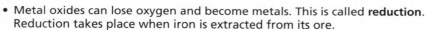

- The equation for the reduction of iron ore with carbon is:

  $2Fe_2O_3$ (s) + $3C$ (s) ⟶ $4Fe$ (s) + $3CO_2$ (g)
  iron oxide + carbon ⟶ iron + carbon dioxide
- Carbon is oxidised and iron oxide is reduced.
- If iron is not protected it will corrode by reacting with oxygen from the air.

  $4Fe$ (s) + $3O_2$ (g) ⟶ $2Fe_2O_3$ (s)
  iron + oxygen ⟶ iron oxide

Reactivity and corrosion

- The more reactive a metal is, the more rapidly it becomes oxidised.
- Many metals form an impermeable layer of metal oxide, which creates a barrier between oxygen and the metal underneath. They do not continue to corrode.
- Iron corrodes when it comes into contact with water and oxygen. You can prevent this by coating the metal, to protect it.
- **Galvanising** is when iron is coated with zinc, a more reactive metal. The zinc corrodes first, protecting the iron. This process is called **sacrificial protection**.

Improve your grade

Pricing metals

Higher: Aluminium is the most common metal in the Earth's crust, yet 100 g of aluminium costs about ten times more than 100 g of iron. Explain the reasons for this difference in value. *AO1* [5 marks]

Metals – uses and recycling

Properties dictate uses

- The different properties of metals makes them useful for different purposes.

Metal	Properties	Uses
Aluminium	Low density, strong for its weight, corrosion resistant, highly reflective	Aircraft, drinks cans, overhead electricity cables, bicycle frames, window frames, mirrors and reflectors
Copper	Excellent conductor of heat and electricity, does not corrode in water, **malleable** and **ductile**	Plumbing, electrical wiring
Gold	Excellent electrical conductor, does not corrode, very reflective	Jewellery, dentistry, electronic connectors, reflectors and radiation shields

Alloys

- An alloy is a mixture of different metal atoms. Alloying changes the properties of the metal, e.g. steel is an alloy of iron.

Element added	Change in properties
Carbon	Harder, stronger, more brittle
Chromium	Very corrosion resistant (stainless steel)
Titanium	Stronger, lighter, more corrosion resistant

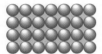 

> **Remember!**
> In a compound the different atoms are in a fixed ratio. In a mixture there can be any ratio of atoms.

In pure metals the atoms are aligned in a very regular pattern (top left), but in alloys the atoms of different substances disrupt the alignment of the metal atoms (top right).

- Pure metals have atoms of identical size. The layers of atoms easily slide over each other, making the metal soft and malleable.

- Mixing different sized atoms interferes with this and makes the metal stronger.

- Pure gold is too soft to be useful, so it is alloyed with silver and copper. The carat and **fineness system** indicates the percentage of gold.

% gold	99.9%	75%	50%	37.5%
Carat rating	24	18	12	9
Fineness rating	999	759	500	370

- Shape memory alloys return to their original shape after being deformed. For example, nitinol is an alloy of nickel and titanium. Uses include:
  - medical stents to keep blood vessels open
  - dental braces to pull teeth into position
  - spectacle frames.

- Scientists are learning to design metals like shape memory alloys to meet specific requirements.

Recycling

- Metal ores are a **non-renewable** resource.

- Recycling of metal brings both economic and environmental advantages:
  - reduces energy use in mining and transport
  - causes less environmental damage from mining
  - reduces the amount of land used up by dumping waste rock and waste metal
  - preserves the supply of metal ore.

Improve your grade

The right metal

Higher: A town council is trying to decide on the best metal to choose as a building material for a bridge over the local river.

Explain what factors they should take into account and suggest a suitable metal. Give reasons for your choice.

AO2 [5 marks]

Hydrocarbons and combustion

Hydrocarbons and fractional distillation

- **Crude oil** is a mixture of lots of different **hydrocarbon** molecules. Hydrocarbons are made from hydrogen and carbon atoms only.
- Different molecules have different lengths, and this gives them different boiling temperatures. We can use the different boiling points to separate the molecules.

- In fractional distillation, crude oil is vaporised and the vapour is slowly cooled. As the temperature drops, first the larger and then the smaller molecules turn to liquid and can be collected. This separates the molecules into groups (fractions) with similar sizes.
- The longer the average carbon chain in the fraction, the higher the boiling point and viscosity and the lower the flammability.
- The different fractions are much more useful than crude oil.
- Products from fractional distillation include gases for heating and cooking, petrol for cars, kerosene for aircraft fuel, diesel oil for some cars and trains, fuel oil for ships and power stations, and bitumen for tarmac and roofing.

> **Remember!**
> The fractions from fractional distillation are still *mixtures* of different molecules.

- A **homologous series** is a family of similar **compounds**. Each successive member of the family has one more CH_2 group than the previous member.
- The molecules in liquid fractions of crude oil are held together by intermolecular forces. As the molecules get longer, the intermolecular forces get stronger. The stronger the force the more kinetic energy (higher temperature) needed to boil the fraction.

Combustion

- Combustion is burning, a type of **oxidation reaction** that produces heat and light.
- Burning hydrocarbon fuels produces carbon dioxide and water.

- Carbon dioxide turns limewater cloudy because it forms solid calcium carbonate.

$$Ca(OH)_2 \text{ (aq)} \quad + \quad CO_2 \text{ (g)} \quad \longrightarrow \quad CaCO_3 \text{ (s)} \quad + H_2O \text{ (l)}$$
calcium hydroxide (limewater) + carbon dioxide → calcium carbonate + water

- Living organisms use oxidation reactions inside cells to transfer energy from food. This is why we need a constant supply of oxygen and we breathe out carbon dioxide.

Incomplete combustion

- When hydrocarbons burn in plenty of oxygen they produce carbon dioxide (CO_2).
- When there is not enough oxygen they produce **carbon monoxide** (CO). This is called **incomplete combustion**.
- Carbon monoxide is very poisonous. It is difficult to detect because it has no odour or colour.
- It is very important to use all heaters that burn hydrocarbons in a well-ventilated space. Then there is plenty of oxygen and no carbon monoxide is made.

- A yellow, sooty flame means incomplete combustion. The soot is particles of carbon (C).
- Carbon monoxide combines permanently with **haemoglobin** in **red blood cells**. This prevents them from carrying oxygen to the body cells.

- Carbon particles released from incomplete combustion can cause breathing problems, especially for asthmatics.
- Particles in the atmosphere also result in global dimming and encourage cloud formation.

Improve your grade

Making crude oil

Foundation: Explain how and why kerosene is made from crude oil.   *AO2* [4 marks]

Acid rain and climate change

Destruction from the sky

- Hydrocarbon fuels naturally contain some atoms of sulfur. When the fuels burn, the sulfur atoms are oxidised to sulfur dioxide.
- Sulfur dioxide reacts with oxygen and water vapour and becomes sulfuric acid. This forms **acid rain**.
- The sulfur dioxide gas is usually carried away in the air and falls as acid rain far away from where it was made.
- Acid rain damages buildings, trees, life in streams and ponds, washes valuable minerals from the soil and releases toxic metals.

- When acid rain falls on trees it damages the leaves. The leaves do not photosynthesise efficiently and eventually the tree dies.
- Acid rain causes damage to the surface of limestone structures because it reacts with the calcium carbonate in limestone.

> **Remember!**
> If the acid level is *high* then the pH is *low*.

- The UK government has pledged to reduce sulfur dioxide emissions. Methods include:
  - removing sulfur from fuels before they are burned
  - trapping sulfur dioxide released after burning fuels
  - swapping to fuels with lower sulfur content, such as low sulfur coal and methane.

Climate change and the greenhouse effect

- Some gases in the atmosphere act like a blanket around the Earth and prevent heat from escaping into space. This warming effect is essential for life on the planet.
- Gases that can do this are called **greenhouse gases**. Important examples are carbon dioxide, water vapour and methane.
- The temperature of the planet may be affected by changes in solar activity and changes in the amounts of greenhouse gases in the atmosphere.
- Humans have increased the amount of carbon dioxide in the atmosphere by burning hydrocarbons and by cutting down and burning forests.
- Scientists are experimenting with ways to reduce the amount of carbon dioxide and other greenhouse gases.

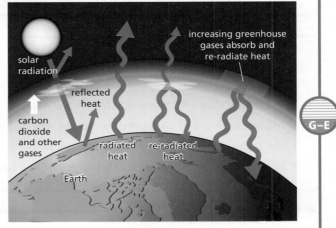

The greenhouse effect.

- The warm Earth radiates **infrared radiation** out towards space. Greenhouse gases absorb this radiation and so trap the energy on the planet. This increases the global temperature (the **greenhouse effect**).
- There is a correlation between the amount of carbon dioxide in the atmosphere and the temperature of the Earth.
- Most scientists consider that the rise in the Earth's temperature has been caused by human activities, which have increased the level of carbon dioxide in the atmosphere.
- Some scientists believe that the global temperature rise has a different cause.

Removing carbon dioxide from the atmosphere

- **Algae** remove carbon dioxide from the atmosphere by **photosynthesis** and by forming carbonate shells. Growth of algae is usually limited by a lack of iron in ocean water. Scientists are experimenting with seeding the oceans with iron to increase algal growth.
- Carbon dioxide can be reduced back into hydrocarbons using experimental **nanotechnology** and energy from the Sun.
- A sure way of preventing further increases in atmospheric carbon dioxide is to reduce energy consumption.

Improve your grade

Causes of climate change

Higher: Discuss the evidence that the activities of humans have resulted in climate change.   *AO2* [5 marks]

Biofuels and fuel cells

Fuels from plants

- Petrol, diesel and kerosene are **fossil fuels** made from crude oil. Fossil fuels are a **non-renewable resource** that will eventually run out.
- **Biofuels** are made from plants. Plants are a **renewable resource** because more can be grown.
- Ethanol is a biofuel that can be made from sugar beet or sugar cane. It can be mixed with petrol so that less petrol is needed.
- If fuel crops are grown instead of food, this may put up food prices.
- When fuel crops grow they take in the carbon dioxide that will be released when the fuel is burned.

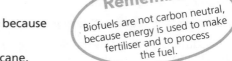

Remember!
Biofuels are not carbon neutral, because energy is used to make fertiliser and to process the fuel.

- A good fuel will:
  - be easy to ignite and keep alight
  - not produce much ash, smoke or polluting gases
  - release a lot of energy per kg
  - be easy to store and transport
  - be cheap to produce and use.

- **Fermentation** is the name given to the process that uses the **enzymes** in yeast cells to convert plant carbohydrate into ethanol. The overall reaction is:

  $C_6H_{12}O_6$ (aq) $\longrightarrow$ $2C_2H_5OH$ (aq) + $2CO_2$ (g)

- Enzymes are biological **catalysts** that speed up the rate of reactions.

Cells and electricity

- Hydrogen makes a good fuel because:
  - it releases a large amount of energy
  - it produces only water as a waste product
  - it can be made from water, which is a cheap and plentiful.
- There are problems with using hydrogen as a fuel for cars because it is flammable and explosive.
- The technology for using hydrogen as a fuel is not completely ready yet.
- When oxygen and hydrogen react together in a **fuel cell**, the energy released is captured as electricity. This can be used to power a car.

Comparing fuels

- The energy released by different fuels can be compared using a burner and a **calorimeter**.
- The temperature of the water is measured before and after burning the fuel.
- It is important to keep the control variables the same in all experiments. These are the volume of water and the mass of fuel burned.
- The independent variable is the type of fuel and the dependent variable is the temperature rise.

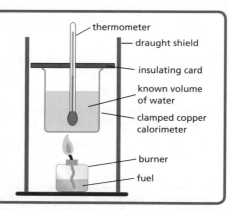

thermometer

draught shield

insulating card

known volume of water

clamped copper calorimeter

burner

fuel

A basic calorimeter.

Where does the hydrogen come from?

- Generating hydrogen by electrolysis of water requires electricity, which is mainly produced by burning fossil fuels. This means that using hydrogen-fuelled cars will result in the burning of fossil fuels and carbon dioxide emissions, unless renewable methods of generating electricity are used.
- Supplying the hydrogen to vehicles using fuel cells is a problem. There is no network of refuelling stations for hydrogen. One solution is to produce hydrogen in the vehicle by reacting petrol with steam.

Improve your grade

Energy from ethanol

Foundation: Describe an experiment that you could do to decide whether ethanol or hexane releases the most energy. Ethanol and hexane are both liquids.

AO2 [4 marks]

Topic 5: 5.17, 5.18, 5.19, 5.20, 5.21, 5.22, 5.23, 5.24

Alkanes and alkenes

Natural gas

- Most of the **hydrocarbons** in crude oil are **alkanes**.
- All alkanes:
  - have the formula $C_nH_{(2n+2)}$
  - have a name which ends in -ane
  - are **saturated** (all carbons atoms have four single bonds to four different atoms).
- The first three alkanes in the family are methane, ethane and propane. They are found in natural gas.

Hydrocarbon	Formula and structure	No. of carbon atoms	State
Methane	CH_4 	1	Gas
Ethane	C_2H_6	2	Gas
Propane	C_3H_8	3	Gas

The structure and formulae of methane, ethane and propane.

- Refinery gas is a mixture of methane (70–90%), ethane and propane.
- The methane is separated and used in the home for heating and cooking. It releases more energy and less carbon dioxide than other fuels.
- Ethane is mostly processed further then used to make either **polymers** or other chemicals.
- Propane turns to a liquid easily when put under pressure in a cylinder. It is used in LPG fuel for cars, and for cooking and heating where piped gas is not available.

G–E
D–C

Covalent bonding

- Carbon atoms form four **covalent bonds** because this makes them stable.
- Atoms are made from a central **nucleus** containing **protons** and neutrons and surrounded by **electrons**. Carbon has six protons in its nucleus and six electrons arranged in two **shells** around the nucleus.
- A covalent bond is formed when a pair of electrons is shared between two different atoms. The nuclei of both atoms are attracted to the shared electrons, so the atoms are held together.
- When carbon shares four electrons to make four covalent bonds, it has eight electrons in its outer shell. This makes it chemically stable.

B–A*

Remember!
Bromine water changes from brown to *colourless*, not from brown to *clear*. Clear means transparent – the opposite of cloudy.

Unsaturated hydrocarbons

- **Alkenes** are hydrocarbons that have a carbon-carbon double bond. This is two covalent bonds between the same two carbons.
- Molecules with a double bond are called **unsaturated**.
- Bromine water changes from brown to colourless when it reacts with an alkene. Alkanes do not decolourise bromine water.

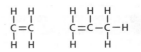

The structure of ethene and propene.

G–E

Organic compounds

- **Organic compounds** are molecules that contain carbon.
- The hydrocarbons in crude oil make very good starting points from which chemists can manufacture other useful organic molecules, such as medicines.
- Organic chemicals can be named in a systematic way so that the name tells us the structure of the compound.
- The prefix to the name gives the number of carbon atoms.
- The suffix gives the family or **homologous group** to which the molecule belongs.

D–C
B–A*

No. of carbon atoms	Prefix
1	Meth-
2	Eth-
3	Prop-
4	But-
5	Pent-

Prefixes used in naming organic compounds.

Improve your grade

Ethane and ethene

Higher: Most of the ethane obtained from natural gas is converted into ethene and made into polymers.

How could you distinguish between ethane and ethane? Illustrate your answer with drawings of the molecules concerned.

AO2 [5 marks]

Cracking and polymers

Cracking

- Crude oil from different sources contains different amounts of each fraction. The shorter-chain fractions are the most valuable.

- **Cracking** is a process that splits long-chain alkanes into shorter alkanes and alkenes. To crack an alkane you pass the alkane vapour over a heated **catalyst**.

- Cracking is a **thermal decomposition** reaction.

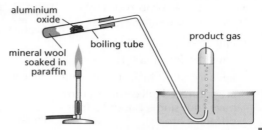

Laboratory equipment to crack hydrocarbons.

- Cracking uses a catalyst of aluminium oxide or zeolites.

- There is a mismatch between supply and demand for the fractions of crude oil. Cracking increases the supply of shorter-chain alkanes and provides alkenes for the polymer industry.

Making polymers

- Alkenes are used to make **polymers**. Many alkene molecules (**monomers**) link together to make a very long polymer molecule. This is **polymerisation**.

- The name of the polymer tells you the name of the monomer. Poly(*ethene*) is made from ethene. Poly(*propene*) is made from propene.

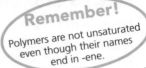

Remember!
Polymers are not unsaturated even though their names end in -ene.

- To make ethene into poly(ethene) you need a high temperature and pressure, and a catalyst.

- One bond from the double bond breaks and is used to join one alkene monomer to another in a long chain. This process of adding the monomers together is called **addition polymerisation**.

- The longs chains of the polymer can be spun into threads or moulded into any shape.

- Different alkenes can be used as monomers for polymerisation. This gives polymers with different properties.

- The equation below shows polymerisation for PTFE.

fluoroethene   a strand of poly(tetrafluoroethene)

Disposing of polymers

- Disposing of unwanted polymers is a problem. Polymers put into landfill remain there for a very long time because they are not **biodegradable**. Burning polymers often releases toxic fumes.

- **Recycling** solves the problem of what to do with unwanted polymers. It also saves oil, energy used in making new polymers, and space in landfill sites.

- Scientists have produced new polymers that are biodegradable.

- Polymers must be sorted into different types before they can be recycled. Melting a mixture of polymers gives a poor-quality product with few uses.

- International recycling codes make it easier to identify and sort polymers.

- Not all polymers are easily recycled, and the quality of the recycled product is not as good as the original.

- Adding biodegradable components into the polymer mixture (like starch grains) helps the polymer break down more easily.

- Polymers made from **starch** and **cellulose** are renewable and biodegradable. There is potential to develop these so they have the required properties to replace oil-based polymers.

Improve your grade

Polymers and energy

Higher: Explain why making bin-liners from new polymers uses so much more energy than using recycled polymers. Suggest why only a small proportion of polymers are recycled.   *AO2* [4 marks]

C1 Summary

The Earth's sea and atmosphere

The early atmosphere was formed from volcanic activity and comprised mainly carbon dioxide and water vapour.

Evidence for the early atmosphere is found in gases trapped in rocks and in the oxidation of iron in rocks.

Early oceans formed as water vapour condensed.

They absorbed carbon dioxide to make carbonate rock.

Photosynthesis eventually caused decreased CO_2 and increased O_2 in the atmosphere.

The modern atmosphere is mostly nitrogen and oxygen with tiny amounts of carbon dioxide.

Materials from the Earth

Igneous rock solidifies from molten rock. Intrusive igneous rock cools below the surface, forming large crystals; extrusive rock cools on the surface, forming small crystals.

In thermal decomposition, a metal carbonate decomposes to form a metal oxide and carbon dioxide.

Metamorphic rock forms when other rocks come under heat and pressure.

Limestone becomes marble.

Sedimentary rock forms from eroded rock fragments cemented together.

It is relatively soft and easily eroded, and may contain fossils.

Limestone is quarried for building, making cement and glass, and neutralising soil.

Quarrying destroys habitats and causes pollution, but provides jobs.

Acids

Acids are neutralised by bases, which are metal oxides, hydroxides or carbonates.

Neutralising acids produces salts.

Indigestion remedies are used to neutralise stomach acid.

Electrolysis is the splitting up of compounds using electricity (d.c.).

HCl splits to H_2 (g) and Cl_2 (g); H_2O splits to H_2 (g) and O_2 (g).

Obtaining and using metals

Metals are extracted from ores in the Earth.

Less reactive metals are reduced from their compounds with carbon; more reactive metals are reduced by electrolysis.

Recycling preserves supplies of ore and reduces environmental damage from mining and extraction.

Alloying changes the properties of a metal, e.g. it becomes harder or stronger.

Steel is iron + carbon + other metals.

Fuels

Alternative fuels include:
- Biofuels made from plants (renewable).
- Ethanol made by fermenting sugar cane and beet.
- Hydrogen, which is non-polluting.

Hydrocarbon fuels are distilled from crude oil. They are mostly alkanes (C_nH_{2n+2}).

Complete combustion gives CO_2 + H_2O; incomplete combustion gives toxic CO + C (soot).

Carbon dioxide is a greenhouse gas. Greenhouse gases trap heat on Earth.

Human activity has increased the level of greenhouse gases, and this may be causing climate change.

Polymers are made by polymerising alkenes (unsaturated molecules formed by cracking alkanes).

Artificial polymers are not biodegradable.

Recycling and producing biodegradable polymers reduces landfill usage.

Matter and mass

- **Atoms** are the smallest building blocks of **elements**. They are made from three types of subatomic particle: **protons**, **neutrons** and **electrons**.

- Protons and neutrons are held tightly together in a *tiny* space in the centre of the atom called the **nucleus**. Electrons move around in a *large* area surrounding the nucleus.

- Protons have a positive charge. Electrons have a negative charge. Neutrons are neutral (they have no charge).

- There are the same number of negative electrons as positive protons. This means that an atom has no overall charge.

- Elements are made from only one type of atom. Different elements have different numbers of protons in the nucleus of their atoms.

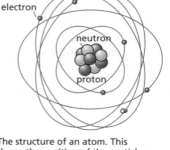

The structure of an atom. This shows the position of the particles, but really the nucleus is thousands of times smaller than the space that the electrons move in.

- The mass of a proton is 1 **atomic mass unit**. The mass of other particles are compared to this.

Name of particle	Relative mass	Relative charge
Proton	1	+1
Neutron	1	0
Electron	1/1836	−1

Remember!
Atoms are too tiny to be seen or weighed. The mass numbers are *relative*.

The periodic table

- In 1869, Dmitri Mendeleev arranged the elements known at that time in a table in order of increasing atomic mass. He put elements with similar properties underneath each other.

- Mendeleev left gaps in the table to make the elements fit the pattern. He correctly predicted that new elements would be discovered to fill the gaps. He was able to predict the properties of these elements by looking at the properties of the elements around them.

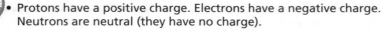

The modern periodic table. Rows are referred to as periods and columns are called groups.

- The modern **periodic table** shows each element like this:

Mass number. The number of protons + neutrons

Atomic number. The number of protons

$$^{12}_{6}C$$

A capital letter or capital followed by a small letter is the symbol for the element

- Elements appear in order of their **atomic number**. Elements in the same group have similar properties.

- Non-metal elements are at the top right. All the other elements are metals.

Isotopes

- All atoms of the same element have the same number of protons in their nucleus.

- **Isotopes** are atoms of the same element with different numbers of neutrons in their nucleus. They have the same number of protons and electrons, and the same chemical properties, but a different mass.

- Hydrogen has three isotopes: ^{3}H, ^{2}H, ^{1}H

- **Relative atomic mass** is the average mass of an atom of the element, taking into account the number and abundance of all the different isotopes.

- Because of the existence of isotopes, not all relative atomic masses are whole numbers.

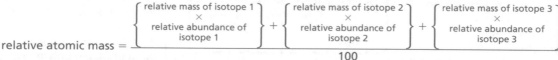

$$\text{relative atomic mass} = \frac{\left\{\begin{array}{c}\text{relative mass of isotope 1} \\ \times \\ \text{relative abundance of isotope 1}\end{array}\right\} + \left\{\begin{array}{c}\text{relative mass of isotope 2} \\ \times \\ \text{relative abundance of isotope 2}\end{array}\right\} + \left\{\begin{array}{c}\text{relative mass of isotope 3} \\ \times \\ \text{relative abundance of isotope 3}\end{array}\right\}}{100}$$

Improve your grade

Atomic structure
Foundation: Describe the structure of an oxygen atom.

AO1 [4 marks]

Electrons

Completing the picture

- The number of electrons in an atom is the same as the number of protons in the nucleus.

- The electrons are arranged in **shells** around the nucleus. Electrons in the same shell have the same energy.

- The nearer the nucleus, the lower the energy of the electrons in the shell. Electrons always go to the lowest energy shell they can.

- The first shell can hold up to two electrons, the second can hold eight electrons, the third holds eight electrons before the fourth shell begins to fill up.

- The position of electrons in an atom is shown using the 2.8.8 convention. This is called the **electron configuration**, e.g. sodium has 11 electrons: two in the first shell, eight in the second shell and one in the third shell. The electron configuration of sodium is 2.8.1.

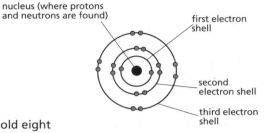

nucleus (where protons and neutrons are found)

first electron shell

second electron shell

third electron shell

The arrangement of electrons in an atom of argon.

- The table below shows the electron configurations of the first three periods of the periodic table.

Element	Atomic number	Electron configuration	Element	Atomic number	Electron configuration
Hydrogen	1	1	Neon	10	2.8
Helium	2	2	Sodium	11	2.8.1
Lithium	3	2.1	Magnesium	12	2.8.2
Beryllium	4	2.2	Aluminium	13	2.8.3
Boron	5	2.3	Silicon	14	2.8.4
Carbon	6	2.4	Phosphorus	15	2.8.5
Nitrogen	7	2.5	Sulfur	16	2.8.6
Oxygen	8	2.6	Chlorine	17	2.8.7
Fluorine	9	2.7	Argon	18	2.8.8

G–E

Remember!
Electrons always fill the lowest energy shell available.

Location, location, location

- Elements in the same group of the periodic table have the same number of electrons in their outer shell.

- The number of shells shows which period an element is in. The number of electrons in the outer shell shows which group it is in.

D–C

Periodicity

- Elements with the same number of electrons in their outer shell react in a similar way in chemical reactions. For example, all group 2 elements react with oxygen to form a compound with the formula XO (put any group 2 element in place of X).

- Mendeleev arranged the elements in order of increasing atomic mass. He noticed that at regular intervals (periodically), elements showed the same properties. We now know that this is because they have a similar electronic structure. This repeating nature is called **periodicity**.

B–A*

How science works

You should be able to:

- understand the process by which scientific hypotheses are developed, proven and accepted. For example, Mendeleev used his arrangement to make predictions about the properties of new elements that had yet to be discovered. When these elements were discovered and his predictions found to be correct, Mendeleev's periodic table was accepted.

Improve your grade

Similar reactions

Higher: Lithium and potassium both react in a very similar way when they are added to water.

Use your knowledge of atomic structure to explain why lithium and potassium react in a similar way, even though they are different elements. *AO2* [4 marks]

Ionic bonds and naming ionic compounds

Bonding

- A compound is two or more different atoms that are chemically bonded together.

- An atom that has gained extra electrons is a negative **ion**. An atom that has lost electrons is a positive ion.

- Positive and negative ions form when one atom transfers electrons to a different atom. For example, sodium (Na) transfers an electron to chlorine (Cl) to make a sodium ion (Na^+) and a **chloride** ion (Cl^-).

- Positive and negative ions are held together by **electrostatic** attraction. This is called **ionic bonding**.

- Compounds held together by ionic bonding are called **ionic compounds**.

Making ions

- An atom that has a full outer shell of electrons is very unreactive (stable).

- Elements in group 0 of the periodic table (the noble gases) have full outer shells of electrons and are very stable.

- When atoms form ions, they give or receive electrons to gain a full outer shell of electrons.

- The electronic configuration of an atom tells us what type of ion it will form:
  - Oxygen 2.6 will gain two electrons to fill up the second shell, so there are eight electrons. It forms an O^{2-} ion.
  - Magnesium 2.8.2 will lose two negative electrons so that the full second shell becomes the outer shell. It forms an Mg^{2+} ion.

- Negative ions change the ending of their element name to -ide, e.g. a fluorine atom becomes a fluoride ion.

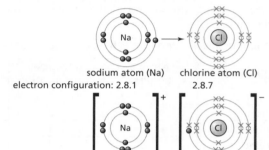

sodium atom (Na)   chlorine atom (Cl)
electron configuration: 2.8.1   2.8.7

sodium ion (Na^+)   chloride ion (Cl^-)
electron configuration: 2.8   2.8.8

Sodium and chloride ions being formed.

Remember!
Forming ions only involves electrons. The number of protons and neutrons in the nucleus does not change.

Ionic bonds

- All metal atoms form positive ions by giving away electrons. Positive ions are called **cations**.

- Non-metal atoms form negative ions by receiving electrons. Negative ions are called **anions**.

- Ions can also be compounds. Examples are OH^-, NO_3^-, HCO_3^-, CO_3^{2-}, SO_4^{2-}, NH_4^+.

Naming ionic compounds

- The name of an ionic compound tells us which ions it contains.

- When the negative ion is an element, the name ends in -ide

potassium bromide

The first word gives the name of the positive ion K^+ — The second word gives the name of the negative ion Br^-

- When the negative ion is a compound containing oxygen, the ending (usually) changes to -ate.

magnesium carbonate

The first word gives the name of the positive ion Mg^{2+} — Shows the negative ion contains carbon — -ate shows the negative ion is a compound with oxygen CO_3^{2+}

Improve your grade

Ionic compounds

Higher: Explain the meaning of 'ionic compound'. Illustrate your answer with a diagram that shows an example of how ionic compounds form.   *AO1* [4 marks]

Writing chemical formulae

Symbols for ions

- The formula for an ion shows the symbol and the charge.
- Monoatomic ions are formed from atoms of only one element.
  - Monoatomic cations have the same name as the element from which they were made. A sodium atom becomes sodium ion.
  - Monoatomic anions have the same name as their atoms but with the ending changed to -ide. A chlorine atom becomes chloride ion.
- **Polyatomic** cations are formed from atoms of more than one element. The different symbols show the different elements from which they are formed.
- When ions join to form ionic compounds, the total number of negative charges always equals the total number of positive charges.
- This means that the number of positive and negative ions is not necessarily the same. Some examples are shown in the table below.

	cations			anions	
1+ ions	2+ ions	3+ ions	2- ions	1- ions
H^+ hydrogen				
Li^+ lithium	Be^{2+} beryllium		O^{2-} oxide	F^- fluoride
Na^+ sodium	Mg^{2+} magnesium	Al^{3+} aluminium	S^{2-} sulfide	Cl^- chloride
K^+ potassium	Ca^{2+} calcium			Br^- bromide

Some monoatomic ions (made from one atom).

cations	anions	
1+ ions	1- ions	2- ions
NH^+ ammonium	OH^- hydroxide	CO_3^{2-} carbonate
	NO_3^- nitrate	SO_4^{2-} sulfate

Some polyatomic ions (made from more than one atom).

Cation	Anion	Compound
Na^+	Cl^-	$NaCl$
Na^+	S^{2-}	Na_2S
Mg^{2+}	Cl^-	$MgCl_2$
Mg^{2+}	S^{2-}	MgS

Writing formulae for ionic compounds

- The **chemical formula** of an ionic compound shows how many and which type of ions it contains.
- When the compound contains more than one polyatomic ion, the whole ion has brackets around it. For example:

  $Ca(NO_3)_2$ means $2 \times NO_3$ so $Ca(NO_3)_2$ contains $1 \times Ca$, $2 \times N$ and $6 \times O$ atoms

- To work out the formula of an ionic compound:
  1 Write the name of the compound.   Calcium nitrate
  2 Write the ions it contains. Ca^{2+} NO_3^-
  3 Multiply the number of ions so that the number of positive charges equals the number of negative charges. $1 \times Ca^{2+}$ $2 \times NO_3^-$
  $= 2 \times +$ $= 2 \times -$
  4 Write the formula. Show the number of each type of ion as a subscript. Remember to put brackets around the compound ions before writing the subscript. $Ca(NO_3)_2$

> **Remember!**
> The formula of an ionic compound never has a charge.

Balancing equations

- To convert a word equation into a formula equation:
  1 Write the **word equation**.
  2 Work out the formula of all reactants and products.
  3 Count the number of each type of atom in the reactants. Add coefficients to balance the numbers of each atom in the reactants with the numbers in the products.

> **EXAM TIP**
> Many students try to balance ionic equations that contain compound ions like SO_4^{2-} by breaking up the sulfate ion to form oxygen. In fact, in most reactions studied at GCSE, sulfate ions in the reactants appear as sulfate ions in the product. Always try to balance an equation first by keeping compound ions intact.

Improve your grade

Formulae equations

Higher: Potassium iodide and lead nitrate react together to form lead iodide. Lead forms a Pb^{2+} ion.

Decide the name of the other product and write a balanced formula equation for this reaction.

AO2 [4 marks]

Ionic properties and solubility

Substances made of ions

- All ionic compounds have similar properties because their particles are joined together in the same way. Positive and negative ions are arranged one after the other in three dimensions.

- This means they often form crystals.

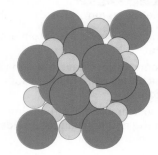

- Ionic compounds:
  - have high melting points and boiling points
  - are brittle and hard
  - conduct electricity only when dissolved or molten
  - may be soluble in water.

A model of a small part of a crystal of sodium chloride. The green balls are chloride ions and the yellow balls are sodium ions.

Structure of ionic compounds

- Ionic substances form giant **lattice** structures with strong **electrostatic forces** between positive and negative ions.

- A large amount of energy is needed to break strong ionic bonds, so the melting point is high.

- The regular arrangement of millions of ions gives a crystalline structure.

- Ionic substances conduct electricity when molten or dissolved because the charged ions are able to move towards oppositely charged electrodes. They do not conduct electricity when solid because the ions are not able to move.

- The strength of the ionic bonding is higher if the ions have a higher charge. For example, magnesium oxide, MgO (Mg^{2+} and O^{2-}), has stronger bonding than sodium chloride, NaCl (Na$^+$ and Cl$^-$).

Remember!
There are no individual molecules in an ionic compound, just a giant ionic lattice containing millions of ions. The formula shows the ratio of ions.

Solubility of ionic compounds

- There are patterns in the solubility of ionic compounds, as shown in the table below.

General rule	Compounds that break the rule
Compounds are *soluble* if the positive ion is: sodium; potassium; ammonium	None
Compounds are *soluble* if the negative ion is: nitrate; chloride; sulfate	Silver chloride, lead chloride, lead sulfate, barium sulfate, calcium sulfate
Compounds are *insoluble* if the negative ion is: carbonate; hydroxide	Sodium carbonate, potassium carbonate, ammonium carbonate
	Sodium hydroxide, potassium hydroxide, ammonium hydroxide

Precipitates

- Sometimes two soluble salts form an insoluble salt when mixed together. This is called a **precipitation reaction**.

- **State symbols** in an equation show if a reactant or product is dissolved (aq), a solid (s), a liquid (l) or a gas (g). For example:

  magnesium sulfate (aq) + sodium carbonate (aq) ⟶ sodium sulfate (aq) + magnesium carbonate (s)

- To decide if a precipitation reaction will occur:
  - Look at the ions in each of the soluble reactants.
  - If any combination of these ions would make an insoluble compound (see table above), then a **precipitate** will form.

Improve your grade

Ionic compounds

Foundation: Jon has a test tube containing white crystals. He wonders if the white crystals are ionic.

What properties will the crystals have if they are ionic? Suggest a simple experiment Jon could carry out to test for one of these properties.

AO2 [5 marks]

Preparation of ionic compounds

Making an insoluble salt

- An insoluble **salt** can be made by a precipitation reaction in the following way:

Step	Example	
Name the insoluble salt you want to make and decide which ions are in it.	silver chloride	
	silver ions	chloride ions
Use the solubility rules to choose a soluble compound for each ion.	*silver* nitrate	sodium *chloride*
Mix solutions of the two soluble compounds to make a precipitate of the insoluble salt.	silver chloride	

- To make a pure sample of an insoluble salt, follow this method:
  - Mix solutions of the reactants.
  - Filter to separate the insoluble salt.
  - Wash the residue in the filter paper to remove impurities.
  - Allow to dry.

Remember!
The solid trapped in the filter paper is the **residue**, the liquid that passes through the filter paper is the **filtrate**.

Using salts in X-rays

- Barium sulfate is insoluble and X-rays cannot pass through it. Doctors can use these properties to diagnose gut problems.

- The patient drinks a suspension of barium sulfate (**barium meal**). Once it has passed into the gut the patient is X-rayed. The X-ray shows the silhouette of the gut and any abnormalities can be seen.

- Barium sulfate is toxic, but because it is very insoluble it is not absorbed into the bloodstream and so is safe to drink.

Testing for ions

- Metal ions make colours when they are put into a flame. Different metals make different colours, helping to identify which metals are in a compound. Some examples are shown in the table opposite.

- To conduct a **flame test**:
  - Dip a nichrome wire in acid.
  - Dip it into the compound to be tested.
  - Put the wire into a Bunsen flame.

Metal ion	Colour
Na^+	Yellow/orange
K^+	Lilac
Ca^{2+}	Brick red
Cu^{2+}	Blue/green

Testing for anions

- Flame tests do not work for negatively charged anions, but other tests can be carried out.

- To test for a carbonate, add a dilute acid. If a gas bubbles off, test it with limewater. If it turns the limewater cloudy then the gas is carbon dioxide and the carbonate is confirmed.

  acid + carbonate ⟶ salt + water + carbon dioxide

- To test for sulfate ions, add hydrochloric acid and barium chloride solution. If a white precipitate forms then the solution contains sulfate ions.

  sulfate ions (aq) + barium chloride (aq) ⟶ barium sulfate (s) + chloride ions (aq)

- To test for chloride ions, add silver nitrate. If a white precipitate forms it contains chloride.

  chloride ions (aq) + silver nitrate (aq) ⟶ silver chloride (s) + nitrate ions

Spectroscopy

- Emission **spectroscopy** can be used to detect the presence of individual elements.

- Each element produces a unique and characteristic spectrum when heated, like a chemical fingerprint.

- The **emission spectrum** of an unknown substance can be compared with standard spectra of elements to see which one it matches. This led to the discovery of rubidium and caesium.

- The method can detect very small amounts and can also measure the quantity of each element.

 Improve your grade

Preparing copper carbonate
Higher: Describe how a pure sample of copper carbonate could be made.   *AO2* [5 marks]

Covalent bonds

Covalent molecules

- Covalent molecules are groups of atoms joined by **covalent bonds**. A covalent bond is a shared pair of electrons.
- Covalent substances can be elements like oxygen (O_2) or compounds like water (H_2O).
- Covalent compounds are made from non-metals.

- Atoms are held together in a covalent bond because the nuclei of two different atoms are both holding onto the same pair of electrons.
- No electrons are transferred from one atom to another.
- Atoms share electrons because they are more stable when they share. The outer shell of each atom in the molecule fills up with shared electrons. A full outer shell of electrons makes atoms stable.

Stable configurations

- The number of covalent bonds that an atom can form depends on how many more electrons are needed to fill the outer shell. For example:
    - Carbon needs four electrons, so it can form four bonds.
    - Oxygen needs two electrons, so it can form two bonds.

- We can predict the formula of a covalent molecule by looking at how many covalent bonds each atom can form.
- Sometimes two atoms share two or three pairs of electrons to form **double bonds** and **triple bonds**.
- Some elements form **diatomic** molecules (molecules containing two atoms), e.g. H_2, O_2, N_2, F_2, Cl_2, Br_2, I_2.

Remember!
No electrons are transferred when covalent bonds form, and there are no charged particles.

Drawing covalent bonds

- We can show covalent bonds in molecules using **dot and cross diagrams**.
- Dot and cross diagrams represent the electron configuration in the outer shells of the combining atoms.
- Dots represents the electrons in the outer shell of the left-hand atom. Crosses represents the electrons in the outer shell of the other atom.
- Overlapping areas show the shared electrons.

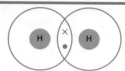

Two hydrogen atoms combining to form a hydrogen molecule (H_2). Hydrogen has just one electron so there is one dot and one cross.

- Carbon has four electrons in its outer shell. It can share them to form four covalent bonds. Hydrogen has one electron to share in a covalent bond.
- Four hydrogen atoms share with one carbon atom to form methane. Carbon now has eight electrons in its outer shell and each hydrogen atom has two electrons.
- A hydrogen chloride molecule contains one hydrogen atom and one chlorine atom. How would this molecule be drawn as a dot and cross diagram?

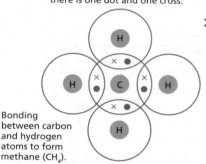

Bonding between carbon and hydrogen atoms to form methane (CH_4).

Double bonds

- Oxygen atoms share two pairs of electrons to form an oxygen molecule with a double bond.
- Carbon forms double bonds with two oxygen atoms to form carbon dioxide.
- Carbon atoms can bond together to make chains and rings. This allows the formation of the large molecules needed for life to exist.

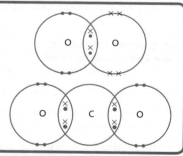

Covalent bonding in an oxygen molecule and a carbon dioxide molecule.

Improve your grade

Bonding in water

Foundation: Describe the type of bonding that holds the atoms together in a molecule of water. Illustrate your answer with a diagram.

AO2 [4 marks]

Properties of elements and compounds

Classifying substances

- Covalent and ionic substances have different properties. The properties of an unknown substance can help you to decide if it is ionic or covalent.

- Properties that can identify a substance as covalent or ionic include:
  - solubility in water
  - **melting point** and **boiling point**
  - electrical conductivity.

- The methods for investigating some of these properties are shown in the diagrams opposite.

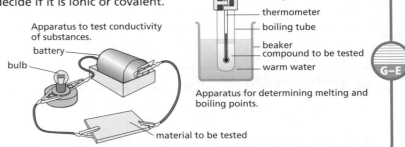

Apparatus to test conductivity of substances.

- battery
- bulb
- material to be tested

- clamp
- thermometer
- boiling tube
- beaker
- compound to be tested
- warm water

Apparatus for determining melting and boiling points.

G–E

Properties of compounds

- Most covalent substances form small molecules. Their structure is called simple molecular. Examples are water, methane and hexane.

- The covalent bonds between the atoms of the molecules are strong, but the forces holding the molecules together are weak.

- Simple molecular substances have low melting and boiling points because the weak forces between molecules are easily broken. They are often gases or liquids at room temperature, or they melt easily.

- Simple molecular substances do not conduct electricity because there are no charged particles.

- Most simple molecular substance do not dissolve in water. There are some exceptions, such as sucrose (sugar).

- Some covalent substances form giant networks of atoms. Their structure is known as giant molecular. Diamond, graphite and sand are examples.

- Giant molecular substances have high melting points and do not dissolve in water or conduct electricity.

- The table below shows the properties of substances with different structures.

D–C

Ionic	Covalent	
Giant lattice	Simple molecular	Giant molecular
High mpt	Low mpt	High mpt
Often soluble	Usually insoluble	Never soluble
Conducts electricity when molten or dissolved	Non-conductor	Non-conductor (except graphite)

EXAM TIP

Many students confuse the covalent bonds *within* simple covalent molecules and the weak forces *between* molecules. When simple covalent molecules boil, the covalent bonds do not break. H_2O (g) contains exactly the same two covalent bonds as H_2O (l).

Diamond and graphite

- Diamond and graphite are both covalent substances with giant molecular structures. They have different properties because their bonds are arranged differently.

- The electrons in the weak bonds between the layers of graphite can move when a voltage is put across them. So, graphite conducts electricity.

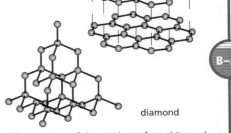

graphite

diamond

The structure of tiny sections of graphite and diamond lattices.

Diamond	Graphite
Four strong covalent bonds	Three strong covalent bonds + one weak bond
Three-dimensional network structure, strong in all directions	Layered structure
Very hard	Layers slide and rub off easily
Poor electrical conductor	Good electrical conductor
Used in cutting tools	Used to make electrodes and to lubricate moving parts

B–A*

Remember!
Diamond and graphite are both the element carbon.

Improve your grade

Using graphite

Higher: Sodium is extracted from sodium chloride by electrolysis. A graphite electrode is inserted into the molten compound and then electricity is passed through it.

Describe the properties of graphite that make it particularly useful as an electrode for this purpose, and explain why graphite has these properties.

AO2 [5 marks]

Separating solutions

Separating immiscible liquids

G–E

- **Immiscible** liquids are liquids that do not mix but separate into layers. Oil and water are examples.
- Immiscible liquids can be separated using a separating funnel.
- Put the mixture of liquids into a separating funnel. Open the tap and collect the bottom layer in a beaker. Close the tap when the top layer enters it. Change the beaker then open the tap to collect the top layer.

Fractional distillation

D–C

- Miscible liquids are liquids that completely mix together. Ethanol and water are miscible, as are the different alkanes in crude oil.
- Miscible liquids can be separated by **fractional distillation**, as shown in the diagram opposite.
- Each liquid in the mixture has a different boiling point.
  - The temperature in the flask rises until it reaches the boiling point of liquid 1.
  - Liquid 1 turns to gas and moves into the condenser, where it cools and turns to liquid on the walls of the condenser.
  - When no more liquid is collected, the container is changed.
  - The temperature in the flask rises until it reaches the boiling point of the next liquid.

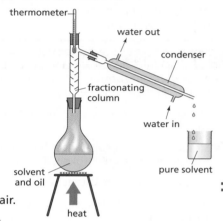

Laboratory fractional distillation apparatus.

B–A*

- Oxygen and nitrogen gas are produced by fractional distillation of air.
  - Dust, water vapour and carbon dioxide are removed from the air.
  - Air is cooled to –200 °C and all gases become liquids.
  - The temperature is gradually allowed to rise, and at about –196 °C nitrogen vaporises and is collected as gas.
  - The remaining liquid is mostly oxygen.

Chromatography

G–E

- **Chromatography** can be used to separate and identify components in substances such as colours in foods:
  - Draw a pencil line about 2 cm up from the bottom of a sheet of chromatography paper.
  - Put a spot of the mixture of colours on the line.
  - Put the paper in a container with solvent and a lid; make sure the solvent does not cover the spot.
  - Wait for the solvent to rise up the paper, then remove the paper and let it dry.
- Different colours move different distances up the paper, so you can see which colours were in the mixture.

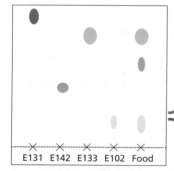

E131 E142 E133 E102 Food

A chromatogram of food dyes. Which colouring in this food needs further investigation?

D–C

- A developed **chromatogram** shows a spot for each substance in a mixture.
- To identify what was in the mixture, compare the spots with known substances.
- The distance travelled by one component of the mixture can be described using **R_f values**.

$$R_f = \frac{\text{distance travelled by component}}{\text{distance travelled by solvent}}$$

B–A*

- R_f values can be used to help identify a component when no standard is available.
- Forensic science and the food industry make use of chromatography.

Remember!

Scientists often use chromatography to identify colourless substances like amino acids and sugars. The invisible spots can be seen by spraying the paper with a locating reagent. This reacts with the spots to produce a colour.

Improve your grade

Identifying colours

Foundation: A sweet manufacturer wants to know what colours have been used in a chewy sweet. Describe a method that they could use to find this out.

AO2 [5 marks]

Classifying elements

Properties of substances

- Scientists can use physical properties to find out about the structure of a substance.
- **Physical properties** include:
  - **Melting point** (the temperature when it changes from a solid to a liquid).
  - **Boiling point** (the temperature when it changes from a liquid to a gas).
  - **Solubility** (how easily it dissolves in water).
  - **Electrical conductivity** (how well it conducts electricity).
- **Chemical properties** describe how a substance reacts in a chemical reaction.
- Elements and compounds are classified as:
  - **Ionic compounds**, which contain positively charged metal ions and negatively charged non-metal ions.
  - **Simple molecular covalent compounds**, which are small molecules consisting of only non-metallic atoms.
  - **Giant molecular covalent compounds**, which are large structures with many non-metallic atoms held together with covalent bonds.
  - **Metallic compounds**, which are individual metal ions surrounded by electrons.

G–E

- A high melting point substance has strong forces holding its particles together. A low melting point substance has weak forces holding its particles together.
- Each type of element and compound has relative properties, as shown in the table below.

Type	Relative melting point	Relative boiling point	Relative solubility in water	Electrical conductivity
Ionic	High	High	Soluble	Good conductors in aqueous solutions or when molten
Simple molecular covalent	Low	Low	Insoluble	Non-conductors as solids, liquids and in solutions
Giant molecular covalent	Very high	Very high	Insoluble	Non-conductors (except graphite)
Metallic	High	High	Insoluble	Good conductors as solids or liquids

D–C

Classifying elements into groups

- Elements are grouped by similar properties in the **periodic table**.
- Some groups are given special names, including **alkali metals**, **transition metals**, **halogens** and **noble gases**.
- Metals are **malleable** and can conduct electricity.
- Most of the metal elements are transition metals. They have high melting points.
- When transition metals react with other elements they often make coloured compounds.

G–E

- All metals have the same structure – a regular arrangement of positive metal ions surrounded by a sea of delocalised electrons.
- Metals are malleable because the layers of positive ions can slide over each other in the sea of electrons.
- Metals conduct electricity because the delocalised electrons can move when a voltage is applied.

Remember!
When molten or dissolved, ionic substances conduct electricity. However, it is not electrons that carry the charge but the ions themselves.

D–C

- The sea of delocalised electrons in metals is formed from the outer-shell electrons of the metal atoms. They are described as delocalised because they are no longer associated with just one atom, but can move between the metal ions.
- The metal atoms are held together in a strong metallic bond because all the ions are attracted to the same sea of delocalised electrons.
- Lots of energy is required to break these bonds so the melting point is high.

B–A*

Improve your grade

Electrical conductivity

Higher: Use ideas about structure and bonding to explain why solid copper oxide cannot conduct electricity while solid copper can.

AO2 [5 marks]

Alkali metals

Group 1 elements

- **Alkali metals** are in group 1 of the periodic table. They have one electron in their outer shell. This gives them similar properties.

- Compared to transition metals, alkali metals are soft and have low melting points.

- They are very reactive and must be stored in oil to prevent them reacting with the air.

- As you go down the group from lithium to caesium the metals:
  - get more reactive
  - become softer
  - have a lower melting point
  - have one more shell of electrons.

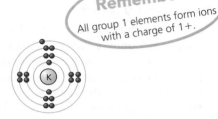

Remember!
All group 1 elements form ions with a charge of 1+.

The electron shells of the first three alkali metals.

Reactivity

- When alkali metals are added to water they float and skid across the surface. Hydrogen fizzes off and the alkali metal gradually disappears. A metal hydroxide is formed, which dissolves into the water. The water becomes alkaline and turns universal indicator purple.

  alkali metal + water ⟶ metal hydroxide + hydrogen

- The reactions of the first three alkali metals – lithium, sodium and potassium – with water demonstrate that they get more reactive going down the group.

- Lithium moves slowly across the surface of the water and gradually gets smaller as it turns into lithium hydroxide and hydrogen.

- Sodium moves quickly across the surface. It melts and forms a ball, then rapidly gets smaller as it turns to sodium hydroxide and hydrogen.

- Potassium melts and moves very fast across the water. The hydrogen produced often catches fire. The flame is lilac because of the potassium present.

- The reaction of the alkali metals with water all have the same equation. (Just put the symbol for one of the alkali metals in the place of X.)

  $2X\,(s) + 2H_2O\,(l) \longrightarrow 2XOH\,(aq) + H_2\,(g)$

- The reaction becomes more vigorous as you go from lithium to caesium because:
  - the outer-shell electron gets further from the positive nucleus
  - there are more inner shells of electrons to shield it from the positive pull
  - it is therefore held to the atom less tightly
  - and is thus more easily lost, to allow the atom to become a stable ion.

- The trend in reactivity going from lithium to potassium allows us to make predictions about other members of the group.

- Caesium, at the bottom of the group, reacts explosively with water. We can predict that francium would be even more reactive, but it is very rare.

How science works

You should be able to:

- predict how reactive certain metals would be when added to water

- describe the safety precautions you would take when testing your predictions, and explain how you would minimise the risks

- understand and describe the trends you see in the results from testing your predictions.

Improve your grade

Observing a reaction

Foundation: Sarah's teacher demonstrates the reaction of potassium with water. She carefully cuts a small piece of potassium and drops it into a large trough of water.

Describe what Sarah would see.

AO2 [5 marks]

Halogens and noble gases

Group 7 elements

- **Halogens** are in group 7 of the periodic table. Each only needs one more electron to have a full outer shell.

- The colours and states of the first four halogens at room temperature are described in the table below.

Halogen	State	Colour
Fluorine	Gas	Pale yellow
Chlorine	Gas	Pale green
Bromine	Liquid	Red/brown
Iodine	Solid	Grey

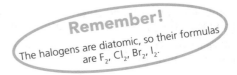

Remember!
The halogens are diatomic, so their formulas are F_2, Cl_2, Br_2, I_2.

G–E

- Halogens get less reactive going down the periodic table from fluorine to iodine.

- Halogens react with hydrogen to form hydrogen halides.

- Hydrogen halides form acids when they dissolve in water.

- Halogens react with metals to form ionic compounds as the halogens take electrons from the metal.

- In the reaction, the halogen becomes negatively charged because of the electrons it gains and the metal becomes positively charged because it has lost electrons to the halogen.

- The ions then form ionic bonds, making metal halides. For example:

  iron + bromine ⟶ iron bromide

  $2Fe (s) + 3Br_2 (l) \longrightarrow 2FeBr_3 (s)$

D–C

Halogen displacement

- A more reactive halogen will displace a less reactive halogen from its compound in solution. This is called a **displacement reaction**.

- Halogen compounds contain halide ions. These are colourless, but halogen atoms are coloured.

- When a displacement reaction occurs, there is a colour change because a different halogen is produced.

chlorine water	+	potassium iodide	⟶	iodine	+	potassium chloride
green		colourless		brown		colourless
$Cl_2 (aq)$	+	$2KI (aq)$	⟶	$I_2 (aq)$	+	$2KCl (aq)$

B–A*

Noble gases

- The **noble gases** (helium, neon, argon, krypton and xenon) form group 0 of the periodic table. They are monoatomic.

- Helium is less dense than air, so it can be used to make balloons and airships float. It is non-flammable, which makes it safer to use than hydrogen.

- Argon is used in filament bulbs and in welding because it is very **inert**. This prevents the unwanted reactions that can occur if air is used.

- The noble gases are inert because they have a full outer shell of electrons. They do not become any more stable by losing, gaining or sharing electrons.

G–E

- The noble gases were discovered in 1894 as a result of observation, **hypothesis** and experimentation.
  - Observation: nitrogen produced from air had a different **density** from nitrogen produced in a chemical reaction.
  - Hypothesis: the nitrogen produced from air also contains other unknown gases.
  - Experiment: fractional distillation of air separated the noble gases from nitrogen.

D–C

- The boiling point and density of elements increase going down group 0 of the periodic table.

- The boiling point and density of any noble gas will be midway between those of the gases above and below it in the group.

B–A*

Improve your grade

Extracting bromine

Higher: Bromine is extracted from the sea on a commercial basis. The first step is to bubble chlorine through sea water. Sea water contains sodium bromide.

Write a symbol equation for the reaction that occurs. Explain what you would see and why. *AO2* [4 marks]

Endothermic and exothermic reactions

Energy changes

- In a chemical reaction, the atoms of the reactants are rearranged to form the products. There is always an energy change.

- Most reactions are **exothermic**. In exothermic reactions, **chemical energy** is transferred to heat energy, so the temperature rises.

- Some reactions are **endothermic**. In endothermic reactions, heat energy is taken in and transferred to chemical energy, so the temperature falls.

- All reactions start by breaking the bonds between the reactant atoms. Heat energy is taken in when bonds are broken.

- Next, the new bonds between atoms of the product are made. Heat energy is given out when bonds are made.

- In exothermic reactions, less energy is taken in to break the reactant bonds than is given out when the product bonds are made.

- In endothermic reactions, more energy is taken in than is given out.

Measuring change

- To measure the energy change in a reaction:
  - Place a solution of reactant 1 in an insulated cup.
  - Record the temperature of the solution.
  - Add a solution of reactant 2 and stir (or add powdered reactant 2).
  - Wait for the temperature to finish changing, then record the new temperature.
  - Calculate the difference in temperature before and after the reaction.

- An increase in temperature means the reaction is exothermic. A decrease means it is endothermic.

- The insulated cup reduces energy transfer in and out of the cup. Stirring makes an even temperature throughout the mixture.

- Examples of exothermic reactions include: combustion, explosions, metal displacement reactions, precipitation reactions, many neutralisation reactions.

- Examples of endothermic reactions include: photosynthesis, thermal decomposition reactions, many salts dissolving in water (e.g. ammonium nitrate).

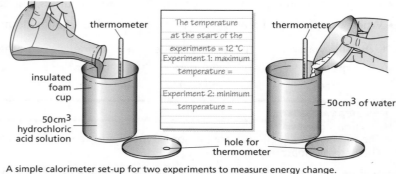

thermometer · thermometer · The temperature at the start of the experiments = 12 °C · Experiment 1: maximum temperature = · Experiment 2: minimum temperature = · insulated foam cup · $50\,cm^3$ hydrochloric acid solution · $50\,cm^3$ of water · hole for thermometer

A simple calorimeter set-up for two experiments to measure energy change.

Energy profile diagrams

- The breaking and making of bonds in a chemical reaction can be described using an **energy profile diagram**.

- For exothermic reactions, the energy of the products is less than the energy of the reactants. The temperature rise in the experiment comes from the energy released.

- For endothermic reactions, the energy of the products is more than the energy of the reactants. The temperature fall in the experiment comes from energy being removed from the surroundings.

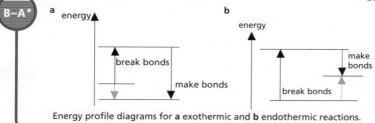

a energy — break bonds — make bonds
b energy — make bonds — break bonds

Energy profile diagrams for **a** exothermic and **b** endothermic reactions.

Remember!

Exothermic reactions show the energy going down while the temperature goes up. Remember that the diagram shows the *chemical energy* of the reactants and products that goes down. The energy lost is transferred to *heat energy*, so the temperature goes up.

Improve your grade

Proving exothermic reactions

Foundation: Andy says that adding iron filings to copper sulfate solution is an exothermic reaction. Describe an experiment he could do to show this.

AO2 [4 marks]

Reaction rates and catalysts

Understanding reaction rates

- Chemical reactions happen when particles collide.
- Reactions happen at different speeds, from very slow to extremely fast. The rate of a reaction is how fast the products are made or how fast the reactants disappear.
- Four factors can increase the rate of a reaction:
  - Increasing the concentration of reactants.
  - Increasing the temperature of the reaction.
  - Breaking a large solid reactant into smaller pieces to increase the surface area.
  - Using a catalyst.

- You can measure the rate of a reaction by recording how much product is made per second. The diagram below shows methods of measuring temperature, concentration and surface area on the **rate of reaction** of marble chips and hydrochloric acid.
- A faster rate of reaction occurs if the concentration of hydrochloric acid is increased, the temperature is higher or the same mass of marble is broken into smaller pieces.
- A slower rate of reaction occurs when a lower acid concentration, lower temperature or smaller surface area is used.

cotton wool bung to stop spray escaping

conical flask

hydrochloric acid and marble chips

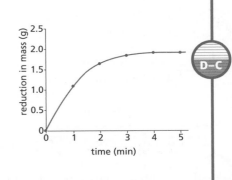

An experimental set-up to study the rate of reaction of hydrochloric acid and calcium carbonate.

Collision theory

- Not all collisions lead to a reaction. To react, they must have sufficient energy and have the correct orientation.
- The rate of a reaction depends on the frequency of effective collisions.
- When the concentration of reactants increases, there are more particles per cm³. This means there are more collisions per second.
- When the temperature increases, the reactants have more energy so a higher percentage of the collisions are effective. The reactants also collide more frequently.
- Increasing the surface area of a solid reactant increases the frequency of collisions.

Remember!
Increasing the *volume* of reactants does not increase the rate of reaction.

Catalysts

- A **catalyst** speeds up the rate of a reaction, but is not used up by the reaction.
- Catalytic converters in vehicles reduce the amount of carbon monoxide and unburned fuel that come from the exhaust pipe.

- The platinum in a catalytic converter is spread in a thin layer over a honeycomb ceramic structure to give a large surface area. This increases the number of reactions catalysed per second.
- Catalysts work better at higher temperatures. Catalytic converters do not work well until the car warms up.
- Two important reactions that are catalysed in a catalytic converter are:

carbon monoxide + oxygen ⟶ carbon dioxide

hydrocarbons + oxygen ⟶ carbon dioxide and water

 Improve your grade

Collision theory

Higher: In glow sticks, two chemicals react to form a product that glows for a short time. Use collision theory to explain why manufacturers recommend keeping glow sticks in the fridge to make them last longer.

AO2 [4 marks]

Mass and formulae

Calculating mass

- To find the **relative formula mass** (M_r) of a compound, such as calcium carbonate, $CaCO_3$:

1 Work out the number of each type of atom	$Ca \times 1$	$C \times 1$	$O \times 3$
2 Look up the relative atomic mass of each	40	12	16
3 Multiply the mass by the number	$40 \times 1 = 40$	$12 \times 1 = 12$	$16 \times 3 = 48$
4 Add them all together	$40 + 12 + 48 = 100$		

- To find the **percentage composition** of a compound, such as the percentage oxygen in water, divide the mass of oxygen (16) by the total mass of water (18) and multiply by 100 = 88.89%.

- **Empirical formula** is the simplest ratio of atoms, e.g. formula of ethane = C_2H_6 and empirical formula of ethane = CH_3.

- To calculate the empirical formula from experimental results:

1 Write down the symbol for each element	Fe	Cl
2 Write down the experimental mass of each element	22.4	42.6
3 Divide the mass of each element by its A_r	$\dfrac{22.4}{56}$	$\dfrac{42.6}{35.5}$
The result is the ratio of atoms in the compound	0.4 : 1.2	
4 Make it into a whole number ratio by dividing the biggest number by the smallest	$\dfrac{Cl}{Fe} \dfrac{1.2}{0.4} = 1:3$	
5 Write the formula	$FeCl_3$	

Calculating yields

- You never get 100% of the possible **yield** because some reactants may not have reacted, the product may stick to the apparatus or otherwise get lost, or because unwanted products may be created by side reactions.

- The **theoretical yield** is the maximum amount of product that could be made if all the reactants were converted into product.
- **Percentage yield** is: $\dfrac{\text{actual yield}}{\text{theoretical yield}} \times 100\%$

Reacting masses

- You can calculate the masses of all reactants and products if you know the equation and the mass of one substance.
- What mass of Na_2SO_4 will be made from 10 g of NaOH? The mass of NaOH is known and the mass of Na_2SO_4 is unknown.

1 Write the equation.	$H_2SO_4 + 2NaOH \longrightarrow Na_2SO_4 + 2H_2O$	
2 Calculate the M_r of known and the unknown	40	142
3 Multiply the M_r by the balancing number	$2 \times 40 = 80$	$1 \times 142 = 142$
4 Divide the unknown by the known and multiply by the mass of the known.	$\dfrac{142}{80} \times 10 = $ **17.8 g** of Na_2SO_4 will be made	

Commercial chemistry

- In industry, the unwanted products of a reaction must be disposed of. This can be costly and must avoid damaging the environment or causing problems to people living nearby.

- Economic considerations drive industry to search for reactions that have a high percentage yield, make no unwanted products and occur at a suitable rate.

Improve your grade

Calculating mass

Foundation: Which compound contains the highest percentage by mass of nitrogen, KNO_3 or NH_4Cl? Show your working.

AO1 [4 marks]

C2 Summary

Atomic number = number of protons. All atoms of an element contain the same number of protons.

Mass number = number of protons + neutrons.

Isotopes have the same number of protons but a different number of neutrons.

Atomic structure and the periodic table

The periodic table lists all the elements in order of increasing atomic number.

Rows are called periods. Columns are called groups and contain elements with similar properties.

Ionic compounds and analysis

Ionic compounds form when the outer-shell electrons from metal atoms are transferred to the outer shell of non-metals.

Ionic compounds have high melting points and only conduct electricity when dissolved or molten.

Insoluble salts are made as precipitates by mixing two suitable solutions.

Many cations give coloured flames. Sodium is yellow, potassium is violet, calcium is brick red, copper is green.

Anions can be identified by chemical tests.

Covalent molecules form when atoms share electrons to make covalent bonds.

Simple molecular covalent substances have low melting points. Giant molecular covalent structures have high melting points. Neither conduct electricity.

Covalent compounds and separation techniques

Immiscible liquids can be separated using a separating funnel.

Miscible liquids can be separated by distillation.

Mixtures in solution can be separated by paper chromatography.

Most elements are metals. Metals consist of regular arrangements of metal ions in a sea of delocalised electrons.

Groups in the periodic table

Transition metals have a high melting point and form coloured compounds.

The noble gases are very unreactive because they have full outer shells of electrons

Halogens react with hydrogen to form acids and with metals to form metal halides. A more reactive halogen will displace a less reactive halogen.

Alkali metals are soft and react with water to form hydroxides and hydrogen.

Chemical reactions

Exothermic reactions give out energy; endothermic reactions take in energy.

A reaction is exothermic if the energy needed to break bonds is less than the energy released when bonds are made. The reverse is true for endothermic reactions.

The rate of a reaction increases if the concentration of reactants, the surface area or the temperature increases, or if a catalyst is used.

Catalytic converters in cars catalyse reactions to oxidise carbon monoxide and unburned hydrocarbons.

Relative formula mass is the sum of the atomic masses of atoms in a compound.

Percentage composition is the atomic mass divided by the relative formula mass × 100%.

The formula equation can be used to calculate the masses of reactants and products.

Yield is the amount of product. Percentage yield is the actual yield divided by theoretical yield × 100%.

Quantitative chemistry

Disposing of waste products from reactions may cause economic, environmental and social problems.

Industrial chemists must consider the percentage yield, the rate of reactions and the use of all products to make a process economically viable.

Testing for ions

Analysis of ionic compounds

- **Qualitative analysis** tells you if your sample contains any of the chemical you are testing for.
- **Quantitative analysis** tells you how much of the chemical there is.
- One qualitative test for some dissolved metal ions is to add sodium hydroxide solution.

What you do	If you see	Then the solution contains
Put the solution to be tested in a test tube and add a few cm³ of sodium hydroxide solution	Pale blue solid	Copper 2+ ions (Cu^{2+})
	Grey-green solid	Iron 2+ ions (Fe^{2+})
	Brown solid	Iron 3+ ions (Fe^{3+})
	White solid	Either calcium ions (Ca^{2+}) or aluminium ions (Al^{3+})
Add more sodium hydroxide solution	The white solid dissolve	Aluminium ions (Al^{3+})
	The white solid is still there	Calcium ions (Ca^{2+})

- A qualitative test to see if a sample contains ammonium ions (NH_4^+):
  - Add a few cm³ of sodium hydroxide solution. Gently warm the tube. Put a piece of damp red litmus paper at the open end of the tube. If it goes blue there are ammonium ions in the sample.
  - Qualitative tests for halide ions:

What you do	If you see	The solution contains
Add silver nitrate solution and dilute nitric acid	A white precipitate	Chloride ions (Cl^-)
	A pale yellow precipitate	Bromide ions (Br^-)
	A yellow precipitate	Iodide ions (I^-)

You can use the results of the test for metal cations (positive ions) and non-metal anions (negative ions) to write the name of the compound present. For example, if adding sodium hydroxide gives a blue precipitate it means copper ions are present. If adding silver nitrate gives a white precipitate it means chloride ions are present. Compound present = copper chloride.

Remember!
You can also use flame colours and tests for carbonates and sulfates to identify compounds.

Ionic equations

To write an ionic equation:

Write out the word equation	silver nitrate + sodium chloride ⟶ silver chloride + sodium nitrate
Write the balanced formula equation	$AgNO_3(aq)$ + $NaCl(aq)$ ⟶ $AgCl(s)$ + $NaNO_3(aq)$
Write the (aq) compounds as separate ions	$Ag^+(aq)$ + $NO_3^-(aq)$ + $Na^+(aq)$ + $Cl^-(aq)$ ⟶ $AgCl(s)$ + $Na^+(s)$ + $NO_3(aq)$
Cross out anything that is on both sides of the arrow	$Ag^+(aq)$ + ~~$NO_3^-(aq)$~~ + ~~$Na^+(aq)$~~ + $Cl^-(aq)$ ⟶ $AgCl(s)$ + $Na^+(s)$ + ~~$NO_3(aq)$~~
What remains is the ionic equation.	$Ag^+(aq)$ + $Cl^-(aq)$ ⟶ $AgCl(s)$

Improve your grade

Iron in drinking water

Higher: A student tested a solution with silver nitrate and nitric acid. A white precipitate formed. State which ion is present in the solution. Write an ionic equation for the reaction that formed the precipitate.

AO1 [4 marks]

Ions in industry

Ions in blood and water

- Chemists working in the water industry use quantitative tests to measure the amount of different ions dissolved in drinking water. High levels of some ions may be damaging to health.

- Chemists working in hospitals measure the quantity of ions dissolved in the patients' blood. This helps doctors to decide which treatment to use.

- A summary of how to test for some ions:

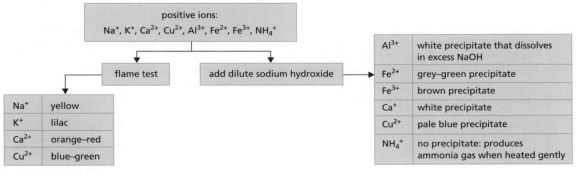

positive ions:
Na^+, K^+, Ca^{2+}, Cu^{2+}, Al^{3+}, Fe^{2+}, Fe^{3+}, NH_4^+

flame test		add dilute sodium hydroxide

Na^+	yellow
K^+	lilac
Ca^{2+}	orange–red
Cu^{2+}	blue–green

Al^{3+}	white precipitate that dissolves in excess NaOH
Fe^{2+}	grey–green precipitate
Fe^{3+}	brown precipitate
Ca^+	white precipitate
Cu^{2+}	pale blue precipitate
NH_4^+	no precipitate: produces ammonia gas when heated gently

Flowchart to identify positive ions.

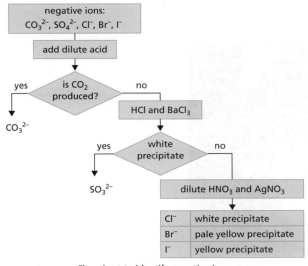

negative ions:
CO_3^{2-}, SO_4^{2-}, Cl^-, Br^-, I^-

add dilute acid

is CO_2 produced?

yes → CO_3^{2-}

no → HCl and $BaCl_3$

white precipitate

yes → SO_3^{2-}

no → dilute HNO_3 and $AgNO_3$

Cl^-	white precipitate
Br^-	pale yellow precipitate
I^-	yellow precipitate

Flowchart to identify negative ions.

Quantitative testing

- Instrumental techniques can give quantitative results even when the concentration of ions is very low. For example, an atomic absorption spectrometer uses the principle of the flame test but records the exact brightness of the flame and the frequency of the light produced. This identifies both the type of ion and the quantity of that ion.

EXAM TIP
If the question asks you to say what you would see, you must describe the change, not write an equation.

Improve your grade

Chloride in drinking water

Foundation: The water board want to test the levels of chloride ions in the drinking water. Say why it is important to test water for ions. Explain which would give the best answer a quantitative or a qualitative method.

A02 [3 marks]

Hard water

Hard and soft water

- Hard water has lots of calcium and magnesium ions dissolved in it.
- The calcium and magnesium ions get into the water when rain washes through certain types of rocks. Some parts of the country have lots of these rocks. These are hard water areas.
- Calcium and magnesium ions react with soap to make scum. This stops the soap from making lather.

- Hard water can be made into soft water by removing calcium and magnesium ions.
- **Temporary hard water** contains calcium hydrogencarbonate or magnesium hydrogencarbonate. Heating makes the dissolved calcium and magnesium hydrogencarbonate decompose (break down). The magnesium or calcium ions then clump together with carbonate ions to form solid calcium or magnesium carbonate and so remove the ions from the water. Solid calcium or magnesium carbonate is called **limescale**.

$$Mg(HCO_3)_2(aq) \longrightarrow MgCO_3(s) + H_2O(l) + CO_2(g)$$

Magnesium hydrogencarbonate $\longrightarrow$ magnesium carbonate + water + carbon dioxide

- **Permanent hard water** contains calcium or magnesium sulfate. It cannot be made soft by boiling because calcium and magnesium sulfate do not decompose.
- Both temporary and permanent hard water can be softened using ion exchange resins. The hard water runs through a column of resin beads. The calcium and magnesium ions stick to the resin and sodium ions from the resin are washed into the water. Household water softeners use ion exchange resin. The calcium and magnesium ions can be washed from the resin with concentrated sodium chloride solution.

> **Remember!**
> The ions in hard water are dissolved, they cannot be removed by filtering.

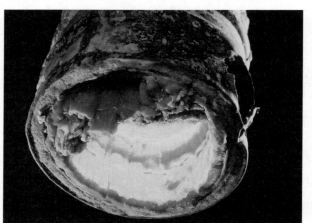

A water pipe containing limescale.

Problems with hard water

- Positive calcium and magnesium ions in water react with negative ions in the soap to form solid scum. The soap will only lather once all the calcium and magnesium have precipitated as scum, so people in hard-water areas use more soap.

> **EXAM TIP**
> Avoid using 'it' in answers. Name the thing you are writing about.

- The hydrogencarbonates in temporary hard water decompose when hot water is used. This means that limescale precipitates in pipes, radiators and washing machines. Pipes are narrowed and energy is wasted heating up the limescale, which reduces the heating efficiency.

 Improve your grade

The problem of limescale

Higher: It has been estimated that hard-water scale costs thousands of pounds a year in lost efficiency. Explain where hard-water scale comes from. Include a word equation in your answer.   *AO2* [4 marks]

Measuring masses

Concentrations of solutions

- To work out the concentration of a solution in grams per cubic decimeter:

What to do	e.g.
Find the mass of the solid to be dissolved in grams	15 g of copper sulfate
Find volume of the liquid it is being dissolved in dm³	0.25 dm³ of water
Divide the mass by the volume	15 ÷ 0.25
This is the concentration in g/dm³	= 60 g/dm³

- To change the units from cm³ to dm³ divide by 1000, e.g. 50 g/**cm³** = 0.05 g/dm³

- To change the units from dm³ to cm³ multiply by 1000, e.g. 0.2 dm³ = 200 cm³

- To calculate the mass of solute you need when you know the concentration and the volume you want:
  - mass of solute = concentration in g/dm³ × volume in dm³

- To find the mass of a solute in a solution:
  - i Measure the volume of the solution
  - ii Weigh an empty evaporating basin then pour the solution into it
  - iii Heat the solution gently in the evaporation basin until all the water has evaporated
  - iv Weigh the evaporating basin again
  - v Subtract the starting mass of the basin from the final mass. This is the mass of solute in the volume of solution you added.

Remember!
The solute is the substance dissolved, the solvent is the liquid it is dissolved in.

Comparing masses

- There are different ways of describing the amount of a substance: number of particles or mass.

- In practical experiments the mass of substances is measured in grams, but chemical equations show how many *particles* are reacting.

- The mass of each particle is very small, e.g the mass of a carbon atom is 0.000000000000000000000199 g, so we weigh out particles in moles (groups of 6.02×10^{23}).

- 6.02×10^{23} is known as Avogadro's number. One **mole** of anything contains 6.02×10^{23} particles but one mole of different things has a different mass, e.g.
  - 6.02×10^{23} carbon atoms = 1 mole carbon = 12 g carbon.
  - 3.01×10^{23} carbon atoms = .5 mole carbon = 6 g carbon.
  - 6.02×10^{23} methane molecules = 1 mole of methane molecules = 16 g methane.

EXAM TIP

Always show your working out and describe what you are doing at each step. This helps you to remember where you are in the calculation.

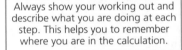

- The balancing number (coefficient) in equations shows how many moles of each substance react exactly with each other.

Equation	CH_4	+	$2O_2$	→	CO_2	+	$2H_2O$
Number of moles	1		2		1		2
Number of particles	6.02×10^{23}		12.04×10^{23}		6.02×10^{23}		12.04×10^{23}
Mass (g)	16		64		44		36

 Improve your grade

The concentration of salt solution

Foundation: Alec dissolved 6 g of sodium chloride in 50 cm³ of water. What is the concentration of the solution in g/dm³? *AO1* [3 marks]

Mass, moles and concentrations

From masses to moles

- The mass of one mole of atoms of an element is its **relative atomic mass** (A_r or RAM) in grams. To find A_r look up the element in the Periodic table. The A_r is the number at the top of the element symbol.

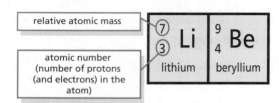

It is easy to find the relative mass of the atoms of each element by looking at the periodic table. This section shows Li and Be.

- The mass of one mole of a compound is called the **relative formula mass** (M_r or RFM). To work it out, add together the atomic masses of all the atoms in the formula.

Formula	Atoms	A_r	M_r
Na_2CO_3	Na × 2	23 × 2	46 +
	C	12	12 +
	O × 3	16 × 3	48
			106
$(NH_4)_2SO_4$	N × 2	14 × 2	28 +
	H × 8	1 × 8	8 +
	S	32	32 +
	O × 4	16 × 4	64
			132

> **Remember!**
> Some **elements** form diatomic molecules, e.g. H_2, O_2, N_2, F_2, Cl_2, Br_2, I_2. To calculate the mass of one mole of these molecules multiply the A_r by two.

> **EXAM TIP**
> Don't worry if the number of moles is small. Chemists often deal with fractions of a mole, remember, 1 mole = 6×10^{23}.

- To find the number of moles when you know the mass of substance, divide the mass of substance by the mass of one mole of the substance: moles = mass/M_r.

Mass(g)	Formula	M_r	Calculation	Number of moles
200	$CaCO_3$	100	200 ÷ 100	2
5	$Ca(OH)_2$	74	5 ÷ 74	0.068

- If you know the number of moles and you want to know the mass, multiply the number of moles by the mass of one mole: mass = moles × M_r.

Number of moles	Formula	M_r	Calculation	Mass (g)
4	$(NH_4)_2SO_4$	132	4 × 132	528
0.15	Al_2O_3	102	0.15 × 102	15.3

Molar concentrations

- Concentrations of solutions can be measured in grams per dm^3 (g/dm^3) or moles per dm^3 (mol/dm^3).
- To convert from g/dm^3 to mol/dm^3 divide by the M_r of the solute.

Formula	Concentration (g/dm^3)	M_r solute	Calculation	Concentration (mol/dm^3)
NaOH(aq)	20	40	20 ÷ 40	0.50

- To convert from mol/dm^3 to g/dm^3 multiply by the M_r of the solute.

Solution	Concentration (mol/dm^3)	M_r solute	Calculation	Concentration (g/dm^3)
HCl	1.5	36.6	1.5 × 36.5	54.75

Improve your grade

Calculating solutions

Higher: The chemistry technician needs to make up 1 dm^3 of a solution of sodium iodide (NaI) concentration 0.1 mol/dm^3. How many grams of NaI must she weigh out?   *AO1* [3 marks]

Salts from acids

What are salts?

- A salt is an ionic compound made from positive metal ions and negative non-metal ions. A salt is made when an acid is neutralised.

- The name of the negative ion in the salt depends on which acid is neutralised.
  - Hydrochloric acid makes chloride ions (Cl^-)
  - Sulfuric acid makes sulfate ions (SO_4^{2-})
  - Nitric acid makes nitrate ions (NO_3^-)

G–E

Preparing salts

- Salts can be made by reacting acids with insoluble bases or metals. Metal oxides are examples of insoluble bases.

What you do	Why you do it
Warm the acid	To make the reaction go faster
Add solid base or metal until no more will dissolve	To make sure all the acid has reacted
Filter the mixture	To remove the excess solid base or metal
Evaporate the water	To allow the pure salt to form crystals

Remember!
Moles = concentration × volume. All volumes must be measured in dm³.

Stage 1 Mix the reactants and stir. Ensure the copper oxide is in excess

Stage 2 Filter off the excess copper oxide

Stage 3 Leave the filtrate to evaporate in an evaporating basin or crystallising dish

D–C

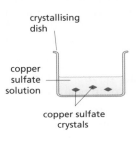

Apparatus for making copper sulfate from copper oxide and sufuric acid.

- Acid + alkali → salt + water. Alkalis are soluble bases. If acid and alkali are mixed in exactly the correct proportions then a pure salt can be made.

- Find out the exact volumes that must be mixed together by titration.

What you do	Why you do it
Put a known volume of acid into a conical flask	You can swirl a conical flask to mix the contents without spillage
Add some indicator	So you can tell when the acid has been neutralised
Put the alkali in a burette	So you can add it little by little and measure the volume added
Add a small portion of alkali to the acid and swirl the flask until the indicator changes colour	So that you can add just enough to neutralise the acid but no more. There is only salt and water in the flask, with no left-over acid or alkali
Note the volume of alkali added	So that you know exactly what volume of this concentration of alkali is needed to just neutralise this volume of acid
Add the same volume of acid and alkali together without indicator. Evaporate the water	To obtain a pure sample of salt without contamination by the indicator

B–A*

Improve your grade

Preparing copper sulfate

Foundation: Students were asked to make a sample of copper sulfate by adding acid to copper oxide. Which acid should they use and what equipment will they need? *AO1* [4 marks]

Acid-base titrations

What is happening during neutralisation?

- Acids are solutions which contain hydrogen ions (H^+), alkalis are solutions which contain hydroxide ions (OH^-).
- In a neutralisation reaction the H^+ and OH^- react together to make water.

$$H^+ \text{ and } OH^- \longrightarrow H_2O$$

Titrations

- Titrations can be used to work out the concentration of a solution. You must know the equation for the reaction. E.g. $HCl + NaOH \longrightarrow NaCl + H_2O$ and the concentration of one of the solutions.

What you do

- Rinse and fill a burette with alkali solution and ensure jet space is filled
- Use a pipette to measure 25 cm³ acid into a conical flask
- Add a few drops of an indicator
- Put the flask on a white tile under the burette
- Read and record the volume of NaOH in the burette
- Open the burette tap and add NaOH to the flask, with swirling to mix the contents, until the indicator changes colour – the end point. Swirl the flask to mix the contents.
- Record the volume in the burette
- Repeat everything, but this time add the alkali drop by drop near the end point
- Repeat several times and calculate the average volume needed

Remember!
It doesn't matter if you put the acid in the burette and the alkali in the flask or the other way around.

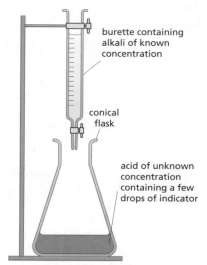

burette containing alkali of known concentration

conical flask

acid of unknown concentration containing a few drops of indicator

Titration apparatus. *Not to scale.*

To calculate a concentration from the results of a titration	Example 0.1 mol/dm³ NaOH titrated against 25 cm³ of HCl
Calculate the average volume used of the reactant in the burette	Average volume of NaOH used = 22.4 cm³
For one reactant you know the concentration and the volume used: (reactant 1) Convert cm³ to dm³ by dividing by 1 000 Multiply conc. × volume (in dm³) to find moles of reactant 1	22.4 cm³ of 0.1 mol/dm³ NaOH = 0.0224 dm³ 0.1 × 0.0224 = 0.00224 mol NaOH
Look at the equation to find the molar ratio of the reactants	$HCl + NaOH \longrightarrow NaCl + H_2O$ Molar ratio 1:1
Multiply the moles reactant 1 by the molar ratio to find the moles reactant 2	0.00224 × 1 = 0.00224 mol HCl
Divide the moles of the reactant 2 by the volume of reactant 2 (in dm³) to find the concentration	Vol HCl = 25 cm³ = 0.025 dm³ 0.0224 ÷ 0.025 = 0.09 mol/dm³ HCl

Improve your grade

Calculating concentration

Higher: A student carried out a titration using 0.25 mol/dm³ H_2SO_4(aq) and 25 cm³ of KOH(aq). 20.5 cm³ of the H_2SO_4 was needed to reach the end point of the titration. What was the concentration of the KOH?

AO3 [5 marks]

Electrolytes and sodium

G–E

Ions and charges

- **Electrolytes** are ionic substances that are molten or dissolved. They can conduct electricity.

- Ionic compounds contain positive ions and negative ions held together by electrostatic attraction. They have a high melting point. They do not conduct electricity when they are solids because the ions cannot move and there are no free electrons.

- If you put electrolytes into an electrical circuit (see diagram below) cations move towards the cathode and anions move towards the anode. The negative electrode is called the cathode and cations are the positive ions. The positive electrode is called the anode and anions are the negative ions.

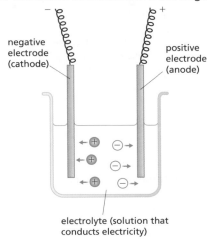

negative electrode (cathode)

positive electrode (anode)

electrolyte (solution that conducts electricity)

Key:

⊖ negative ion moves towards anode ⊕ positive ion moves towards cathode

The movement of ions during electrolysis.

Uses of sodium

- Yellow streetlights contain the element sodium. Sodium is heated inside the lamp until it becomes a gas. When electricity passes through the sodium gas it gives out a bright yellow light.
- Sodium is a good conductor of heat. It is used as a coolant in some nuclear reactors. It carries the heat energy away from the reactor so that it can be used to generate electricity.

Electrolysis of molten sodium chloride

D–C

- Naturally occurring sodium is always found as a compound, not as an element. This is because it is very reactive.

- Sodium metal is made by electrolysis of sodium chloride. **Electrolysis** means splitting up a compound using electricity.

  - Sodium chloride is heated to a high temperature until it melts.

  - Electricity is passed through the molten liquid.

  - The chloride ions move towards the anode, lose electrons and form chlorine gas.

  - The sodium ions move towards the cathode, gain electrons and form sodium metal.

  - The sodium metal floats to the surface and is collected.

> **Remember!**
> In a molten ionic compound it is the **ions** that carry the electric current, not **electrons**.

B–A*

- Sodium works well as a coolant in nuclear power plants because it has a high boiling point and need not be used under pressure. It does not cause corrosion like some other coolants and it is able to absorb a large amount of heat without getting too hot.

- In the electrolysis of molten sodium chloride:

At the anode, chloride ions are oxidised: $2Cl^- (l) \longrightarrow Cl_2(g) + 2e^-$

At the cathode, sodium ions are reduced: $Na^+(l) + e^- \longrightarrow Na(l)$

Sodium rises to the top of the mixture because it is less dense than the molten sodium chloride.

Improve your grade

Uses of sodium

Foundation: How is sodium metal made and what is it used for?   *AO1* [4 marks]

Oxidation and reduction

Electrolysis

* A reaction is called oxidation:
  – when oxygen has been added, or
  – when electrons have been lost.

  E.g. When calcium reacts with oxygen it is oxidised: calcium + oxygen ⟶ calcium oxide.

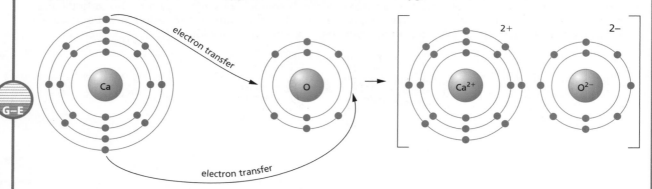

The transfer of electrons from calcium to oxygen is really what happens when oxidation occurs.

The calcium **atoms** lose electrons and become calcium **ions**, they are oxidised.

* A reaction is called reduction:
  – when oxygen has been lost
  – when electrons have been gained.

Remember!
Oxidation Is Loss of electrons,
Reduction Is Gain of electrons
– OIL RIG

* The oxygen **atoms** gain electrons when they react with calcium and become oxide ions, they are reduced.

* During electrolysis, reduction happens at the cathode. Positive ions move to the cathode and when they touch the electrode they pick up electrons. They are reduced from positive ions to atoms.

* Oxidation happens at the anode. Negative ions move towards the anode and when they touch the electrode they lose electrons. They are oxidised from negative ions to atoms.

  E.g. during electrolysis of hydrochloric acid, HCl

hydrogen ion   hydrogen atom   chloride ion   chlorine atom

* Chlorine atoms then combine to make chlorine molecules and hydrogen atoms combine to make hydrogen molecules.

* Reactions where one substance is oxidised while another is reduced are known as redox reactions.

Half equations

* Redox reactions can be described using different types of equations.

Type of equation	Example
Balanced formula equations show the number and formula of all elements and compounds in the reaction	$CuCl_2(aq) \longrightarrow Cu(s) + Cl_2(g)$
Ionic equations show all dissolved ions as separate particles	$Cu^{2+}(aq) + 2Cl^-(aq) \longrightarrow Cu(s) + Cl_2(g)$
Half equations show what happens to one element at a time	$2Cl^-(aq) \longrightarrow Cl_2(g) + 2e^-$ $Cu^{2+}(aq) + 2e^- \longrightarrow Cu(s)$

* Oxidation reactions show the **electrons lost** on the right-hand side of the arrow. Reduction reactions show **electrons gained** on the left-hand side of the arrow. The charges from the ions and electrons on one side of the equation must balance with those on the other side.

Improve your grade

Electrolysis of lead bromide

Foundation: Lead bromide is an ionic solid that will conduct electricity when it is molten. Give the name of the ion that will move towards the anode and explain why it moves this way.   *AO1* [3 marks]

Electrolysing sodium chloride solution

Electrolysis in the lab

- When electricity is put through sodium chloride solution three products are made: hydrogen gas, chlorine gas and sodium hydroxide solution.

- You can demonstrate the electrolysis of sodium chloride in the lab using the apparatus in the diagram below.

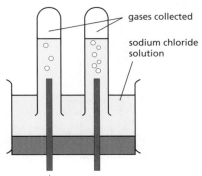

gases collected

sodium chloride solution

Laboratory set-up for the electrolysis of sodium chloride solution.

G–E

- Chlorine bubbles up from the positive electrode (anode). You can show that it is chlorine by holding damp indicator paper in the gas. If it is chlorine it will go white.

- Hydrogen bubbles up from the negative electrode (cathode). You can show that it is hydrogen by putting a lighted splint into it. If it makes a popping sound it is hydrogen.

- The solution remaining after the electricity has passed though contains sodium hydroxide. You can show that it is alkaline by testing with red litmus. If it turns blue the solution is alkaline (or with universal indicator paper it will turn blue/purple).

Thinking about the products

- Pure water contains some hydrogen ions (H^+) and some hydroxide ions (OH^-). When sodium chloride is dissolved in water, the solution contains positive sodium ions + positive hydrogen ions (from the water) and negative chloride ions + negative hydroxide ions (from the water).

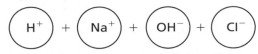

hydrogen ion   sodium ion   hydroxide ion   chloride ion

The ions in sodium chloride solution.

D–C

- During electrolysis of sodium chloride solution, the hydrogen and sodium ions move towards the cathode (negative electrode). The hydrogen ions are better at receiving electrons from the anode than the sodium ions. The hydrogen ions gain electrons and become hydrogen atoms, which then combine to form hydrogen molecules (H_2). Sodium ions do not gain electrons but stay as sodium ions. Hydrogen gas is given off at the cathode.

- The chloride ions are better than the hydroxide ions at giving electrons to the anode so chloride ions lose electrons and become chlorine atoms which then combine to form chlorine molecules. Chlorine is given off at the anode.

- The sodium ions and the hydroxide ions stay in the solution. If the water is evaporated from the solution, sodium hydroxide (NaOH) can be collected.

- At the cathode, H^+ and Na^+ compete to be reduced. H^+ is more easily reduced than Na^+, so hydrogen is produced at the cathode.
  $$2H^+(aq) + 2e^- \longrightarrow H_2(g)$$

- At the anode chloride ions are oxidised.
  $$2Cl^-(aq) \longrightarrow Cl_2(g) + 2e^-$$

- The overall reaction is
  $$2NaCl(aq) + 2H_2O(l) \longrightarrow H_2(g) + Cl_2(g) + 2NaOH(aq)$$

Remember!
Electrolysis of molten sodium chloride gives **sodium** and chlorine but dissolved sodium chloride gives **hydrogen** and chlorine.

B–A*

Improve your grade

Electrolysis of sodium chloride

Higher: Passing electricity through molten sodium chloride and through aqueous sodium chloride gives different results. Name the products formed in each case and explain why they are different.

AO1 [5 marks]

Products of electrolysis

Electrolysis using copper electrodes

- Weigh two pieces of copper and use them as electrodes. Put the electrodes into copper sulfate solution. (See diagram below.)

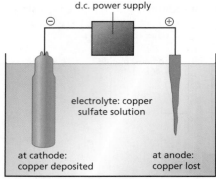

d.c. power supply

at cathode:
copper deposited

electrolyte: copper
sulfate solution

at anode:
copper lost

Electrolysis using copper electrodes.

- Turn on the power supply and let the electricity run thorough the system.

- Turn off the electricity, remove the copper electrodes and dry them. Weigh them again.

- The cathode (negative electrode) will weigh more than at the start. The anode (positive electrode) will weigh less than at the start. Copper atoms have been lost from the anode. Copper atoms have been added to the cathode.

- The mass of copper lost from the anode is the same as the mass of copper gained by the cathode.

Electrolysis using inert electrodes

- Copper electrodes take part in the reaction when copper sulfate is used as an electrolyte. An anode made from copper gradually gets lighter because the copper atoms turn to copper ions and dissolve into the solution. A cathode made from copper gradually gets heavier because copper ions from the solution turn into copper atoms and stick to the electrode.

- Inert electrodes do not change during electrolysis. Graphite and platinum are examples of inert electrodes.

- The products of electrolysis of some electrolytes with inert electrodes are shown below.

Electrolyte	What is produced at the cathode	What is produced at the anode	What is left in the solution
Copper sulfate solution	Copper	Oxygen	Sulfuric acid
Copper chloride solution	Copper	Chlorine	Water
Sodium sulfate solution	Hydrogen	Oxygen	Sodium sulfate
Molten lead bromide	Lead	Bromine	–

Electrolyte	Reduction reaction at cathode	Oxidation reaction at the anode
Copper sulfate solution	$Cu^{2+} + 2e^- \longrightarrow Cu$	$4OH^- \longrightarrow O_2 + 2H_2O + 4e^-$
Copper chloride solution	$Cu^{2+} + 2e^- \longrightarrow Cu$	$2Cl^- \longrightarrow Cl_2 + 2e^-$
Sodium sulfate solution	$2H^+ + 2e^- \longrightarrow H_2$	$4OH^- \longrightarrow O_2 + 2H_2O + 4e^-$
Molten lead bromide	$Pb^{2+} + 2e^- \longrightarrow Pb$	$2Br^- \longrightarrow Br_2 + 2e^-$

- General rule: If the electrolyte is a solution then H_2 will be discharged at the cathode unless the metal is less reactive than hydrogen. O_2 will be discharged at the anode unless a halogen is present.

Improve your grade

Products of electrolysis

Foundation: Joe does an experiment on the electrolysis of copper sulfate using copper electrodes. Describe what happens to the electrodes.   *AO1* [3 marks]

Industrial electrochemistry

Purification and electroplating

- Very pure copper is needed for electrical wiring. Copper can be purified by electrolysis.

- The piece of copper which needs to be purified is used as the anode (positive electrode). A thin piece of very pure copper is used as the cathode. Copper sulfate solution is used as the electrolyte (the solution that the electricity travels through).

- The impure copper electrode dissolves into the solution and the impurities fall to the bottom of the cell. The pure copper electrode picks up new copper atoms from the solution.

- Once the cathode has gained enough pure copper it is removed so that the copper can be used.

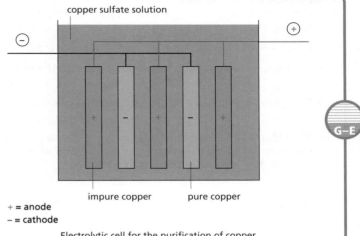

+ = anode
– = cathode

Electrolytic cell for the purification of copper.

- Electrolysis can be used to coat one metal with a very thin layer of another metal. This is called **electroplating**.

- The item to be plated is used as the cathode and is placed in a solution of an electrolyte. The electrolyte contains ions of the metal which will form the coating. When they are connected into a circuit, the metal ions in the electrolyte are attracted to the cathode and stick to the item.

- Reasons for electroplating include preventing corrosion and improving the appearance by coating with a shiny or brighter coloured metal.

Example of electroplating	Reason
Chromium motorbike parts/taps/kettles	Gives bright appearance, reduces corrosion
Silver/gold plating jewellery	Remains shiny, gives gold appearance at a low cost
Copper plating coins	Reduces costs of making solid copper coins
Nickel plating car parts	Reduces corrosion and improves appearance
Zinc plating steel bolts and nuts	Reduces corrosion

The reactions as equations

- When copper is purified by electrolysis, copper is oxidised at the anode and copper ions are reduced at the cathode.
  - Anode reaction: $Cu \longrightarrow Cu^{2+} + 2e^-$ oxidation
  - Cathode reaction: $Cu^{2+} + 2e^- \longrightarrow Cu$ reduction
  - The concentration of copper ions in the electrolyte remains the same, since every copper ion that is reduced at the cathode is replaced by oxidation of a copper atom at the anode.

- In electroplating the important reaction is the reduction of the metal ions at the cathode. Examples of equations for electroplating with:
  - Chromium $Cr^{3+} + 3e^- \longrightarrow Cr$
  - Silver $Ag^+ + e^- \longrightarrow Ag$
  - Nickel $Ni^{2+} + 2e^- \longrightarrow Ni$

The electrolyte is a soluble salt of the metal.

Remember!

Cations are reduced at the cathode. Metal ions are cations.

Improve your grade

Purifying copper

Higher: Draw a labelled diagram of the apparatus that could be used to purify a sample of copper and write an ionic equation for the reaction occurring at the cathode. *AO1* [5 marks]

Volumes of gases

How much gas?

- One mole of any gas occupies the same volume at the same temperature and pressure. So 50 cm³ of ethene and 50 cm³ of helium contain the same number of moles at the same temperature and pressure.

- One mole of any gas occupies 24 dm³ at room temperature (25 °C) and pressure (1 atmosphere).

- To convert the number of moles of a gas into the volume it would occupy:

    Moles × 24 = volume of gas in dm³

- To convert the volume of gas into number of moles of that gas:

    Volume of gas in dm³ ÷ 24 = moles of gas

- The volumes of all gases change in the same way when the temperature and pressure change. So for reactions involving gases only, the molar ratio of the reactants and products is the same as the volume ratio, if they are under the same conditions:

$$CH_4(g) + 2O_2(g) \longrightarrow CO_2(g) + 2H_2O(g)$$

Equation	CH_4	+	$2O_2$	→	CO_2	+	$2H_2O$
Molar ratio	1		2		1		2
Volume ratio	1		2		1		2
E.g.	15 cm³	reacts with	30 cm³	and makes	15 cm³	and	30 cm³
E.g.	2.38 dm³	reacts with	4.76 dm³	and makes	2.38 dm³	and	4.76 dm³

There is no need to convert volumes to moles when calculating reaction volumes.

- In reactions where some of the reactants and products are gases and others are solids or liquids, convert moles of gas into volumes using 1 mole = 24 dm³ and volumes into moles using moles = volume ÷ 24

E.g. to calculate the volume of hydrogen produced by 11 g of zinc in the following reaction:

$$Zn(s) + 2\ HCl\ (aq) \longrightarrow ZnCl_2(aq) + H_2(g)$$

Equation	$Zn(s)$	+	$2\ HCl\ (aq)$	→	$ZnCl_2(aq)$	+	$H_2(g)$
Mole ratio	1		2		1		1
Mass used	11 g						
Calculate moles using moles = mass/M_r (M_r Zn = 65)	11/65 = 0.17						
Use mole ratio to calculate moles of product							0.17
Calculate volume of H_2 using vol = moles × 24							0.17 × 24 = 4.1 dm³

E.g. to calculate the mass of $CaCO_3$ needed to produce 40 cm³ of carbon dioxide in the following reaction:

$$CaCO_3(s) + 2HCl(aq) \longrightarrow CaCl_2(aq) + CO_2(g)$$

Equation	$CaCO_3(s)$	+	$2HCl(aq)$	→	$CaCl_2(aq)$	+	$CO_2(g)$
Molar ratio	1		2		1		1
Volume needed							40 cm³
Convert volumes into dm³							40 ÷ 1000 = 0.04 dm³
Calculate moles of gas using moles = vol ÷ 24							0.04 ÷ 24 = 0.0017 moles
Use mole ratio to calculate moles of reactant	0.0017						
Convert moles to mass using mass = moles × M_r (M_r $CaCO_3$ = 100)	0.0017 × 100 = 0.17 g						

Improve your grade

Filling balloons

Higher: Jake wants to fill a balloon with carbon dioxide. The volume of the balloon is 2 dm³ and he plans to use the reaction between sodium hydrogencarbonate and vinegar:

$$NaHCO_3 + CH_3COOH \longrightarrow CO_2 + H_2O + CH_3COONa$$

If he uses 10 g of $NaHCO_3$ and plenty of vinegar, will this fill the balloon? Show your calculation.

AO2 [5 marks]

Topic 4: 4.1, 4.2, 4.3

Fertilisers

Nitrogenous fertilisers

- Plants only grow well if there are plenty of nitrogen compounds in the soil. Adding nitrogenous fertilisers to the soil adds nitrogen compounds. This increases the yield of crops (how much you get from an acre of ground).

- Chemists make nitrogen compounds from ammonia. Examples are ammonium nitrate and potassium nitrate.

- Ammonia can be made from nitrogen and hydrogen. The reaction to make ammonia is called the Haber process. The manufacturers get the nitrogen they need from the air. They get the hydrogen by reacting natural gas with steam to produce hydrogen.

nitrogen + hydrogen ⇌ ammonia

- Using too much fertiliser causes **eutrophication**.
  - Unused fertiliser gets washed away by rain (leached).
  - Fertiliser collects in rivers and ponds and fertilises water plants.
  - Water plants grow and multiply excessively, which clogs the water.
  - Eventually water plants die and are attacked by decomposers.
  - Decomposers multiply excessively and use up all the oxygen in the water.
  - Fish and other organisms die for lack of oxygen.

- Over-use of fertiliser can also result in nitrates in the drinking water.

Nitrogen compounds

- Nitrate compounds are very water-soluble. This explains why they are easily leached from the soil and collect in waterways. It also explains why it is difficult to remove them from the drinking water supply.

- Plants use nitrates from the soil to make proteins. Although nitrogen makes up approximately 80% of air it cannot be used directly by plants. When nitrogen from the air is converted into compounds it is called 'nitrogen fixing'.

- Nitrogen molecules (N_2) have a triple bond between the atoms, which requires a lot of energy to break. This means it is difficult to make nitrogen compounds from nitrogen gas.

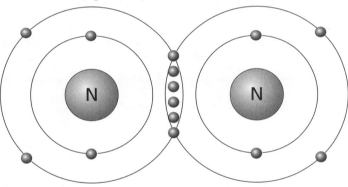

A nitrogen molecule.

- Lightning provides enough energy to allow nitrogen to react with oxygen in the air. The nitrogen oxides formed enter the soil when it rains. Some bacteria are able to fix nitrogen using enzymes.

Remember!
Air contains 78% nitrogen.

- Fritz Haber was the first person to discover a way to convert nitrogen ($N_2(g)$) into the nitrogen compound ammonia (NH_3) using high pressures. Once the nitrogen is converted into ammonia it is easier to convert it into different nitrogen compounds such as nitrates.

- The production of artificial fertilisers allows many more people to live on planet Earth than would otherwise be possible.

Improve your grade

Overuse of fertiliser

Foundation: Explain why farmers add nitrogen fertilisers to their crops. Why is it not a good idea to add too much fertiliser? *AO1* [3 marks]

Dynamic equilibrium

Back and forth

- Some chemical reactions can go backwards (from products to reactants) as well as forwards (from reactants to products). For example, when blue (hydrated) copper sulfate crystals are heated they become white:

  hydrated copper sulfate $\rightleftharpoons$ anhydrous copper sulfate + water

- This symbol is used to show that the reaction is reversible $\rightleftharpoons$.

- The reaction used to manufacture ammonia is a reversible reaction called the Haber process (after the chemist who discovered it):

  $$N_2(g) + 3H_2(g) \rightleftharpoons 2NH_3(g)$$

Dynamic equilibrium

- If the **Haber process** takes place in a sealed container it never converts all the hydrogen and nitrogen to ammonia. It reaches equilibrium where there is a mixture of hydrogen, nitrogen and ammonia.

- At equilibrium the forward and backward reaction are going at the same rate. There is no change in the quantity of reactants or products.

- Both reactions are happening at the same time. If we could follow one nitrogen atom it would sometimes be in an ammonia molecule and sometimes in a nitrogen molecule. So the equilibrium is called **dynamic** equilibrium.

Changing conditions

- Increasing the pressure in the reaction chamber increases the percentage of ammonia in the mixture at equilibrium. It moves the position of equilibrium to the right, towards the products.

Pressure (atm)	% of ammonia in the mixture at equilibrium at 200 °C
25	63.6
50	74.0
100	81.7
200	89.0

- Increasing the temperature decreases the percentage of ammonia in the mixture at equilibrium. It moves the position of equilibrium to the left, towards the reactants.

Temperature °C	% of ammonia in the mixture at equilibrium at 50 atm pressure
100	94.5
200	74.0
300	39.5
400	14.3

- Using a catalyst does not affect the amount of ammonia in the mixture at equilibrium but it reduces the time taken to reach equilibrium.

- To get the maximum amount of ammonia in the mixture at equilibrium (maximum yield of ammonia) a very high pressure and a very low temperature should be used. Manufacturers of ammonia use only moderately high pressure and quite high temperatures.

- Very high pressures are expensive to produce and there is a danger of explosions. Equipment must be very strong to withstand the pressures, and this is costly. A compromise pressure gives an acceptable yield at reasonable cost and risk. Typically between 50 and 150 atm pressure.

- Very low temperatures mean a very slow reaction. Lots of ammonia is made in each batch but very few batches can be made per day. More ammonia can be made per day using a higher temperature and making many batches with a lower percentage of ammonia.

- Using an iron catalyst speeds up the reaction at lower temperatures.

Improve your grade

Industrial compromise

Higher: At temperatures of below 100 °C the Haber process gives ammonia yields of greater than 90%. Explain why manufacturers of ammonia use temperatures of between 400 °C and 500 °C even though this gives a lower yield.

AO1 [3 marks]

Ethanol production

Fermentation and distillation

- Ethanol is the chemical name for the alcohol in drinks like beer, wine and whisky. It is made by microorganisms (yeasts) when they use glucose as food. This is called **fermentation**.

$$\text{Glucose} \xrightarrow{\text{yeast}} \text{ethanol} + \text{carbon dioxide}$$

- Yeast only makes ethanol if there is no oxygen present. This means air must be kept out of the fermentation container. Keeping oxygen out is called using **anaerobic conditions**.

- The yeast/glucose mixture must be kept warm during fermentation. This is because yeast cells use **enzymes** to make ethanol and enzymes only work at warm temperatures. 37 °C is the best temperature.

G–E

- When the alcohol level in the mixture gets too high it kills the yeast. This means fermentation never gives more than about 14% alcohol.

- To get a higher percentage of ethanol, such as to make spirits, the ethanol must be separated from the water by fractional distillation. The water and ethanol separate because they have different boiling points.

- When the temperature reaches 78 °C the liquid ethanol turns to vapour and moves to the cold condenser. The vapour condenses back into liquid and runs into the collecting vessel. Everything else remains in the flask.

D–C

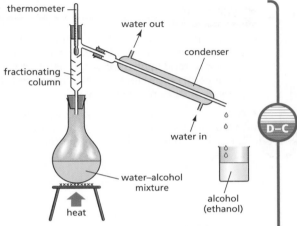

Apparatus for fractional distillation in the laboratory.

Ethanol from fermentation versus ethanol from ethene

- Ethanol is widely used as a fuel or fuel additive, as a solvent and as a reactant in many industrial chemical processes.

- It can be produced by the chemical reaction of ethene with steam. (Ethene is obtained from the cracking of crude oil fractions.)

$$\text{ethene} + \text{steam} \rightleftharpoons \text{ethanol}$$
$$CH_2CH_2(g) + H_2O(g) \quad CH_3CH_2OH(g)$$

Decisions about which method to use depend on a number of factors:

Considerations	Fermentation	Chemical reaction
Cost and availability of raw materials	In some countries sugar cane or beet are easily and cheaply grown and make suitable sources of glucose.	Often cheaper than fermentation but costs of ethene made from crude oil will vary with crude oil costs and is expensive where oil must be imported.
Sustainability	Raw materials are renewable. They can be re-grown	Crude oil is non-renewable.
Environmental factors	Growing plants reduces the overall carbon footprint from the energy costs of manufacture.	Carbon from the crude oil in the ground adds to the carbon footprint from the energy costs of manufacture.
Cost of manufacture and purification of the product	Fractional distillation is required to obtain a high percentage of ethanol from a mixture of yeast, flavour compounds, water and ethanol. Production is slow and must be done in batches.	Fractional distillation is required but the product obtained is largely ethanol and water. Production is fast and continuous.
Uses of the product	Flavour compounds are important for beverages but are an impurity in industrial use.	Not suitable for drinks. Suitable for solvents and chemical processes.

B–A*

Improve your grade

Fermentation

Foundation: Write a word equation for the fermentation of glucose. Describe two important conditions needed for fermentation.   *AO1* [4 marks]

Homologous series

Alkanes

- A homologous series is a family of organic chemical compounds like the alkanes or the alkenes.
- Things that are the same about members of a homologous series
  - The general chemical formula
  - The chemical properties
- Things that are different between members of a homologous series
  - The number of carbon atoms
  - The physical properties

Alkenes

- Every member of a homologous family is the same as the last member but with an added CH_2. There is a trend in physical properties, that is, the physical properties gradually change as the number of carbon atoms increases.
- Alkenes contain a double bond between carbon atoms and have the general formula C_nH_{2n}. Examples are shown in the table.

The first three alkenes.

Name	Formula	Structure	Boiling point (°C)
Ethene	C_2H_4		−104
Propene	C_3H_6		−48
Butene	C_4H_8		−6

Functional groups

- Each homologous series has a specific functional group. This is the part of the molecule that decides the chemical properties that the series will have.
- The increasing length of the carbon chain in a homologous series is the reason for the trend in physical properties. For example, as the carbon chain gets longer the intermolecular bonds get stronger. More energy is needed to break the stronger intermolecular bonds so the viscosity and boiling point get higher.

Name of homologous series	Functional group
Alcohols	−OH
Alkenes	C=C
Carboxylic acids	
Esters	

The first three members of the alcohol homologous series.

Name	Formula	Structure	Boiling point (°C)
Methanol	CH_3OH		65.0
Ethanol	C_2H_5OH		78.6
Propanol	C_3H_7OH		97.5

The first three carboxylic acids.

Name	Formula	Structure	Boiling point (°C)
Methanoic acid	HCOOH		100.7
Ethanoic acid	CH_3COOH		118.0
Propanoic acid	C_2H_5COOH		141.0

Improve your grade

Homologous series

Foundation: Give an example of a homologous series and say what differences you would expect to see between different members of your series.

AO1 [3 marks]

Ethene, ethanoic acid, ethanol and society

Alcohol content

- Different drinks contain different amounts of alcohol. The % vol shows how many cm^3 of pure alcohol are in 100 cm^3 of the drink. 10 cm^3 of ethanol is called 1 unit.

	Beer	Cider	Wine	Sherry	Spirits
Typical percentage alcohol	4–6	4–8	11–14	17–20	40–60
Units in a typical drink	½ pint = 1–2	1–2.5	Small glass 1.5–2	1	1.0–1.5

G–E

Drinking too much alcohol damages your liver and makes you more likely to get heart disease and cancer. The UK government recommends drinking no more than 2–3 units a day for women or 3–4 units a day for men. Children under 15 should never be given alcohol.

- Alcohol affects your brain and changes people's behaviour. People who have been drinking are more likely to be involved in violence or accidents in the home or the streets. Drinking causes many days of work to be missed each year.

Carboxylic acids

- The ethanol in wine can be oxidised by the air. It forms ethanoic acid, which is the main compound in vinegar. This spoils the flavour of the wine.

- Ethanoic acid has a low pH. Most bacteria and microorganisms are not able to grow at a low pH. Food can be preserved by storing it in vinegar (pickling). Many people enjoy the flavour of vinegar.

- Ethanoic acid is an example of a carboxylic acid. Carboxylic acids are weak acids. They turn blue litmus paper red and universal indicator red/orange.

General reaction	Reaction of ethanoic acid
Acid + base ⟶ salt + water	Ethanoic acid + sodium hydroxide ⟶ sodium ethanoate + water
Acid + carbonate ⟶ salt + carbon dioxide + water	Ethanoic acid + sodium carbonate ⟶ sodium ethanoate + carbon dioxide + water
Acid + metal ⟶ salt + hydrogen	Ethanoic acid + magnesium ⟶ magnesium ethanoate + hydrogen

D–C

- Carboxylic acids and alcohols react together to form compounds called esters.

    E.g. ethanoic acid + ethanol ⇌ ethyl ethanoate + water

    carboxylic acid + alcohol ⇌ ester + water

- The reaction is called an **esterification** and uses a catalyst of concentrated sulfuric acid. The bond which holds the acid and alcohol together is called an ester bond.

- Esterification is a reversible reaction.

carboxylic acid functional group   alcohol functional group   ester functional group

CH_3COOH (l) + CH_3CH_2OH (l) ⇌ $CH_3COOCH_2CH_3$ (aq) + H_2O (l)

B–A*

Dehydration of alcohols

- Alcohols can be converted to alkenes by a dehydration reaction. Two atoms of hydrogen and one atom of oxygen are removed from the alcohol molecule and a double bond forms between the carbon atoms. A catalyst is required for this reaction.

B–A*

Improve your grade

Esterification

Higher: Give a named example of an ester and describe the chemical reaction that could be used to make this ester. Illustrate your answer with an equation.   *AO1* [5 marks]

Esters, fats and soaps

Uses of esters

- **Esters** are compounds with a low boiling point that have a sweet smell. They are used in perfumes and also as artificial flavourings in foods. Many natural flavours and aromas are esters.
- Fats and oils are also types of esters.

- **Polyesters** are polymers formed from very many monomers joined together by an ester bond. The polymer can be melted and moulded or spun into fibres to make cloth.
- One type of polyester used for plastic bottles is called PET (polyethylene terephthalate). Bottles made from PET are strong but easily recycled.
- One use of recycled polyester is to make fleece fabric for clothing.

- Fats and oils are mixtures of different triesters. These are formed from three long chain carboxylic acids and glycerol.

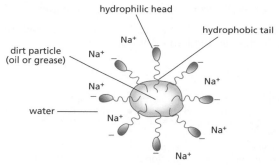

Forming a triester from fatty acids and glycerol.

Soap

- When fats are heated with alkali the ester bonds in the molecule break down. The products are soaps and glycerol. Soaps are the sodium or potassium salts of carboxylic acids which have long chains of carbon atoms. Common chain lengths are 16 or 18 carbon atoms.

- One end of a soap molecule can dissolve in water (the **hydrophilic** end) and the other end can dissolve in fatty substance (the **hydrophobic** end).

How soap washes away dirt and grease.

- The hydrophilic end stays in the water while the hydrophobic end dissolves into the fatty dirt. This allows the dirt to be carried away in the washing water.

Manufacturing margarine

- Liquid oils can be hardened into solid fats by hydrogenation. The carbon–carbon double bonds (unsaturated groups) in the oils are reacted with hydrogen using a nickel catalyst. Hydrogenation is important in the manufacture of margarine.

Improve your grade

Useful esters

Foundation: Give two examples of how esters are used. Describe the properties of the ester that make it useful.

AO1 [3 marks]

C3 Summary

To test for Cl⁻, Br⁻, I⁻, add diute nitric acid and silver nitrate solution to get a precipitate Cl⁻ white, Br⁻ pale yellow, I⁻ yellow.

Test for ammonium ions – add sodium hydroxide solution, warm and see if the vapours turn damp red litmus paper blue.

Qualitative analysis

Qualitative tests detect whether an ion is present or not.
Sodium hydroxide solution gives a coloured precipitate with ions, e.g. Cu^{2+} – blue, Fe^{2+} – green, Fe^{2+} – brown. Al^{3+} and Ca^{2+} – white but Al^{3+} dissolves in excess NaOH.

To find concentration in g/dm^3, divide mass of solute by volume of solvent.
To convert g/dm^3, into mol/dm^3, divide mass of solute by M_r of solute.

Quantitative analysis

Soluble salts can be prepared by either warming acid with an insoluble base, then filtering off excess base or titrating acid against alkali to discover the exact reacting proportions. The concentration of solutions can be measured by titration.

Hard water contains dissolved Ca^{2+} or Mg^{2+} and forms scum with soap. Temporary hard water becomes soft when boiled. Permanent hard water can only be softened using ion exchange resins.

Sodium is used in street lights and as coolant in nuclear reactors. It can be produced by electrolysis of molten sodium chloride.
Electrolysis of sodium chloride solution produces chlorine, hydrogen and sodium hydroxide.

Electrolytic processes

Electrolytes contain ions in solution or molten liquids. During electrolysis positive ions move to the cathode and are reduced and negative ions move to the anode and are oxidised.

Electrolysis using inert electrodes sometimes gives products from water rather than from dissolved ions.

Electrolysis is used to purify copper. Electroplating coats a metal object with a thin layer of metal by using it as a cathode in a solution of metal ions.

One mole of any gas occupies 24 dm^3, at room temperature and pressure. Moles of gas = volume ÷ 24.

Gases, equilibria and ammonia

Nitrogenous fertilisers are made from ammonia. Fertilisers may leach into waterways causing excessive growth of water plants.
Nitrogen from the air and hydrogen from natural gas are used to manufacture ammonia in a reversible reaction called the Haber process.

Dynamic equilibrium means the forward and backward reaction are occurring at the same rate. Changing the conditions changes the relative amounts of reactants and products at equilibrium.

Ethanol can be made by fermentation of glucose with yeast or by hydration of ethene. Concentrated ethanol can be obtained by fractional distillation. Ethanol can be oxidised to the weak acid, ethanoic acid.

Organic chemistry

Homologous series of compounds have the same general formula, similar chemical properties and show trends in physical properties.

Ethanol and ethanoic acid react together to form the ester, ethyl ethanoate.
Some esters have sweet smells. Polyesters can be used for fibres and bottles. Fats and oils are esters. Fats can be converted to soaps by boiling with alkali.

Page 4 The changing atmosphere

Foundation: Explain how the early atmosphere changed to become the atmosphere we have today. *AO1* [4 marks]

The atmosphere used to be made by volcanoes but now there is much more oxygen.

> **Answer grade: E.** The answer gains a mark for noting that there is more oxygen in the modern atmosphere, but there is no explanation of how changes occurred. For full marks, list the gases in the early atmosphere, explain that water vapour condensed to make seas and carbon dioxide dissolved into it, describe how photosynthesis increased the oxygen and show your understanding by giving the composition of today's atmosphere.

Page 5 Measuring gases

Higher: The percentage of gases in the atmosphere has remained the same for thousands of years, but recently there have been small changes.

Explain how we can tell when the atmosphere changes and suggest some reasons for the changes. *AO1* [4 marks]

Scientists have instruments like satellites that can measure accurately the amount of gases in the atmosphere and detect when they change. The gases are changing because of burning fossil fuels and volcanoes.

> **Answer grade: C.** For full marks, specific detail and more examples are needed. Explain that burning fossil fuels for energy releases carbon dioxide. There is more deforestation to provide land for agriculture, which means that less carbon dioxide is absorbed by trees for photosynthesis. Some types of farming release nitrogen oxides or methane. Remember – always give specific examples rather than making general statements.

Page 6 Igneous rock formation

Foundation: Scientists can gain a great deal of information by looking at the properties of rocks.

What is igneous rock, and what does the appearance of igneous rock tell scientists about the way it has formed? *AO1* [5 marks]

Igneous rock used to be lava. There are two different types with different sized crystals.

> **Answer grade: E.** Two marks are awarded for describing igneous rock, but there is no explanation of what this tells scientists. Improve to grade C by explaining that igneous rock forms when molten lava or magma cool and solidify. Say what the different sizes of crystals tell us about where the rock formed.

Page 7 Uses of limestone

Foundation: The limestone industry plays an important part in the British economy but it also causes environmental problems.

Explain what limestone is and how it is used. Discuss whether you think that the damage to the environment means we should no longer use it. *AO2* [4 marks]

Limestone is a sedimentary rock. We should still use it because you have to have it to make concrete and other things. You have to take more care about quarrying it so it doesn't do so much damage.

> **Answer grade: E.** This explains what limestone is but does not fully describe its uses or how quarrying damages the environment. To improve to grade C, give specific examples of environmental damage, like dust or road damage. Give more than one example of the uses of limestone. Make a suggestion of how more care could be taken in quarrying, such as repairing the damage to animal habitats after quarrying is finished.

Page 8 Rearranging atoms

Higher: Prakash and John are discussing where all the nitrogen gas in the atmosphere came from. Prakash thinks that the carbon dioxide in the early atmosphere was converted into nitrogen.

$$CO_2 \ (g) \longrightarrow N_2 \ (g)$$
carbon dioxide   nitrogen

John disagrees. Who do you agree with and why? *AO2* [3 marks]

John. The reactants contain carbon and oxygen. The product contains nitrogen so they can't have come from nowhere.

> **Answer grade: B.** The answer correctly identifies the reactants and the product, but greater detail is needed to explain why Prakash is wrong. For full marks, explain that in a chemical reaction the atoms are rearranged to form the products. Atoms cannot change from one type to another, so carbon and oxygen atoms cannot become nitrogen atoms.

Page 9 Limestone reactions

Foundation: Explain the reaction that occurs when limestone is heated and why this makes it more useful. *AO2* [4 marks]

Limestone breaks down when you heat it. It makes calcium oxide, which is used for lots of things.

> **Answer grade: E.** The answer gains 2 marks for explaining what happens when you heat it and naming one of the products. However, it lacks specific examples. To improve to grade C, give the chemical name of limestone and named examples of its uses such as in making glass. You could also gain marks by writing an equation for the reaction.

Page 10 Neutralising acid spills

Higher: Commercial spill kits are available to help deal with acid spills in the workplace. They often contain sodium carbonate.

Explain how such kits would help to prevent damage from a spill of sulfuric acid. Include any reactions that occur in your answer. AO2 [4 marks]

Sodium carbonate can neutralise the acid so it isn't dangerous. It reacts acid + base → salt + water.

Answer grade: C/D. Two marks would be gained for mentioning neutralisation and giving a basic equation. However, the answer does not fully explain the properties of sodium carbonate that enable it to neutralise the acid. For full marks, explain that sodium carbonate is a base/alkali that will neutralise the sulfuric acid, give the full names in the reaction equation, describe the product (sodium sulfate) and explain why it is safe (not harmful/corrosive). If a question uses specifically named chemicals (sodium carbonate, sulfuric acid), use these names in your answer rather than making general statements.

Page 11 Creating chlorine

Foundation: Describe how you could produce a test tube full of chlorine from hydrochloric acid. AO2 [4 marks]

You would make electricity go through it and it would bubble up.

Answer grade: E. The answer gains 1 mark for explaining the need for electricity, but it does not give enough detail on the process of the experiment. You should explain what apparatus you would use to pass electricity through the acid (a beaker with two electrodes) and how you would collect the chlorine gas (from the positive electrode in an upturned test tube filled with water). You could draw a diagram to show you fully understand the process.

Page 12 Pricing metals

Higher: Aluminium is the most common metal in the Earth's crust, yet 100 g of aluminium costs about ten times more than 100 g of iron. Explain the reasons for this difference in value. AO1 [5 marks]

Aluminium is more expensive to extract than iron. You have to use electrolysis.

Answer grade: C. This answer does not explain why aluminium must be extracted by electrolysis or what the method of extraction for iron is. Explain that aluminium is more reactive than carbon and so cannot be extracted by heating with carbon. Iron is less reactive than carbon and so you can use this method, which is much cheaper than electrolysis. Compare the two metals in the answer.

Page 13 The right metal

Higher: A town council is trying to decide on the best metal to choose as a building material for a bridge over the local river.

Explain what factors they should take into account and suggest a suitable metal. Give reasons for your choice. AO2 [5 marks]

They should consider economic and environmental factors. It would be best to use a recycled metal. Aluminium is a good choice because it does not corrode.

Answer grade: B/C. This answer addresses the main points but does not explain or give examples. The answer should include the cost of the metal and the cost of upkeep of the bridge. Aluminium is more expensive because it is costly to extract, but has lower maintenance costs because it does not need to be painted. Recycled metal is best because it reduces damage to the environment from mining and from energy use in extracting the metal. Make sure that you always give specific examples of the type of damage.

Page 14 Making crude oil

Foundation: Explain how and why kerosene is made from crude oil. AO2 [4 marks]

Kerosene is made by fractional distillation. You heat up the oil and it turns into vapour, then it separates into fractions and one of them is kerosene.

Answer grade: D. Two marks would be earned for mentioning fractional distillation and how this works. However, the answer does not include any explanation of how the fractions separate and has not offered any uses for kerosene. For full marks, include the condensation of the fractions at different temperatures because of their different sizes and mention why it is made, such as its use as an aircraft fuel.

Page 15 Causes of climate change

Higher: Discuss the evidence that the activities of humans have resulted in climate change. AO2 [5 marks]

Humans have burned fossil fuels to provide energy. This has meant that a lot of carbon dioxide has been produced. Carbon dioxide is a greenhouse gas which traps energy on the Earth. So this has caused global warming.

Answer grade: B. This answer includes some important points about global warming but it does not fully discuss the evidence. To improve to grade A, discuss the correlation between the carbon dioxide levels in the atmosphere and the global temperatures over a number of years. Alternative ideas about why global temperatures have risen should be mentioned. It is a common misconception that all the carbon dioxide produced by burning hydrocarbons remains in the atmosphere. In fact, most is absorbed by the oceans or used in photosynthesis.

Page 16 Energy from ethanol

Foundation: Describe an experiment that you could do to decide whether ethanol or hexane releases the most energy. Ethanol and hexane are both liquids. *AO2* [4 marks]

You could make the ethanol and hexane heat up some water. The one that heated it up the most would be the one that released the most energy.

Answer grade: G. The student probably had a clear idea of the experiment in their head but they have not written enough on paper. To improve, describe how the apparatus would be set up and say how you measure the temperature of the water before and afterwards. Explain how you will get valid results by controlling the volume of water and measuring the mass of fuel burned. A diagram would help.

Page 17 Ethane and ethene

Higher: Most of the ethane obtained from natural gas is converted into ethene and made into polymers.

How could you distinguish between ethane and ethane? Illustrate your answer with drawings of the molecules concerned. *AO2* [5 marks]

You can tell the difference because ethene has a double bond and it will react with bromine water.

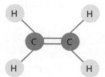 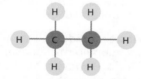

Answer grade: C. Marks are gained here for outlining the characteristics of ethane. The molecules are drawn correctly but they are not labelled. There is no comparison between ethane and ethane. For full marks, explain that ethane does not have a double bond. Give the outcome of the reaction with bromine water and the results with both ethane and ethane.

Page 18 Polymers and energy

Higher: Explain why making bin-liners from new polymers uses so much more energy than using recycled polymers. Suggest why only a small proportion of polymers are recycled. *AO2* [4 marks]

When you make bin-liners from new polymer you have to use up oil. This takes a lot of energy. Recycled polymers don't need oil – they are just made from old polymers melted together. But many people don't recycle their polymers because it is too much trouble.

Answer grade: C: The first sentence mentions the need for oil in the process, gaining a mark, and the last sentence gives one reason why polymers are not recycled. However, the answer does not contain enough specific information. Explain how the energy is used in making polymers (extracting oil, distilling/refining, manufacturing polymer etc.). Identify that some energy is required to recycle polymers (collecting, transporting, sorting and manufacturing) and indicate why it is likely to be less than making new polymer. Demonstrate understanding that mixed polymers cannot be recycled together but must be sorted. Some cannot be recycled. This increases the costs of recycling, making it less economic to recycle.

Page 20 Atomic structure

Foundation: Describe the structure of an oxygen atom. *AO1* [4 marks]

Atoms are made from protons and neutrons. They have electrons going round the nucleus.

> **Answer grade: E.** This answer lists the particles that make up an atom, but it does not make clear how these particles are arranged in an oxygen atom. To gain full marks, state that protons and neutrons are in the nucleus. Explain that an oxygen atom has 8 protons, 8 electrons and 8 neutrons.

Page 21 Similar reactions

Higher: Lithium and potassium both react in a very similar way when they are added to water.

Use your knowledge of atomic structure to explain why lithium and potassium react in a similar way, even though they are different elements. *AO2* [4 marks]

Lithium and potassium are both in the same group of the periodic table. Elements in the same group have similar properties.

> **Answer grade: B/C.** Although the information given is correct, the student has not fully answered the question because they have not explained in terms of atomic structure. To gain full marks, include an explanation of the similarities in the outer-shell electrons of the two elements. Including the electronic structure of both elements would show this clearly.

Page 22 Ionic compounds

Higher: Explain the meaning of 'ionic compound'. Illustrate your answer with a diagram that shows an example of how ionic compounds form. *AO1* [4 marks]

Ionic compounds are compounds formed from ions.

transfer of electrons

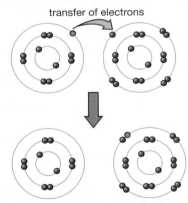

> **Answer grade: B.** The student has forgotten to include the fact that ions are held together by electrostatic attraction. A very good diagram is spoilt because the positive and negative charges on the ions have not been included. Remember – it's not sufficient just to describe an ion as positive or negative, you should always state how many positive or negative charges an ion carries.

Page 23 Formulae equations

Higher: Potassium iodide and lead nitrate react together to form lead iodide. Lead forms a Pb^{2+} ion.

Decide the name of the other product and write a balanced formula equation for this reaction. *AO2* [4 marks]

The other product is potassium nitrate.

$$KI + PbNO_3 \longrightarrow PbI + KNO_3$$

> **Answer grade: B.** The name of the product is correct. However, the formula for lead nitrate is wrong, because lead ions have a 2+ charge while nitrate ions only have a 1+ charge. There should be two nitrate ions for every lead ion. The equation is balanced for this wrong formula, but would not be balanced with the correct formula.

Page 24 Ionic compounds

Foundation: Jon has a test tube containing white crystals. He wonders if the white crystals are ionic.

What properties will the crystals have if they are ionic? Suggest a simple experiment Jon could carry out to test for one of these properties. *AO2* [5 marks]

It will have ionic bonds. It will have a high melting point and conduct electricity. He could see if it melts easily.

> **Answer grade: E.** This answer does not give enough information to gain all the marks available. Saying that a substance has ionic bonds is not naming properties. Ionic substances only conduct electricity if they are dissolved or molten, so Jon's white crystals will not conduct electricity. Give more detail about the test and explain what he would expect to see. For example, Jon should heat the crystals in a strong Bunsen flame. If they do not melt, they have a high melting point.

Page 25 Preparing copper carbonate

Higher: Describe how a pure sample of copper carbonate could be made. *AO2* [5 marks]

A soluble copper compound should be mixed with a soluble carbonate compound. Then you filter it and you have copper carbonate.

> **Answer grade: C.** Marks have been lost because the student did not give enough detail. Suggest the name of a soluble copper and carbonate, state that they must be in solution at the start. Remember to wash and dry the precipitate. Many students think that when an ionic compound dissolves the ions remain in pairs. In fact, each ion is completely separate from all the others and behaves independently.

Page 26 Bonding in water

Foundation: Describe the type of bonding that holds the atoms together in a molecule of water. Illustrate your answer with a diagram. *AO2* [4 marks]

Water molecules are covalent.

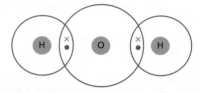

Answer grade: E. This answer names the bonding, but it does not describe it as a shared pair of electrons. The diagram shows the shared pairs of electrons, but the student has forgotten to draw the other outer-shell electron of oxygen. Many students think that it is sufficient to show only the bonding electrons in dot and cross diagrams. It is important to show *all* outer-shell electrons on your diagram.

Page 27 Using graphite

Higher: Sodium is extracted from sodium chloride by electrolysis. A graphite electrode is inserted into the molten compound and then electricity is passed through it.

Describe the properties of graphite that make it particularly useful as an electrode for this purpose, and explain why graphite has these properties. *AO2* [5 marks]

Graphite can conduct electricity. This is because it has free electrons that can move when a voltage is applied.

Answer grade: C. This answer mentions one property of graphite. However, the student has failed to mention a second important property – the high melting point of graphite. The description of the structure of graphite does not contain enough detail to gain full marks. The number of marks available is a clue that more is needed. Describe the layered structure of graphite. A labelled diagram would be helpful.

Page 28 Identifying colours

Foundation: A sweet manufacturer wants to know what colours have been used in a chewy sweet.

Describe a method that they could use to find this out. *AO2* [5 marks]

You could use paper chromatography. You put the colour on the bottom of the paper, and when it is ready you can tell which colours are in it.

Answer grade: E. This answer does not describe the method clearly enough to gain more than 2 of the 5 marks available. To improve, describe what the sweet manufacturer should do with the paper once the mixture has been spotted onto it. Explain what will happen to the different colours in the mixture and how the manufacturer can tell what the colours are.

Page 29 Electrical conductivity

Higher: Use ideas about structure and bonding to explain why solid copper oxide cannot conduct electricity while solid copper can. *AO2* [5 marks]

Copper oxide is ionic, because it is made from copper ions and oxide ions in a giant lattice. This means that it cannot conduct electricity unless it is molten or dissolved. Solid copper is metallic, so it can conduct electricity as a solid.

Answer grade: C. This answer has described the structure and bonding in copper oxide accurately, but has not explained why this means that it cannot conduct electricity. The description of copper only repeats the information in the question so it does not gain any marks. For full marks, describe the structure and explain that the delocalised electrons can move to carry the electricity.

Page 30 Observing a reaction

Foundation: Sarah's teacher demonstrates the reaction of potassium with water. She carefully cuts a small piece of potassium and drops it into a large trough of water.

Describe what Sarah would see. *AO2* [5 marks]

The potassium would fizz and shoot around on the water. It would turn into potassium hydroxide.

Answer grade: E. This answer would gain no more than 2 marks and a grade E, because the description is incomplete. Remember that the potassium would melt and form a ball and would get smaller. There might be a flame. Although the chemistry is good, there are no marks for saying that potassium turns into potassium hydroxide because the question asks what Sarah would *see*. Always read the question carefully. It is not always necessary to explain the chemistry behind what you are describing. If the question asks what would you see then you should only describe things that can be seen.

Page 31 Extracting bromine

Higher: Bromine is extracted from the sea on a commercial basis. The first step is to bubble chlorine through sea water. Sea water contains sodium bromide.

Write a symbol equation for the reaction that occurs. Explain what you would see and why. *AO2* [4 marks]

$NaBr + Cl \longrightarrow NaCl + Br$

You would see the water turn brown.

Answer grade: C. The student has forgotten that the halogens are diatomic, so the formula for chlorine is Cl_2 and for bromine is Br_2. Thus, two parts of the formula equation are incorrect. Although the answer correctly identifies that the water would turn brown, there is no explanation of *why* the brown colour appears.

Page 32 Proving exothermic reactions

Foundation: Andy says that adding iron filings to copper sulfate solution is an exothermic reaction.

Describe an experiment he could do to show this. *AO2* [4 marks]

He could put some iron filings in copper sulfate and see if the temperature goes up.

Answer grade: D/E. This answer would gain 2 marks for mentioning iron filings and the use of temperature as a measure. However, the answer is not detailed enough to achieve full marks. To improve, describe the experiment including the apparatus needed. Remember that the temperature must be measured before and after. The student has not said whether a rise in temperature confirms that the reaction is exothermic or demonstrates that it is not.

Page 33 Collision theory

Higher: In glow sticks, two chemicals react to form a product that glows for a short time.

Use collision theory to explain why manufacturers recommend keeping glow sticks in the fridge to make them last longer. *AO2* [4 marks]

Keeping the sticks in the cold slows down the rate of reaction. The reactants have less energy so there will be less collisions.

Answer grade: C. This answer would receive half marks at best because collision theory is not fully explained. The important fact is that there are fewer effective collisions per second. Explain that lowering the temperature means that the reactants have less energy so a lower percentage of collisions will be effective. For this reason, the reaction will take longer to complete.

Page 34 Calculating mass

Foundation: Which compound contains the highest percentage by mass of nitrogen, KNO_3 or NH_4Cl? Show your working. *AO1* [4 marks]

$M_r \, KNO_3 \; 39 + 14 + 16 = 69 \; \dfrac{14}{69} \times 100\% = 20.3\%$

$M_r \, NH_4Br \; 14 + (4 \times 1) + 80 = 98 \; \dfrac{98}{14} \times 100\% = 700\%$

KNO_3 has the highest percentage nitrogen.

Answer grade: E. The student has shown their working very clearly, and this means that they would gain some marks, even though there are mistakes in the calculation.

KNO_3 – the student has forgotten to multiply the oxygen by three so has the wrong M_r but still gets credit for doing the correct calculation for the percentage mass.

NH_4Br – the student has the numbers the wrong way up for the percentage mass – the clue was that the answer is higher than 100%.

Many students panic when they see a calculation, but they can be one of the easiest ways to pick up marks. Stay calm, follow the method you have learned and always show your working!

Page 36 Iron in drinking water

Higher: A student tested a solution with silver nitrate and nitric acid. A white precipitate formed. State which ion is present in the solution. Write an ionic equation for the reaction that formed the precipitate. *AO1* [4 marks]

It was chlorine ions. $Cl^- + Ag^+ \longrightarrow AgCl$

Answer grade: C. The student has used the name chlorine instead of chloride. They have forgotten to add state symbols in the ionic equation.

Page 37 Chloride in drinking water

Foundation: The water board want to test the levels of chloride ions in the drinking water. Say why it is important to test water for ions. Explain which would give the best answer a quantitative or a qualitative method. *AO2* [3 marks]

They need to know the levels of ions. A quantitative test is best.

Answer grade: E. To improve to a C explain that they need to know the levels of chloride ions **because** they may affect people's health. Say that a quantitative test is best **because** it tells you how much chloride is present but a qualitative test only tells you that there is some chloride present.

Page 38 The problem of limescale

Higher: It has been estimated that hard water scale costs thousands of pounds a year in lost efficiency. Explain where hard water scale comes from. Include a word equation in your answer. *AO2* [4 marks]

Hard water contains ions that have been leached out of the rocks. When it is heated it decomposes. $Ca(HCO_3)_2 \longrightarrow CaCO_3 + H_2O + CO_2$

Answer grade: C. The student has said what hard water is but not what hard water **scale** is. They have not read the question carefully. A correct formula equation has been given but the question asked for a *word* equation.

Page 39 The concentration of salt solution

Foundation: Alec dissolved 6 g of sodium chloride in 50 cm³ of water. What is the concentration of the solution in g/dm³? *AO1* [3 marks]

0.12

Answer grade: D. The student has not noticed that the volume of water is in cm³. Divide this volume by 1 000 before dividing it into the mass and give units to gain full marks.

Page 40 Calculating solutions

Higher: The chemistry technician needs to make up 1 dm³ of a solution of sodium iodide (NaI) concentration 0.1 mol/dm³. How many grams of NaI must she weigh out? *AO1* [3 marks]

M_r NaI 23 + 107 = 130   <u>1.3 g</u>

Answer grade: C. The M_r has been incorrectly calculated as A_r I = 127, not 107 and the final answer is wrong. If the calculation had been shown the student could have obtained a mark for using the correct method even though the answer was wrong.

Page 41 Preparing copper sulfate

Foundation: Students were asked to make a sample of copper sulfate by adding acid to copper oxide. Which acid should they use and what equipment will they need? *AO1* [4 marks]

You need sulfuric acid otherwise it won't make copper sulfate. You need a beaker to mix the reactants.

Answer grade: E. The student has not given enough detail in this answer. To improve to C grade remember to include filter funnel and filter paper. A labelled diagram is often helpful.

Page 42 Calculating concentration

Higher: A student carried out a titration using 0.25 mol/dm³ $H_2SO_4(aq)$ and 25 cm³ of KOH(aq). 20.5 cm³ of the H_2SO_4 was needed to reach the end point of the titration. What was the concentration of the KOH? *AO3* [5 marks]

$0.25 \times 20.5 = 5.125$ $5.125 \div 25 = 0.205$

Answer grade: C. *The student has lost marks by not using any units. They have forgotten to convert cm³ into dm³ twice. Even though these errors have cancelled out to give the correct numerical answer, marks are lost for wrong working. The student has not written out the reaction equation and has failed to notice that the mole ratio for this reaction is 2 moles alkali to 1 mole acid.*

Page 43 Uses of sodium

Foundation: How is sodium metal made and what is it used for? *AO1* [4 marks]

Sodium metal is made by electrolysis. It is for lights and nuclear reactors.

Answer grade: D. The answer does not give enough detail. The student is assuming that the examiner knows what is meant instead of actually writing it down. To improve to a C grade explain what electrolysis is, i.e. passing an electric current through molten sodium chloride. Give detail of what kind of lights and what sodium does in a nuclear reactor.

Page 44 Electrolysis of lead bromide

Foundation: Lead bromide is an ionic solid that will conduct electricity when it is molten. Give the name of the ion that will move towards the anode and explain why it moves this way. *AO1* [3marks]

The bromine ion will move towards the anode because it is attracted to it.

Answer grade: G. Negative ions have the ending –ide so the name of the ion is bromide. Explain that the bromide ion is attracted to the anode because it has a negative charge while the anode has a positive charge.

Page 45 Electrolysis of sodium chloride

Higher: Passing electricity through molten sodium chloride and through aqueous sodium chloride gives different results. Name the products formed in each case and explain why they are different. *AO1* [5 marks]

Molten sodium chloride gives sodium and chlorine, but dissolved sodium chloride gives hydrogen and chlorine. This is because of the water in the dissolved sodium chloride, which means that you don't get sodium.

Answer grade: B. To improve explain that the only ions in the molten sodium chloride are sodium and chloride ions but the solution also contains hydrogen and hydroxide ions. State that hydrogen ions are more easily reduced than sodium ions. Don't forget that sodium hydroxide is also a product.

Page 46 Products of electrolysis

Foundation: Joe does an experiment on the electrolysis of copper sulfate using copper electrodes. Describe what happens to the electrodes. *AO1* [3 marks]

One gets bigger and one gets smaller.

Answer grade: E. The student has not described that the cathode gets heavier while the anode gets lighter. It is better to describe changes in mass rather than changes in size.

Page 47 Purifying copper

Higher: Draw a labelled diagram of the apparatus that could be used to purify a sample of copper and write an ionic equation for the reaction occurring at the cathode. *AO1* [5 marks]

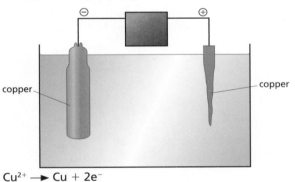

copper   copper

$Cu^{2+} \longrightarrow Cu + 2e^-$

Answer grade: B. Correct apparatus but the diagram needs to be more carefully labelled. The anode should be labelled 'impure copper', and the electrolyte has not been named. The ionic equation has the electrons on the wrong side of the equation. It should read $Cu^{2+} + 2e^- \longrightarrow Cu$.

Page 48 Filling balloons

Higher: Jake wants to fill a balloon with carbon dioxide. The volume of the balloon is 2 dm³ and he plans to use the reaction between sodium hydrogencarbonate and vinegar:

$NaHCO_3 + CH_3COOH \longrightarrow CO_2 + H_2O + CH_3COONa$

If he uses 10 g of $NaHCO_3$ and plenty of vinegar, will this fill the balloon? Show your calculation. *AO2* [5 marks]

M_r $NaHCO_3$ = 84, moles $NaHCO_3$ = 84 ÷ 10 = 8.4, so moles CO_2 = 8.4, 8.4 × 24 = 201.6 dm³

Answer grade: B. The calculation is well laid out but the student has made the error of not checking the formula before calculating moles from mass and has divided by the mass instead of dividing by the M_r. In addition, the student has not answered the question about whether the balloon will be filled but simply left the answer as a volume.

Page 49 Overuse of fertiliser

Foundation: Explain why farmers add nitrogen fertilisers to their crops. Why is it not a good idea to add too much fertiliser? *AO1* [3 marks]

Fertiliser makes plants grow better but too much means that the fish can die.

Answer grade: E. To improve to C grade explain why it is important to farmers that the plants grow better. Explain the steps that show why the fertiliser might cause the fish to die.

Page 50 Industrial compromise

Higher: At temperatures of below 100 °C the Haber process gives ammonia yields of greater than 90%. Explain why manufacturers of ammonia use temperatures of between 400 °C and 500 °C even though this gives a lower yield. *AO1* [3 marks]

Low temperatures make the reaction slow so the higher temperature is a compromise.

Answer grade: C. The student has not demonstrated their understanding of yield. Explain that the slow rate means that the high yield takes a long time to achieve and manufacture of the same amount of ammonia can be achieved in less time by using a higher temperature and running the reaction several times.

Page 51 Fermentation

Foundation: Write a word equation for the fermentation of glucose. Describe two important conditions needed for fermentation. *AO1* [4 marks]

Glucose + oxygen ⟶ ethanol + carbon dioxide. The mixture must be kept warm and with no air.

Answer grade: D. The student has stated that there must be no air during fermentation but has then written oxygen in the equation. Always read back through what you have written to check for mistakes.

Page 52 Homologous series

Foundation: Give an example of a homologous series and say what differences you would expect to see between different members of your series.
AO1 [3 marks]

Hydrocarbons are an example of a homologous series. They all get a higher boiling point as you go up.

Answer grade: C. Hydrocarbon is not a description of a homologous series. The student is muddling hydrocarbons and alkanes, which are a type of hydrocarbon. A trend of physical properties is described but the description is not clear enough. Compare the property with the carbon chain length to gain full marks.

Page 53 Esterification

Higher: Give a named example of an ester and describe the chemical reaction that could be used to make this ester. Illustrate your answer with an equation.
AO1 [5 marks]

Ethyl ethanoate is an example of an ester. An esterification reaction will make it.

$$CH_3CH_2COOH + CH_3CH_2OH \rightarrow CH_3COOCH_2CH_3$$

Answer grade: B. Give more detail about the esterification reaction, name the reactants, sulfuric acid catalyst as well as the product. Take care when writing equations. The formula of the carboxylic acid does not match the ester produced.
The equation need a reversible arrow and lacks water as a product on the right hand side.

Page 54 Useful esters

Foundation: Give two examples of how esters are used. Describe the properties of the ester that make it useful. *AO1 [3 marks]*

Esters are used for perfumes and for flavours. They make nice perfumes.

Answer grade: D. Being a nice perfume is not a property. To move to grade C you must say that esters are sweet-smelling or esters have a low boiling point.

How Science Works

Data, evidence, theories and explanations

As part of your Science and Additional Science assessment, you will need to show that you have an understanding of the scientific process – How Science Works.

This involves examining how scientific data is collected and analysed. You will need to evaluate the data by providing evidence to test ideas and develop theories. Some explanations are developed using scientific theories, models and ideas. You should be aware that there are some questions that science cannot answer and some that science cannot address.

Practical and enquiry skills

You should be able to devise a plan that will answer a scientific question or solve a scientific problem. In doing so, you will need to collect data from both primary and secondary sources. Primary data will come from your own findings – often from an experimental procedure or investigation. While working with primary data, you will need to show that you can work safely and accurately, not only on your own but also with others.

Secondary data is found by research, often using ICT – but do not forget books, journals, magazines and newspapers are also sources. The data you collect will need to be evaluated for its validity and reliability as evidence.

Communication skills

You should be able to present your information in an appropriate, scientific manner. This may involve the use of mathematical language as well as using the correct scientific terminology and conventions. You should be able to develop an argument and come to a conclusion based on recall and analysis of scientific information. It is important to use both quantitative and qualitative arguments.

Applications and implications of science

Many of today's scientific and technological developments have both benefits and risks. The decisions that scientists make will almost certainly raise ethical, environmental, social or economic questions. Scientific ideas and explanations change as time passes and the standards and values of society change. It is the job of scientists to validate these changing ideas.

How science ideas change

From the information you have learnt, you will know that science is a process of developing, then testing theories and models. Scientists have been carrying out this work for many centuries and it is the results of their ideas and trials that has provided us with the knowledge we have today.

However, in the process of developing this knowledge, many ideas were put forward that seem quite absurd to us today.

In 1692, the British astronomer Edmund Halley (after whom Halley's Comet was named) suggested that the Earth consisted of four concentric spheres. He was trying to explain the magnetic field that surrounds the Earth and suggested that there was a shell of about 500 miles thick, two inner concentric shells and an inner core. Halley believed that these shells were separated by atmospheres, and each shell had magnetic poles with the spheres rotating at different speeds. The theory was an attempt to explain why unusual compass readings occurred. He also believed that each of these inner spheres, which was constantly lit by a luminous atmosphere, supported life.

Reliability of information

It is important to be able to spot when data or information is presented accurately and just because you see something online or in a newspaper, does not mean that it is accurate or true.

Think about what is wrong in this example from an online shopping catalogue. Look at the answer at the bottom of the page to check that your observations are correct.

From box to air in under two minutes!

Simply unroll the airship and, as the black surface attracts heat, watch it magically inflate.

Seal one end with the cord provided and fly your 8-metre, sausage-shaped kite.

- Good for all year round use.

- Folds away into box provided.

- A unique product – not for the faint hearted.

- Educational as well as fun!

Once the airship is filled with air, it is warmed by the heat of the sun.

The warm air inside the airship makes it float, like a full-sized hot-air balloon.

Answer

Black absorbs heat, it does not attract it.

Glossary

Glossary

electrons tiny negatively charged particles within an atom that orbit the nucleus – responsible for current in electrical circuits 17, 20, 21, 22, 26, 29, 30, 31, 43

electroplating coating with another metal using electrolysis 47

electrostatic forces the very strong forces between positive and negative ions in an ionic substance 22, 24

element a substance made out of only one type of atom 8, 20, 21, 22, 23, 25, 27, 29, 30, 31

empirical formula a formula that shows the correct ratio of all of the elements in a compound 35

endothermic reaction a chemical reaction that takes in heat 32

energy profile diagram a diagram showing energy taken in or given out during a chemical reaction 32

enzymes biological catalysts (usually proteins) produced by cells that control the rate of chemical reactions in cells 16, 51

esterification the reaction between an alcohol and a carboxylic acid 53

esters compounds synthesised by the reaction between an alcohol and a carboxylic acid 54

ethene a gas that is an alkene (C_2H_4), which is used to make polymers and is also a plant hormone 17, 18, 53

eutrophication the processes that occur when water is enriched with nutrients (from fertilisers) which allow algae to grow and use up all the oxygen 49

evolution the process whereby organisms change through time – present-day living things are descended from organisms that were different from them 4

exothermic reaction a chemical reaction in which heat is given out 32

F

fermentation the conversion of carbohydrates to alcohol and carbon dioxide by yeast or bacteria 16, 51

fertiliser chemical put on soil to increase soil fertility and allow better growth of crop plants 49

filtrate the soluble material that passes through a filter paper 25

fineness system a system for denoting the purity of gold, platinum and silver, indicating parts per thousand 13

flame test the heating of metal ions in a flame to produce a colour as an aid to identifying the material 25

fossil fuels fuel (coal, natural gas, oil) formed from the compressed remains of plants and other organisms that lived long ago 5, 16

fossils the preserved remains of organisms that lived long ago 7

fractional distillation a method of separating liquid mixtures by evaporation 5, 14, 28

fuel cell a cell that produces energy by combining a fuel and an oxidant 16

G

galvanising a method of corrosion protection that uses a layer of zinc to protect the underlying metal 12

giant molecular covalent compounds very large molecules consisting of non-metals covalently bonded together 29

greenhouse effect a process in which the atmosphere is warmed up by infrared radiation; it then re-radiates some of the infrared radiation back towards the Earth's surface, which warms the surface 15

greenhouse gases gases in the atmosphere whose absorption of infrared solar radiation is responsible for the greenhouse effect, e.g. carbon dioxide, methane and water vapour 15

H

Haber process the process for producing ammonia from nitrogen and hydrogen 50

haemoglobin the chemical found in red blood cells which carried oxygen 14

half equation an equation that shows either the cathode reaction or the anode reaction in an electrolytic cell 44

halogens reactive non-metals in group 7 of the periodic table, e.g. chlorine 29, 31

homologous series a group of compounds that change in some incremental way 14, 17, 52

hydrocarbons molecules containing only carbon and hydrogen – many fuels are hydrocarbons, e.g. natural gas (methane) and petrol (a complex mixture) 5, 14, 15, 17

hydrophilic the part of a molecule that tends to dissolve in water 54

hydrophobic the part of a molecule that tends to be repelled from water 54

hypothesis a possible explanation for an observation 6, 31

I

igneous rock rock formed from magma or lava 6

immiscible two liquids that are completely insoluble in each other 28

incomplete combustion when fuel burns in a small amount of oxygen so that carbon monoxide, particles and water are produced 14

inert an inert substance is one that is not chemically reactive 31

infrared radiation part of the electromagnetic spectrum, thermal energy 15

insoluble a substance that will not dissolve (something that will not dissolve in water may dissolve in other liquids) 9, 24, 25

intrusive rock igneous rock formed by slow cooling when magma oozes into cracks and voids in the Earth's crust 6

ion an atom with an electrical charge (can be positive or negative) 11, 22, 23, 24, 25, 29, 30, 36, 37, 38, 41, 43, 44

ionic bonding chemical bonding between two ions of opposite charge 22, 24

ionic compounds compounds that contain positively charged metal ions and negatively charged non-metal ions 22, 23, 24, 25, 29

isotopes (1) nuclei of atoms with the same number of protons but a different number of neutrons; (2) atoms with the same number of protons but different numbers of neutrons 20

K

kinetic energy the energy that moving objects have 6

L

lattice a criss-cross structure 24, 25

limescale an insoluble precipitate that lines heating elements and pipes, formed when hard water is heated 38

limestone sedimentary rock composed mainly of calcite or dolomite 6, 7, 9

limewater an aqueous solution of calcium hydroxide 9, 14, 25

M

magma hot molten rock found in the mantle, below the Earth's surface 6

malleable capable of being shaped by hammering 13, 29

marble metamorphosed limestone produced by recrystallisation 6, 7, 33

mass the amount of matter inside an object, measured in kilograms 20, 34

mass number the total number of neutrons and protons within the nucleus of an atom (same as the nucleon number) 20

Glossary

melting point the temperature at which a solid becomes a liquid 8, 24, 27, 29, 30

metallic compounds compounds composed of individual metal ions floating in a sea of electrons 29

metamorphic rock sedimentary rock that is transformed by heat and pressure 6, 7

microorganisms single-celled organisms that are only just visible in the light microscope 11

minerals solid metallic or non-metallic substances found naturally in the Earth's crust 7, 12

mole a specific number of particles (6.02×10^{23}): the relative formula mass of a substance expressed in grams will give this number of particles 39

monomer a small molecule that may become chemically bonded to other monomers to form a polymer 18

N

nanotechnology engineering systems constructed at the molecular level 15

neutralisation reaction a reaction between an acid and an alkali that produces a neutral solution 10

neutrons small particles that do not have a charge, found in the nucleus of an atom 17, 20

noble gases elements of group 0 in the periodic table, also called the inert gases 22, 29, 31

non-renewable resources resources which are being used up more quickly than they can be replaced, e.g. fossil fuels; they will eventually run out 13, 16

nucleus the central core of an atom, which contains protons and neutrons and has a positive charge 17, 20, 21

O

ores rocks that contain minerals, including metals, e.g. iron ore 12, 13

organic compounds chemicals containing carbon 17

oxidation reaction a reaction in which molecules gain oxygen 4, 12, 14, 46

P

percentage composition the proportion of a compound's relative formula mass composed of a specific element 34

percentage yield the ratio of actual yield to theoretical yield 34

periodic table a table of all the chemical elements based on their atomic number 20, 21, 22, 29, 28, 31

periodicity The characteristics of repeating patterns of properties in the periodic table 21

permanent hard water hard water that cannot be removed by boiling 38

pH a scale running from 0 to 14 that shows how acidic or alkaline a substance is 9, 10

photosynthesis a process carried out by green plants where sunlight, carbon dioxide and water are used to produce glucose and oxygen 4, 5, 15

physical properties properties that can be observed without changing the chemical composition of a substance, e.g. colour, density, melting point and boiling point 8, 29

polyatomic ions ions containing more than one type of atom 23

polyester polymer created by the polymerisation of alcohols and carboxylic acids using ester bonds 54

polymerisation reaction a chemical process that combines monomers to form a polymer – this is how polythene is formed 18

polymers large molecules made up of chains of monomers 17, 18

precipitate an insoluble solid formed in a solution during a chemical reaction 8, 24, 25

precipitation reaction a reaction that results in an insoluble product 24, 25

product the substance formed in a reaction 5, 8, 23, 32, 33, 34

protons small positively charged particles found in the nucleus of an atom 17, 20, 21

Q

qualitative analysis analysis of a chemical (or chemicals) to find out what's in it 36

quantitative analysis based on quantity 37

quantitative analysis analysis of a chemical (or chemicals) to find out how much is present 36

R

rate of reaction the speed with which a chemical reaction takes place 16, 33

reactant the chemicals that react in a chemical reaction 5, 8, 23, 24, 25, 33, 34

recycling the reprocessing of materials to make new products 13, 18

red blood cells blood cells which are adapted to carry oxygen 14

reduction reaction the removal of oxygen from a compound 12, 46

relative atomic mass the average atomic mass of an element, taking into account the relative abundance of the isotopes of that element 20, 34, 40

relative formula mass the sum of all the relative atomic masses of the atoms in a molecule 34, 40

renewable resources energy resources that can be replenished at the same rate that they are used up, e.g. biofuels – they will not run out 16

residue the solid material collected in a filter paper after filtration 25

R$_f$ value the ratio of how far a substance has moved up chromatography paper relative to the solvent front 28

S

sacrificial protection a method of corrosion protection using blocks of reactive metal to corrode instead of the object being protected 12

salt an ionic compound composed of positive ions (cations) and negative ions (anions) 10, 24, 25, 31

saturated hydrocarbons hydrocarbons that contain no carbon-carbon double bonds 17

sedimentary rock rock formed by the sedimentation of material on riverbeds and ocean floors 6, 7

semiconductor a group of materials with electrical conductivity properties between metals and insulators 9

shells electrons are arranged in shells (or orbits) around the nucleus of an atom 17, 21, 30, 26, 30, 31

simple molecular covalent compounds small molecules consisting of non-metals covalently bonded together 29

solubility the amount of a substance that will dissolve 8, 24, 29

spectroscopy a sophisticated type of flame test: substances are heated until they produce their own unique emission spectrum 25

starch large polysaccharides made by plants as a form of food storage 18

state symbols the symbols that describe the state of a substance: solid, liquid, gas or aqueous (dissolved in water) 4, 24

T

temporary hard water hard water that can be removed by boiling 38

theoretical yield the predicted yield of a chemical reaction based on calculations 34

thermal decomposition the breaking down of a compound due to the action of heat 9, 18

Glossary

titration a common laboratory method used to determine the unknown concentration of a known reactant 10

transition metals elements between group 2 and group 3 in the periodic table 29

triple covalent bond three pairs of electrons shared in a covalent bond 26

U

unsaturated hydrocarbons hydrocarbons that contain carbon-carbon double bonds 17

W

word equations a shorthand way of representing a chemical reaction 5, 23

X

X-rays electromagnetic waves with very short wavelength of the order of 0.000 000 001 m 25

Y

yield useful product made from a chemical reaction 34

Exam tips

The key to successful revision is finding the method that suits you best. There is no right or wrong way to do it.

Before you begin, it is important to plan your revision carefully. If you have allocated enough time in advance, you can walk into the exam with confidence, knowing that you are fully prepared.

Start well before the date of the exam, not the day before!

It is worth preparing a revision timetable and trying to stick to it. Use it during the lead up to the exams and between each exam. Make sure you plan some time off too.

Different people revise in different ways and you will soon discover what works best for you.

> **Remember!**
>
> There is a difference between *learning* and *revising*.
>
> When you revise, you are looking again at something you have already learned. Revising is a process that helps you to remember this information more clearly.
>
> Learning is about finding out and understanding new information.

Some general points to think about when revising

- Find a quiet and comfortable space at home where you won't be disturbed. You will find you achieve more if the room is ventilated and has plenty of light.

- Take regular breaks. Some evidence suggests that revision is most effective when tackled in 30 to 40 minute slots. If you get bogged down at any point, take a break and go back to it later when you are feeling fresh. Try not to revise when you're feeling tired. If you do feel tired, take a break.

- Use your school notes, textbook and this Revision guide.

- Spend some time working through past papers to familiarise yourself with the exam format.

- Produce your own summaries of each module and then look at the summaries in this Revision guide at the end of each module.

- Draw mind maps covering the key information on each topic or module.

- Review the Grade booster checklists on pages 126–128.

- Set up revision cards containing condensed versions of your notes.

- Prioritise your revision of topics. You may want to leave more time to revise the topics you find most difficult.

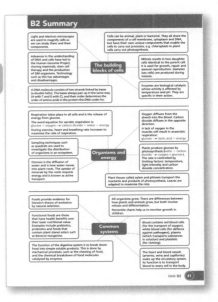

Workbook

The **Workbook** (pages 73–125) allows you to work at your own pace on some typical exam-style questions. You will find that the actual GCSE questions are more likely to test knowledge and understanding across topics. However, the aim of the Revision guide and Workbook is to guide you through each topic so that you can identify your areas of strength and weakness.

The Workbook also contains example questions that require longer answers (**Extended response questions**). You will find one question that is similar to these in each section of your written exam papers. The quality of your written communication will be assessed when you answer these questions in the exam, so practise writing longer answers, using sentences. The **Answers** to all the questions in the Workbook can be cut out for flexible practice and can be found on pages 132–144.

At the end of the Workbook there is a series of **Grade booster checklists** that you can use to tick off the topics when you are confident about them and understand certain key ideas. These Grade boosters give you an idea of the grade at which you are currently working.

Collins Workbook

NEW GCSE

Chemistry

Foundation and Higher

for Edexcel

Author: Alison Dennis

Revision Guide +
Exam Practice Workbook

1 a Which of the following gases was not in the atmosphere 4.5 billion years ago, but is in our modern atmosphere?

G–E

    i Water vapour   **ii** Carbon dioxide   **iii** Oxygen   **iv** Nitrogen

.... **[1 mark]**

2 Scientists analyse the gases that come from volcanoes. How does this help them to understand what the early atmosphere was like?

D–C

....

.... **[2 marks]**

3 Scientists analysed some rocks that contain iron compounds. Those formed more than 4 billion years ago contained iron sulfide (FeS), while rocks that formed only 1.8 billion years ago contain iron oxide (Fe_2O_3).

    a Name the type of reaction that converts iron to iron oxide.

.... **[1 mark]**

B–A*

    b Explain how these rocks have helped scientists understand how the atmosphere of the Earth has changed.

....

....

.... **[3 marks]**

4 a In the modern atmosphere there is about 0.03% carbon dioxide. How does this compare to the amount of carbon dioxide that was in the atmosphere 4.5 billion years ago?

.... **[1 mark]**

D–C

    b Suggest what happened to cause the change.

....

.... **[2 marks]**

5 The diagram opposite shows the gases in the atmosphere 3 billion years ago.

    a Calculate the percentage of oxygen in the atmosphere at that time. Show your working.

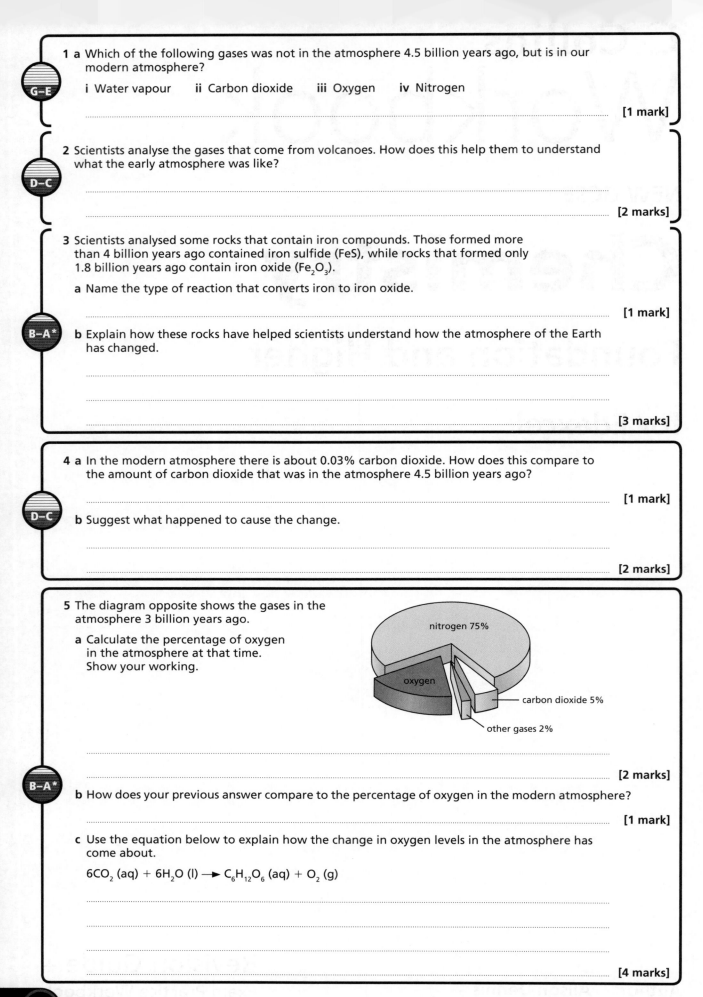

nitrogen 75%

oxygen

carbon dioxide 5%

other gases 2%

....

.... **[2 marks]**

B–A*

    b How does your previous answer compare to the percentage of oxygen in the modern atmosphere?

.... **[1 mark]**

    c Use the equation below to explain how the change in oxygen levels in the atmosphere has come about.

    $6CO_2$ (aq) + $6H_2O$ (l) $\longrightarrow$ $C_6H_{12}O_6$ (aq) + O_2 (g)

....

....

....

.... **[4 marks]**

1 a Which of the following would not be used to measure changes in atmospheric gases?

  i Satellites   **ii** Mass spectrometer   **iii** Digital thermometer   **iv** Fractional distillation

.... [1 mark]

  b Name **two** human activities that can cause changes in the gases in Earth's atmosphere.

....

.... [2 marks]

  c Explain why scientists want to measure the amount of each gas in the atmosphere.

.... [1 mark]

2 a Over the past 100 years there has been a noticeable increase in the percentage of carbon dioxide in the atmosphere. Select the answer that gives the most likely reason for this change.

  i   Carbon dioxide has dissolved into the oceans.

  ii Oxygen has been converted into carbon dioxide by respiration.

  iii Combustion of hydrocarbons has released carbon dioxide.

  iv Volcanoes have erupted, releasing carbon dioxide.

.... [1 mark]

  b It is estimated that 40% of the rainforests of Central America have been cut down over the last 40 years.

  i What effect does cutting down forests have on carbon dioxide and oxygen levels in the atmosphere?

....

.... [2 marks]

  ii Explain why removing trees results in these changes.

....

.... [2 marks]

3 a Balance the following equation.

  _____ CH_4 + _____ O_2 ➙ _____ CO_2 + _____ H_2O [4 marks]

  b Methane, oxygen and carbon dioxide are all gases. Water is a liquid. Explain how you could show this on the equation.

....

.... [3 marks]

  c Many scientists consider that the problem of increasing carbon dioxide levels in the atmosphere would be improved by using hydrogen (H_2) as a fuel instead of hydrocarbons (C_xH_y).

  Explain why burning hydrogen would be better. Use an equation to illustrate your answer.

....

....

....

.... [3 marks]

G–E

D–C

B–A*

1 a Which sentence below describes metamorphic rock?

   i It forms when lava solidifies.   **ii** It forms when magma solidifies.

   iii It forms when rock comes under heat and pressure. **iv** It forms when sediment hardens.

   .... **[1 mark]**

b John has two samples of igneous rock. They formed in different places. One has large crystals and the other has tiny crystals.

  How does the size of the crystals help John to understand where the rocks were formed?

  ....

  .... **[2 marks]**

c Asha reads that chalk is made from the skeletons of plankton that lived in the sea millions of years ago. Describe to Asha what processes occurred to change the skeletons into chalk.

  ....

  .... **[3 marks]**

G–E

---

2 Chen tried an experiment to see what happens when copper sulfate crystals form. First he dissolved as much copper sulfate as he could in 50 cm³ of hot water. Then he poured 25 cm³ of the solution into boiling tube 1 and put the tube in a beaker of ice and water. He poured the remaining 25 cm³ into boiling tube 2 and put the tube into a beaker packed with cotton wool.

The following day he looked at the contents of the tubes and found that both had formed crystals. In one tube the crystals were large and in the other they were small.

a Which tube would have cooled the fastest and why?

  ....

  .... **[2 marks]**

b Which tube would contain the large crystals?

  .... **[1 mark]**

c Chen said that tube 2 is a good model for the formation of granite rock. Do you agree or disagree? Explain why.

  ....

  ....

  .... **[4 marks]**

Copper sulfate solution

Ice and water

Tube 1

Copper sulfate solution

Cotton wool

Tube 2

D–C

---

3 Yellowstone National Park in the USA is the site of an ancient super-volcano.

Geologists studied the rock from different sites around the park and obtained the results shown opposite.

Location	Crystal size (mm)
Obsidian Cliffs	No crystals, smooth glass-like texture
Tower Falls	0.78, 0.92, 1.20, 0.93, 1.1, 0.86, 0.76, 0.61
Hell Roaring Mountain	2.15, 1.76, 0.89, 1.24, 0.98, 1.35, 1.29, 1.17

a What is the difference in average crystal size between the rocks at Tower Falls and those at Hell Roaring Mountain? Show your working.

  ....

  .... **[3 marks]**

b Suggest a difference in the way these three rocks may have formed and explain your suggestion.

  ....

  ....

  ....

  .... **[4 marks]**

B–A*

1 a Link the correct statements.

Cementation | Rock fragments are removed from the surface of the rock.

Weathering | Concentrated solutions of salts stick rock fragments together.

Sedimentation | Rocks break into small fragments.

Erosion | Small fragments of rock are deposited on the sea bed. **[2 marks]**

b Put the four words above in the correct order to describe the formation of sedimentary rock.

.... **[2 marks]**

c Explain how chalk is converted into limestone.

....

.... **[3 marks]**

2 The ancient Greeks believed that animals grew from the Earth. They thought that fossils were animals that had failed to break out on to the surface of the Earth.

Explain what we believe today about the way fossils form and give any evidence that supports this theory.

....

....

....

.... **[4 marks]**

3 The picture shows Idol Rock at Brimham Rocks in Yorkshire.

a Use evidence from the picture to support the view that Idol Rock is made from sedimentary rock.

.... **[1 mark]**

b Use your knowledge of the properties of sedimentary rock and of the way that it forms to suggest how Idol Rock came to be balanced on such a tiny point.

....

.... **[2 marks]**

4 A mining company has asked the local council for permission to quarry limestone just outside a small town. The local residents have prepared a petition against the quarry. What arguments could they use to prevent the quarrying?

....

.... **[3 marks]**

5 Tick the correct boxes for each product.

Ingredient	Glass	Cement	Concrete	Ingredient	Glass	Cement	Concrete
Limestone				Gravel			
Sand				Water			
Clay				Sodium carbonate			

[3 marks]

6 Some forms of industry are unavoidably disruptive to local communities. Contractors are required to provide plans showing how they intend to minimise disruption and long-term damage to the countryside. Write the outline of a suitable plan for a company that wants to build a limestone quarry near a town.

....

....

....

.... **[4 marks]**

Topic 2: 2.3, 2.4, 2.5, 2.6, 2.7, 2.8, 2.9

1 Which of the following is **not** true?

 i   Atoms are the smallest particle of an element.

 ii Atoms from one element change to another element during a chemical reaction.

 iii Atoms are rearranged during chemical reactions.

 iv Different elements have different types of atoms.

.... [1 mark]

2 Below are the instructions that Kelly followed during a chemistry lesson.

 • Hold a piece of grey magnesium metal in the tongs.

 • Put it into the Bunsen flame until it lights.

 • **DO NOT LOOK DIRECTLY AT THE FLAME**

 • When it has finished burning, place the white powdery solid down on the heat-resistant mat.

 a What evidence tells you that Kelly had carried out a chemical reaction?

....

.... [2 marks]

 b The reactants for this reaction were magnesium and oxygen and the product was magnesium oxide. The mass of the magnesium and oxygen added together was 2.0 g. What was the mass of the magnesium oxide?

.... [1 mark]

3 Read the information. Copper carbonate is a green solid. If it is heated in a boiling tube it begins to melt when the temperature reaches 200 °C. If heating is continued to 290 °C it reacts to form copper oxide and carbon dioxide. Copper carbonate reacts with acid to form a salt, water and carbon dioxide.

Identify **one** physical and **one** chemical property of copper carbonate.

....

.... [2 marks]

4

KI solution

$Pb(NO_3)_2$ solution

395.65 g

KNO_3 solution and solid yellow PbI_2

 a Fill in the missing reading on the second balance. [1 mark]

 b Name **one** difference in the physical properties of KNO_3 and PbI_2.

.... [1 mark]

5 Sarah carried out an investigation to discover what mass of carbon dioxide is made when copper carbonate reacts with acid. The equation for the reaction is below:

$2HCl$ (aq)   + $CuCO_3$ (s)   → $CuCl_2$ (aq)   + H_2O (l)   + CO_2 (g)

hydrochloric acid   copper carbonate   copper chloride

She measured the mass of the acid and the copper carbonate in a beaker at the start of the reaction.

Describe the other measurements Sarah must make and the calculation that she must do. Explain why this method enables her to find out how much carbon dioxide is made.

....

....

....

.... [5 marks]

1 Calcium oxide is a very useful chemical that is used to make cement. The starting material for making calcium oxide is limestone.

 a What is the chemical compound in limestone?

.... [1 mark]

 b How can limestone be converted into calcium oxide?

.... [1 mark]

 c What is the other product of this reaction?

.... [1 mark]

 d What name is given to this type of reaction?

.... [1 mark]

2 Magnesium oxide can also be made by a chemical reaction. Suggest a reactant for this reaction and explain how you made your choice.

....

.... [3 marks]

3 a Write the chemical formula for calcium hydroxide.

.... [2 marks]

 b Calcium hydroxide solution is also known as limewater. Describe what limewater is used for and explain the chemistry that allows it to be used in this way.

....

....

....

.... [4 marks]

4 A student decided to investigate which substance decomposed more easily – zinc carbonate ($ZnCO_3$) or copper carbonate ($CuCO_3$). She set up the apparatus as in the diagram opposite.

retort stand — clamp
metal carbonate   test-tube   delivery tube
test-tube
Bunsen burner
B–A*
limewater

 a Write a word equation for the thermal decomposition of zinc carbonate.

.... [2 marks]

 b Write the instructions for experiments that will allow the student to find out whether zinc or copper carbonate decomposes more easily.

....

....

.... [3 marks]

 c Predict the results of the experiment and explain why you made this prediction.

....

.... [2 marks]

5 a Some farmers add calcium compounds to soil. Explain why.

.... [1 mark]

 b Calcium oxide and calcium carbonate are both used to improve some soils. Farmers often choose to use calcium oxide. Explain why.

.... [2 marks]

 c Describe **one** advantage and **one** disadvantage of using calcium oxide rather than limestone to neutralise soil.

....

.... [2 marks]

1 a Which of the following would not neutralise an acid?

    i Sodium hydroxide

    ii Sodium chloride

    iii Calcium oxide

    iv Calcium carbonate

.... **[1 mark]**

b Joe and Folu are discussing the best way to decide how much acid is in two brands of vinegar. They decide to see how much base it takes to neutralise the vinegar. Write a word equation to show the type of products that are formed when an acid and a base react together.

.... **[2 marks]**

c Folu says they must use a base that will dissolve in water. What name is given to this kind of base?

.... **[1 mark]**

d Joe and Folu decide to add drops of base to 5 cm³ of vinegar. Explain how they could tell when the acid had been neutralised and which vinegar contained the most acid.

....

.... **[2 marks]**

G–E

2 A class is planning an experiment to measure the effectiveness of different antacid tablets.

Elsa's plan is as follows:

    • Put an antacid tablet in a beaker.

    • Add some hydrochloric acid to the beaker.

    • When the fizzing has stopped, measure the pH.

    • Repeat these steps with a different type of antacid.

a Improve Elsa's method so that she will get a valid result.

....

....

.... **[3 marks]**

b How will Elsa tell which antacid was the most effective?

.... **[1 mark]**

c Miriam suggests that it would be better to use 25 cm³ of acid and add spatulas of crushed powder to it until the acid is neutralised, then repeat with fresh acid and the second tablet. Do you agree? Explain your answer.

....

....

.... **[2 marks]**

D–C

3 Calcium chloride ($CaCl_2$) is a salt used as a drying agent to remove water from liquids. It can be manufactured by adding acid to limestone ($CaCO_3$).

a Which acid would be added to limestone to form calcium chloride?

.... **[1 mark]**

b The other products of the reaction are carbon dioxide and water. Write a symbol equation for this reaction.

.... **[3 marks]**

B–A*

1 a Which of the following describes a method of obtaining chlorine from sea water?

   i Electroplating   **ii** Filtering

   iii Precipitation   **iv** Electrolysis

.... **[1 mark]**

b Explain why industries that use chlorine gas must be very careful about safety. Suggest **two** safety precautions an industry should use.

....

.... **[3 marks]**

c Name a polymer that requires chlorine for its manufacture.

.... **[1 mark]**

2 a Chlorine can be produced by passing an electrical current through sea water. Which of the following statements is **not** true.

   i Chlorine can be collected from the cathode.

   ii A direct current must be used.

   iii Hydrogen can be collected from the other electrode.

   iv Electrical energy is used to decompose the compound.

.... **[1 mark]**

b Explain what causes substances in the sea water to separate out when an electric current passes through it.

....

.... **[3 marks]**

3 Class 10A carried out an investigation into what happens when electricity passes through water. They recorded the results shown opposite.

a Calculate the average volume of gas collected at the anode and the average at the cathode.

....

.... **[2 marks]**

b What does the relationship between these two values tell you about the compound that is being decomposed?

....

.... **[1 mark]**

Group	Volume of gas at the anode (cm³)	Volume of gas at the cathode (cm³)
1	2.2	4.5
2	4.9	10.0
3	3.2	6.5
4	2.3	4.8
5	2.5	10.3
6	4.6	9.2
7	2.3	4.7
8	4.4	9.1
9	3.3	6.7

c Suggest the identity of the two gases and a test that you could carry out to confirm your suggestions.

....

....

....

.... **[4 marks]**

d Suggest a reason why different groups obtained very different volumes.

.... **[1 mark]**

e Identify the group that obtained an anomalous result and suggest a possible explanation for it.

.... **[1 mark]**

G–E

D–C

B–A*

1 a Which of the following describes a mineral?

i A rock that contains a metal.	**ii** A naturally occurring compound.
iii An unreactive metal.	**iv** A mixture of crystals.

G–E

.... [1 mark]

b Why can gold sometimes be found in the ground as an uncombined element?

.... [1 mark]

2 a What factors need to be considered when estimating the cost of producing metals from their ores?

....

.... [3 marks]

D–C

b What is meant by electrolysis and why is it useful in metal extraction?

....

.... [2 marks]

3 Daniel and Joyce carried out an experiment to simulate the extraction of copper from its ore. The instructions were as follows.

- Weigh out 2 g of charcoal and 2 g of copper oxide.
- Mix the two black powders together in a crucible and heat strongly above a roaring flame for 15 minutes.
- Allow the contents to cool and then pour out onto a heat-resistant mat.

a What is the purpose of adding charcoal to the mixture?

B–A*

.... [2 marks]

b What would Daniel and Joyce have seen at the end of the experiment?

.... [2 marks]

c Joyce suggested repeating the experiment with a different metal oxide. Suggest **one** metal oxide that might give a good result and **one** that would not work in this experiment.

.... [2 marks]

4 a Name the substance oxidised and the substance reduced in the following equation.

Al (s) + Fe$_2$O$_3$ (s) $\longrightarrow$ 2Fe (s) + Al$_2$O$_3$ (s)

.... [2 marks]

b This method could be used to extract iron from iron ore. Suggest why it is not the usual method.

D–C

.... [1 mark]

c Describe the method usually used. Include an equation in your answer.

....

....

.... [4 marks]

5 Steel dustbins are often coated with a layer of zinc to help prevent corrosion.

a Suggest how coating steel helps to prevent corrosion.

....

B–A*

.... [2 marks]

b Explain why zinc is chosen as the coating material.

....

.... [2 marks]

1 Link the metal with its properties and uses.

Gold		Low density		Electronic connectors
Aluminium		Malleable		Plumbing
Copper		Does not corrode		Aircraft

G–E

[3 marks]

2 a Iron is extracted from its ore by heating with carbon. This leaves a product with about 4% carbon atoms mixed in with the iron. What name is given to metals that contain a mixture of atoms?

.... [1 mark]

b The iron is treated to reduce the level of carbon to below 0.3%, which results in a softer metal that is easier to work with. Explain why having carbon atoms mixed in with the iron makes a harder metal. Include a diagram in your answer.

....

....

....

D–C

[3 marks]

c Suggest what metal might be added to make the iron suitable for use in cutlery, and say what property this would give the iron.

....

.... [2 marks]

3 White gold has become a popular choice for jewellery. Explain how gold can be white, and describe the advantages that white gold may have over pure gold.

....

....

....

B–A*

[3 marks]

4 A local business manufactures aluminium drinks cans. They are eager to win a Green Award for environmentally friendly practice. Suggest **three** ways in which they could make their business as environmentally friendly as possible, and explain how your suggestions will help the environment.

....

....

....

D–C

[3 marks]

5 The table below shows the UK percentages for recycling of metals, and the energy savings.

Metal	New metals made using recycled metals	Energy saving
Aluminium	39%	95%
Copper	32%	85%
Lead	74%	60%
Steel	42%	62–74%
Zinc	20%	60%

Explain briefly why these totals should be increased in the coming years. Include a justified opinion on which metal should be the first to target for improved recycling figures.

B–A*

....

....

....

....

....

[5 marks]

1 a Why is crude oil described as a *mixture of hydrocarbons*?

....

.... **[3 marks]**

b What property of the mixture allows it to be separated into fractions?

.... **[1 mark]**

2 Explain why crude oil is processed before use. Illustrate your answer with the names and uses of at least two substances that are made from crude oil.

....

.... **[3 marks]**

3 Use ideas of kinetic energy and intermolecular forces to explain how the molecules in crude oil can be separated into different fractions.

....

.... **[4 marks]**

4 a Which of the following does **not** describe the combustion of a hydrocarbon?

　i It is a reduction reaction.　　**ii** It releases energy as heat and light.

　iii It produces water.　　　　　**iv** It requires oxygen.

.... **[1 mark]**

b Explain why we cannot see the products of combustion of methane.

.... **[2 marks]**

5 Jonas carried out an investigation to find out what happens when a tea light candle burns in a closed system. He measured the height of the wax in the candle. Then he lit the candle on a heatproof mat, put a 250 cm^3 beaker over the top and sealed the edges with plasticine so that no gases could get in or out. After 9 minutes the candle went out. The candle wax was 3 mm lower than at the start.

a Where did the wax go to? .... **[1 mark]**

b Why did the candle go out? .... **[1 mark]**

c What was produced when the candle first began to burn? .... **[2 marks]**

d What different gas was made just before the candle went out? .... **[1 mark]**

e Suggest a test to detect **one** of the gases produced.

....

.... **[2 marks]**

6 a How is carbon monoxide produced and why is it dangerous?

....

.... **[2 marks]**

b Linda suspects that the gas water heater in the holiday flat she is thinking about renting is producing carbon monoxide. What might indicate that Linda is correct, why does this happen and what is it called?

....

.... **[3 marks]**

7 A recent report suggested that Earth may be suffering from global dimming. The underlying cause is thought to be tiny particles (particulates) in the atmosphere. Describe a possible source of these particulates and explain why they might be causing global dimming.

....

.... **[2 marks]**

1 a Which of the following correctly describes damage caused by acid rain?

  i It destroys the ozone layer.   **ii** It raises the pH of ponds.

  iii It causes breathing problems for asthmatics.   **iv** It reduces the yield of some crops.

.... **[1 mark]** G–E

b Explain why northern Norway has problems with acid rain, even though there is no industry in that area.

.... **[2 marks]**

2 a Explain why acid rain is linked with burning hydrocarbon fuels.

....

.... **[3 marks]**

b Give **two** reasons why acid rain might affect the growth of trees.

.... **[2 marks]**

3 The table opposite shows the pH values at which various animals are able to live.

  a Which species would be the first to be affected by acid rain?

.... **[1 mark]**

  b Suggest a reason why the population of perch decreases very fast in water at pH 5.

....

.... **[1 mark]**

	pH6.5	pH5.0	pH5.5	pH5.0	pH4.5	pH4.0
Trout						
Bass						
Perch						
Frogs						
Salamanders						
Clams						
Crayfish						
Snails						
Mayfly						

D–C

4 What advice about use of fuels would you give to an industrialist who wanted to set up a factory with low sulfur emissions?

....

....

.... **[3 marks]**

B–A*

5 Put the statements about the greenhouse effect into the correct order.

  i The warm Earth radiates infrared radiation.   **ii** Some heat radiates back to the surface.

  iii UV radiation passes though Earth's atmosphere and warms the surface of the planet.   **iv** Greenhouse gases absorb some of the radiation.

.... **[3 marks]** G–E

6 a Describe the general pattern of global temperature change over the past 50 years.

.... **[1 mark]**

b Why do most scientists believe that this temperature change is a result of human activity?

.... D–C

....

.... **[2 marks]**

7 Discuss how seeding the oceans with iron might help to solve the problem of global warming.

....

....

.... B–A*

....

.... **[4 marks]**

1 a Why are scientists trying to find alternatives to fossil fuels?

....

.... [3 marks]

b Suggest the name of a biofuel that can be made from sugar beet.

.... [1 mark]

c Why do some people think that using biofuels will put up the cost of food?

.... [1 mark]

2 A company has produced a new fuel from waste products. Suggest **three** factors that should be investigated to see if the fuel is suitable to develop into a petrol substitute.

....

.... [3 marks]

3 Use the information in the table below to compare the suitability of different crops as a raw material for biofuel production and to suggest how biofuel should be made.

Crop	Fuel made	Energy needed to grow and harvest crops and produce the fuel	% of farmland needed to make 50% of current fuel needs
Sugar cane	Ethanol	Medium	46–57
Wood residue	Ethanol or biodiesel	Low	150–250
Rapeseed	Biodiesel	Medium-low	30
Algae	Biodiesel	High	1–2

....

....

.... [4 marks]

4 Give **two** advantages of using hydrogen as a fuel in place of petrol.

....

.... [2 marks]

5 A class tested two fuels to see which one gave out the most energy. They put the fuel in a burner under a beaker holding 100 cm³ of water and measured the temperature of the water. Then they lit the burner and allowed it to burn for two minutes. They measured the highest temperature that the water reached. The results are shown below.

a Group C got a much higher final temperature for fuel 2 than the other groups. Suggest a possible reason for this result.

Group	Fuel 1 starting temperature (°C)	Fuel 1 finishing temperature (°C)	Fuel 2 starting temperature (°C)	Fuel 2 finishing temperature (°C)
A	20	39	21	35
B	21	41	21	34
C	20	38	*	45
D	20	39	21	34
E	20	38	22	34

*forgot to measure

....

.... [1 mark]

b Which fuel gave out the most energy? Explain your answer.

....

.... [2 marks]

c What improvement to the experiment would you suggest to get a more valid result?

.... [1 mark]

6 Explain some problems in achieving carbon-neutral, hydrogen-fuelled cars.

....

.... [3 marks]

1 a Which of the three structures shown is ethane?

.... **[1 mark]**

b Which of the three structures are found in natural gas?

.... **[1 mark]**

A   B   C

c Draw the structure of propane.

[1 mark]

d How can you tell that propane is a saturated molecule?

.... **[2 marks]**

2 a An oil refinery analysed a sample of natural gas. Complete the table of results opposite. **[5 marks]**

b Describe the difference between a molecule of methane and a molecule of propane.

....

....

.... **[2 marks]**

Substance	Mass (g)	% of total
Natural gas	80	100
Methane		80
Ethane	8	
Propane		3
Butane		

c A liquid mix of propane and butane can be used as a fuel for vehicles. It is called LPG and is stored under pressure. Why is LPG stored under pressure?

....

.... **[2 marks]**

3 Give the structural formula of butane and describe the way that the atoms in a molecule of butane are bonded together.

....

.... **[3 marks]**

4 Complete the table opposite.

Propene	True	False
Has four carbon atoms		
Is an unsaturated molecule		
Contains a double bond		
Does not react with bromine water		

[4 marks]

5 Some green activists have suggested that burning crude oil fractions as fuel is madness. Say whether you agree and suggest other uses for crude oil.

....

....

.... **[3 marks]**

6 a Select an unsaturated hydrocarbon with four carbon atoms from the following:

  i Propane   **ii** $C_4H_8Cl_2$

  iii Butene   **iv** C_4H_{10}

.... **[1 mark]**

b Write the name and formula of the unsaturated hydrocarbon with two carbon atoms.

.... **[2 marks]**

1 a The diagram shows the laboratory apparatus to crack hydrocarbons. Label the hydrocarbon and the catalyst. **[2 marks]**

product gas

b What would you have to do to make the cracking reaction happen in this apparatus?

....

.... **[2 marks]**

c What two types of hydrocarbons would be in the product gases?

.... **[2 marks]**

2 a Give a reason to use catalysts in industry.

.... **[2 marks]**

b One process in converting crude oil into petrol uses platinum as a catalyst. Platinum is one of the most expensive metals. How can the industry afford to use such an expensive metal?

.... **[2 marks]**

3 Use the data in the charts to explain why oil companies carry out cracking.

....

....

....

....

....

.... **[4 marks]**

Proportion of each fraction from a sample of crude oil.

bitumen, LPG, fuel oil, petrol, diesel, kerosene

Percentage demand for crude oil fractions.

bitumen, fuel oil, LPG, diesel, kerosene, petrol

4 Use the information in the table to choose a suitable polymer for the following uses:

Polymer name	Polymer properties
Poly(ethene)	Waterproof, easily moulded
Poly(propene)	Can be spun into fibres, strong
Poly(tetrafluoroethene)	Water repellent, shiny
Poly(chloroethene)	Flexible, good insulator

a Rope .... **[1 mark]**

b Plastic bowls .... **[1 mark]**

c Waterproof fabrics .... **[1 mark]**

d Coverings for electrical wires .... **[1 mark]**

5 Put the statements in order so that they describe addition polymerisation.

 i A very long chain of carbon atoms forms, called a polymer.

 ii One bond of the double bond breaks.

 iii The monomers have a double carbon-carbon bond.

 iv A new bond forms between one monomer and the next.

.... **[2 marks]**

6 Most people think that recycling polymers is a good idea. Give **two** reasons to support this view.

....

.... **[2 marks]**

7 Humans only discovered how to manufacture polymers in the 20th century but plants have been making them for millions of years.

a Give the names of two plant polymers.

.... **[2 marks]**

b Explain why plant polymers do not cause the same disposal problems as man-made polymers.

.... **[1 mark]**

c What other advantage would there be to developing polymers from plant materials?

.... **[1 mark]**

G–E

D–C

B–A*

G–E

D–C

G–E

B–A*

Power stations that burn fossil fuels releases gases into the atmosphere. Some of these gases may have damaging effects. Explain how these gases form and why they are damaging to the environment. Suggest ways that this damage could be reduced.

The quality of written communication will be assessed in your answer to this question.

[6 marks]

1 a Which of the following statements correctly describes the nucleus of a helium atom?

    i It contains only positively charged particles.   **ii** It has no overall charge.

    iii It is where the neutrons are found.   **iv** It is the control centre of the atom.

.... **[1 mark]**

b Hydrogen and helium are both elements. Explain **one** way in which an atom of hydrogen and an atom of helium are the same and **one** way in which they are different.

....

.... **[2 marks]**

c In 1808, the chemist John Dalton first suggested that elements were made from atoms. He thought that atoms were like tiny snooker balls.

Describe **two** ways in which modern ideas about atoms differ from Dalton's view.

....

.... **[2 marks]**

2 a Describe the difference between protons and neutrons.

....

.... **[2 marks]**

b What is the relative mass of an atom of lithium that contains three protons, three electrons and four neutrons?

.... **[1 mark]**

3 a Write the symbol of the element that is in group 2 and period 3 of the periodic table.

.... **[1 mark]**

b Use the periodic table to decide the following:

    i The number of protons in an atom of fluorine .... **[1 mark]**

    ii The number of neutrons in an atom of sodium .... **[1 mark]**

    iii The number of electrons in an atom of beryllium .... **[1 mark]**

4 There are two types of chlorine atom. One has a relative mass of 35 and the other a relative mass of 37. Although these atoms are different, they are still atoms of the same element.

a Explain why the two atoms have a different relative mass.

.... **[1 mark]**

b Explain why they are still considered to be the same element.

....

.... **[2 marks]**

5 Explain why the relative atomic mass of magnesium is not a whole number.

....

....

....

.... **[4 marks]**

G–E

D–C

G–E

D–C

B–A*

1 a Complete the table opposite.

Element symbol	Electronic configuration
F	2.7
Al	
	2.8.6

[2 marks]

b The diagram opposite shows an atom.

   i What is the name of the particle labelled a?

.... [1 mark]

   ii How many protons would you find in b?

.... [1 mark]

   iii What do the circles labelled c represent?

.... [1 mark]

---

2 a Write the name and electron configuration of the element that is in group 2 and period 3 of the periodic table.

.... [2 marks]

b In which group of the periodic table would you find the element that has 17 protons in the nucleus? Explain how you can tell.

....

....

....

.... [4 marks]

c Complete the table below.

Element	Atomic number	Electronic configuration
Ne	10	
Ar	18	

[2 marks]

d Use the electronic configuration of Ne and Ar to explain why they have similar properties.

....

.... [3 marks]

e What is the name of the element with electronic structure 2.8.2?

.... [1 mark]

f In which period would you find the element with electronic structure 2.8.8.1?

.... [1 mark]

---

3 a Discuss how Mendeleev was able to create a periodic table similar to the modern one, even though nothing was known about the structure of the atom at the time.

....

....

....

.... [4 marks]

b Explain why Mendeleev's periodic table was eventually accepted by scientists of the day, when other proposed arrangements of elements had been rejected.

....

....

....

.... [4 marks]

G–E

1 Draw lines to match the descriptions with the statements below.

Electrostatic attraction	Atom that has gained electrons
Negative ion	Atom that has lost an electron
Positive ion	Force that holds ions together
Ionic compound	Made from positive and negative ions

[4 marks]

D–C

2 a Use the diagram opposite to explain how magnesium reacts with oxygen to form a positive and a negative ion.

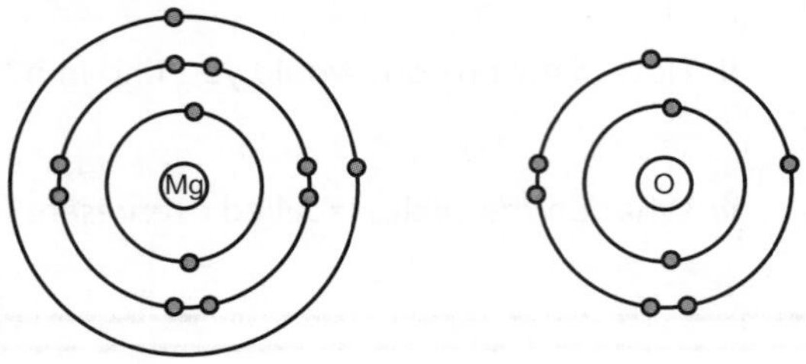

....

....

....

.... **[5 marks]**

b Complete the table to show the formula of the ion formed by each element.

Atom	Ion
F	
Na	
S	
Ca	

[4 marks]

c Explain why potassium forms an ion with a 1+ charge but chlorine forms an ion with a 1– charge.

....

.... **[2 marks]**

B–A*

3 a Calcium carbonate is an ionic compound with the formula $CaCO_3$. Give the formula of the ions that it is made from.

Cation .... **[1 mark]**

Anion .... **[1 mark]**

b Draw a diagram that shows the arrangement of electrons in a fluoride ion. Include the charge on the ion.

[2 marks]

c Suggest why a sodium ion is more stable than a sodium atom.

....

.... **[2 marks]**

D–C

4 a Complete the table below.

Name	Ions	Elements
Sodium chloride	Sodium and chloride	Sodium and chlorine
Potassium fluoride		Potassium and fluorine
		Calcium and oxygen
	Magnesium and nitrate	

[5 marks]

b Name the compounds with the following formulae: $Ca(OH)_2$, NH_4Cl, $MgBr_2$, Na_2CO_3

....

.... **[4 marks]**

B–A*

c Explain the difference between potassium sulfide and potassium sulfate.

....

.... **[2 marks]**

1 a Complete the table below.

Name of ion	Charge	Formula	Name of ion	Charge	Formula
Sulfide	2–	S^{2-}			OH^-
Fluoride					NO_3^-
Hydrogen					Sn^{2+}
Ammonium			Copper	2+	
Potassium			Silver	1+	
Sulfate			Iron	3+	
Carbonate			Iron	2+	

[14 marks]

b Underline **three** errors in the sentence below.

Barium sulfate is an ionic compound that contains barium and sulfur ions. The barium ion is a polyatomic cation and the sulfate ion is a polyatomic cation.

[3 marks]

2 a James and Alex cannot agree on the formula for calcium chloride. James thinks it is $CaCl_2$, but Alex thinks it is CaCl. State who is correct and explain why.

....

.... [4 marks]

b Complete the table below to show the formula of each compound named.

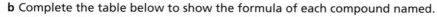

Name	Formula
Potassium fluoride	
Calcium nitrate	
Aluminium oxide	
Ammonium sulfate	

[4 marks]

3 The word equation and formula equation for the reaction between ammonia and sulfuric acid are given below.

Ammonia + sulfuric acid ⟶ ammonium sulfate

$$2NH_3 + H_2SO_4 \longrightarrow (NH_4)_2SO_4$$

a What does the large number in front of the formula for ammonia mean?

.... [1 mark]

b What does the small number after the H in the formula for sulfuric acid mean?

.... [1 mark]

c Explain why there are brackets around the (NH_3) in the formula for ammonium sulfate.

.... [1 mark]

4 a Write word equations for the following formula equations.

i $NaCl + AgNO_3 \longrightarrow AgCl + NaNO_3$

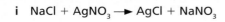

.... [2 marks]

ii $KOH + HCl \longrightarrow KCl + H_2O$

.... [2 marks]

b Write balanced formula equations for the following word equations.

i Sodium sulfate + barium chloride ⟶ barium sulfate + sodium chloride

.... [4 marks]

ii Magnesium nitrate + sodium hydroxide ⟶ magnesium hydroxide + sodium nitrate

.... [4 marks]

1 a Which one of the following best describes an ionic compound?

    i Soft, high melting point.   **ii** Soft, low melting point.

    iii Forms crystals, high melting point.   **iv** Forms crystals, low melting point.

[1 mark]

b Draw a diagram of a sodium chloride crystal and label the two ions.

[2 marks]

2 Keshma wrote the following notes in her science notebook:

We took a sample of the substance in a test tube and heated it. It melted easily in the Bunsen flame. Then we put two electrodes into the liquid. It did not conduct electricity.

Was Keshma testing an ionic compound? Explain your answer.

[2 marks]

3 a Bauxite is a mineral that contains mostly aluminium oxide, an ionic compound. Aluminium can be extracted from it by electrolysis. Extraction is very expensive because large amounts of energy are needed to melt the compound.

Use ideas about the structure of aluminium oxide to explain why large amounts of energy are needed to melt aluminium oxide and why it must be melted before electrolysis.

[3 marks]

b From the list below, choose the compound with the strongest ionic bonding. Explain your choice.

    magnesium chloride   **sodium fluoride**   **calcium oxide**   **potassium sulfide**

[3 marks]

4 Complete the table below.

Name	Soluble? ✓ or ✗
Sodium chloride	
Magnesium nitrate	
Calcium carbonate	
Ammonium carbonate	
Silver chloride	

[5 marks]

5 Which of the following equations describes a precipitation reaction?

    i $CaCO_3$ (s) $\longrightarrow$ CaO (s) + CO_2 (g)

    ii HCl (aq) + NaOH (aq) $\longrightarrow$ NaCl (aq) + H_2O (l)

    iii $AgNO_3$ (aq) + NaCl (aq) $\longrightarrow$ AgCl (s) + $NaNO_3$ (aq)

    iv CH_4 (g) + $2O_2$ (g) $\longrightarrow$ CO_2 (g) + H_2O (l)

[1 mark]

6 Which of the following reactants would you expect to result in a precipitation reaction?

    i Potassium nitrate and sodium chloride   **ii** Silver nitrate and sodium chloride

    iii Potassium sulfate and ammonium carbonate   **iv** Ammonium chloride and sodium carbonate

[1 mark]

1 a Liz wrote this description of how to make an insoluble salt. It has **two** mistakes.

Choose two insoluble compounds. Then dissolve them and mix them together. The insoluble salt that you want will be dissolved in the solution.

Write the description again, but correct Liz's errors.

....

.... [2 marks]

b Name the type of reaction used to make an insoluble salt.

.... [1 mark]

G–E

2 The diagram opposite shows one stage in the preparation of an insoluble salt. Label the diagram.

D–C

[3 marks]

3 Mrs Brown is worried because she has been sent to the hospital to have a barium meal. Explain to her how this will help doctors to spot any abnormalities in her bowels and reassure her about possible toxic effects.

....

....

.... [3 marks]

B–A*

4 Draw lines to match the metal ions to the correct flame colour.

Calcium		Lilac
Sodium		Brick red
Potassium		Green/blue
Copper		Yellow/orange

G–E

[4 marks]

5 a Leroy wants to test a sample of tap water for sodium chloride. Describe the tests that he could carry out and state what the results would be if sodium chloride is present.

....

....

.... [5 marks]

b Sarah added some hydrochloric acid to a sample of white powder. The powder started to fizz and bubble. What do these results tell you about the white powder? What further tests could Sarah do to confirm the result?

....

....

.... [3 marks]

D–C

6 The element helium was first discovered using spectroscopy on the Sun during an eclipse. Explain how it was possible to tell that the Sun contained an unknown element.

....

....

.... [3 marks]

B–A*

1 a Which of the following does **not** have covalent bonds?

    i carbon dioxide   **ii** oxygen   **iii** methane   **iv** iron oxide

.... [1 mark]

b Water is a covalent molecule.

    i Write the formula of water. .... [1 mark]

    ii How many covalent bonds does water have?.. [1 mark]

---

2 a A water molecule contains three atoms. Describe what holds the atoms together in water.

.... [2 marks]

b Why do the atoms in water form covalent bonds?

.... [1 mark]

---

3 Hydrogen always forms H_2 molecules.

    a Explain why hydrogen forms molecules rather than remaining as atoms.

.... [1 mark]

    b Explain why hydrogen forms H_2 molecules and not H_3 or H_4.

....

.... [3 marks]

---

4 Draw a dot and cross diagram
of a hydrogen molecule.

[2 marks]

---

5 a Look at the dot and cross diagram
opposite. Circle two errors.

[2 marks]

    b Draw a dot and cross diagram for a
molecule of methane (CH_4).

[2 marks]

    c i How many electrons surround the carbon atom in methane? .... [1 mark]

    ii How many electrons surround each hydrogen atom in methane? .... [1 mark]

    iii Explain why the two atoms have different numbers of electrons surrounding them.

....

.... [2 marks]

---

6 a Explain what is meant by a double bond. Use a diagram of oxygen to illustrate your answer.

....

....

.... [4 marks]

    b Ethene (C_2H_4) is a molecule with a double bond
between carbon atoms. Draw a dot and cross
diagram of ethene.

[2 marks]

Properties of elements and compounds

1 a Which of the following properties **do not** help us to classify sodium chloride as an ionic substance?

   i It dissolves in water   **ii** It is white

   iii It has a high melting point   **iv** It conducts electricity when molten

.... **[1 mark]**

  b Draw a diagram to show how to test whether a solution conducts electricity.

[4 marks] G–E

  c Which of the substances opposite has the highest melting point?

.... **[1 mark]**

  d Name **one** simple molecular substance and **one** giant molecular substance.

Name	State at room temperature
Methane	Gas
Hexane	Liquid
Sucrose	Solid

.... **[2 marks]**

---

2 a James investigated the properties of three different solids. His results are shown in the table below. Use the results to name the structure and bonding in each of the substances.

Solid	Melted in the Bunsen flame?	Dissolved easily?	Conducted electricity when dissolved?	Structure and bonding
1	Yes	No	No	
2	No	Yes	Yes	
3	No	No	No	

[3 marks]

  b Suzanne and Laurence are investigating the properties of sucrose. They discover that it dissolves easily in water. Suzanne says that this proves it is ionic. What further tests could they do to get more evidence? What results would you expect if Suzanne is right?

....

....

.... **[4 marks]**

D–C

  c Explain why sodium chloride conducts electricity when it is dissolved but carbon dioxide does not.

....

....

.... **[3 marks]**

---

3 a Use ideas about structure and bonding to explain why graphite can be used as a lubricant.

....

....

.... **[3 marks]**

  b Carbon dioxide and silicon(IV)oxide are both covalent substances. Carbon dioxide is a gas and silicon dioxide is a solid. What do the different physical states of these compounds tell us about their structures?

....

....

....

.... **[5 marks]**

B–A*

Separating solutions

1 Perfume manufacturers need to extract the essential oils from lavender flowers. The first step in the extraction gives a layer of lavender oil floating on water. Describe how the lavender oil could be separated from water.

....

....

[3 marks]

2 Put the following statements describing fractional distillation into the correct order.

i   The vapour condenses and is collected as a liquid.

ii The lowest boiling point fraction vaporises.

iii The flask is heated and the temperature rises.

iv The vapour is cooled to below its boiling point in the condenser.

v   The temperature of the flask rises again until the boiling point of the next fraction is reached.

....

[3 marks]

3 Use the data in the table below to explain how a sample of oxygen could be prepared from air.

	Oxygen	Nitrogen	Argon	Carbon dioxide
Melting point (°C)	–219	–210	–189	Sublimes at –78
Boiling point (°C)	–183	–196	–186	

....

....

....

[5 marks]

4 Draw a diagram of a paper chromatogram of some food colouring that contains two different colours.

[2 marks]

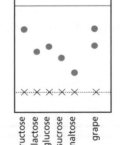

5 Food scientists can identify the sugars present in foods using paper chromatography. Opposite is a diagram of a paper chromatogram of the sugars in grapes. Which sugars are present?

....

....

[2 marks]

6 A groups of students was investigating how quickly the sweetener aspartame breaks down. They boiled aspartame in hydrochloric acid and removed a small sample every five minutes. A chromatogram was made from each sample. The results are shown in the table below.

Time of sample (mins)	0	5	10	15	20	25
Substance A R_f value 0.85	no	small	medium	large	large	large
Substance B R_f value 0.50	no	small	medium	large	large	large
Substance C R_f value 0.15	large	large	medium	small	no	no

a Which substance travelled the furthest up the chromatography paper?

.... [1 mark]

b Which substance is aspartame? .... [1 mark]

c Research suggests that one of the spots is phenylalanine. How could the students confirm which of the substances is phenylalanine?

....

....

[3 marks]

1 a Which of the following structures would you expect to have the highest melting point?

   i Simple molecular covalent or metallic?

.... [1 mark]

   ii Ionic lattice or simple molecular covalent?

.... [1 mark]

b Maltose melts at 160 °C and does not conduct electricity under any circumstances. What is the most likely structure for maltose?

.... [1 mark]

2 a Describe the structure of sodium chloride.

....

.... [2 marks]

b Explain why sodium chloride has a high melting point.

.... [2 marks]

3 Complete the table below.

	Melting point	Solubility	Electrical conductivity	Structure
Silicon carbide	2 730 °C		Non-conductor	
Boron trifluoride	−127 °C	Very soluble	Non-conductor	
Copper(II)oxide	1 201 °C	Insoluble		Ionic
Cerrosafe	74 °C		Conducts as solid	

[6 marks]

4 a What name is given to the elements in group 1 of the periodic table

.... [1 mark]

b Which group in the periodic table is known as the noble gases?

.... [1 mark]

c Which of the statements below does not describe a transition metal?

   i It has a low melting point.

   ii It forms coloured compounds.

   iii It lies between group 2 and group 3 of the periodic table.

   iv It conducts electricity.

.... [1 mark]

5 a Draw a diagram which shows how metal atoms are arranged in a transition metal.

[3 marks]

b Use your diagram to explain why metals are malleable and can conduct electricity.

....

....

.... [4 marks]

6 Copper is a transition metal. Explain why the chemical structure of copper makes it particularly good for use in household wiring.

....

....

.... [4 marks]

G–E

D–C

B–A*

G–E

D–C

B–A*

1 a Which line correctly describes sodium?

A	Less reactive than potassium	Reacts with water to produce oxygen
B	More reactive than potassium	Reacts with water to produce hydrogen
C	Less reactive than lithium	Reacts with water to produce oxygen
D	More reactive than lithium	Reacts with water to produce hydrogen

[1 mark]

b Describe **two** properties of alkali metals that are different from properties of typical metals.

[2 marks]

2 a Kumar watched a demonstration of the reaction of lithium with water. His teacher told him that hydrogen and lithium hydroxide were produced.

  i What would Kumar have seen that suggests that hydrogen was produced?

[1 mark]

  ii What test could he do to confirm it was hydrogen?

[2 marks]

  iii What test could he do to support the claim that lithium hydroxide was produced?

[2 marks]

  iv Write a formula equation for this reaction. Include state symbols.

[5 marks]

b Draw a diagram of a lithium atom and use it to explain why alkali metals always form 1+ ions.

[4 marks]

3 a Describe the trend in reactivity seen in alkali metals.

[1 mark]

b Explain the difference in the reactivity of lithium and potassium.

[4 marks]

c Predict the reaction of rubidium with water. Include an equation in your answer.

[3 marks]

4 In 1817, Johann Döbereiner put forward a 'law of triads'. He had observed that lithium, sodium and potassium had similar properties. He noted that the trend in reactivity in these elements matched the trend in their atomic mass. This early observation was an important contribution to the organisation of the periodic table.

a Describe how the trend in atomic mass of lithium, sodium and potassium matches other trends in these elements.

[2 marks]

b Suggest **two** ways in which Döbereiner might have shared his ideas with other scientists.

[2 marks]

G–E

D–C

B–A*

1 Draw lines to link the halogen with the correct properties.

Fluorine	grey	solid
Chlorine	brown	liquid
Bromine	yellow	gas
Iodine	green	gas

[6 marks]

2 a Which of the following is the correct balanced equation for the formation of hydrogen bromide?

  i H (g) + Br (g) $\longrightarrow$ HBr (g)   **ii** 2H (g) + 2Br (l) $\longrightarrow$ 2HBr (g)

  iii H_2 (g) + Br_2 (l) $\longrightarrow$ 2HBr (g)   **iv** H (g) + Br_2 (g) $\longrightarrow$ 2HBr (s)

[1 mark]

  b Suggest the pH of a solution made by dissolving hydrogen bromide in water.

[1 mark]

3 Pravin carried out an experiment. She mixed chlorine water and then iodine water with potassium bromide solution.

  a Describe the outcome of the experiments. Include any relevant equations.

[3 marks]

  b Explain how the results of this experiment show the relative reactivity of the halogens.

[3 marks]

4 List the following noble gases in order of increasing atomic mass:

Ar   He   Ne   Xe

[2 marks]

5 a Write the electronic structure of neon and argon.

[2 marks]

  b Use the electronic structure you have written above to explain why neon and argon are very chemically inert.

[3 marks]

6 a Use the data in the table below to predict the density of argon.

Element	Density g/dm³	Boiling point °C
Helium	0.1786	−268.93
Neon	0.9002	−246.08
Argon		
Xenon	5.894	−108.12

[1 mark]

  b Use the periodic table and the data in the table above to explain how you could predict the maximum temperature at which radon exists as a liquid.

[4 marks]

1 a Which of the statements below correctly describes an endothermic reaction?

    i The temperature at the end of the reaction is higher than at the start.

    ii The reaction only involves breaking bonds.

    iii Chemical energy is transferred to heat energy.

    iv The reaction takes in energy overall.

    .... **[1 mark]**

b For each of the reactions below, state whether it is endothermic or exothermic.

    i Photosynthesis .... **[1 mark]**

    ii Burning wood .... **[1 mark]**

    iii Dissolving ammonium chloride .... **[1 mark]**

    iv Lighting a firework .... **[1 mark]**

2 Alice and Sanjay want to find out whether the reaction between sodium hydroxide and hydrochloric acid is exothermic or endothermic.

    a Draw a diagram of the apparatus they could use.

        [2 marks]

    b What measurements would they need to take?

    .... **[1 mark]**

    c What results would they see if the reaction was exothermic?

    .... **[1 mark]**

3 Eli's teacher has posters on the wall of the classroom. One says 'Breaking bonds requires energy, making bonds releases energy.' Use this information to explain why some reactions are exothermic.

    ....

    ....

    ....

    .... **[4 marks]**

4 The results of an experiment are shown below. 25 cm³ of silver nitrate solution was mixed with 25 cm³ of sodium chloride solution.

	Silver nitrate	Sodium chloride
Temperature at start of reaction (°C)	22	24
Temperature at end of the experiment (°C)	43	

    a Is the reaction endothermic or exothermic? .... **[1 mark]**

    b Calculate the energy change in the reaction. Show your working.

    .... **[4 marks]**

    c Write a word equation for the reaction.

    .... **[2 marks]**

    d Draw a labelled energy level diagram for this reaction.

        [3 marks]

5 Use ideas about bond breaking and bond making to explain why burning methane is exothermic.

    ....

    ....

    .... **[4 marks]**

1 Sam is cooking carrots. He wants them to cook quickly. Which of the following methods could Sam use to speed up the cooking?

  i Reduce the temperature of the water.   **ii** Cut the carrots into small pieces.

  iii Use large pieces of carrot.   **iv** Use a large volume of water.

.... [1 mark]

2 Ella added acid to chalk and the chalk slowly disappeared. When she added water and acid to chalk it took longer to disappear. Why did this happen?

.... [2 marks]

(G–E)

3 Magnesium reacts with hydrochloric acid to form hydrogen. Design an experiment that would show the rate of reaction for two different concentrations of acid.

  a Draw a diagram of the apparatus you will use.

[3 marks]

  b Say what you will measure.

(D–C)

.... [2 marks]

  c Say how you will present the results.

.... [1 mark]

  d Say what the results will look like.

....

....

.... [2 marks]

4 Hydrogen and iodine react together to make hydrogen iodide. Explain why the number of reactions that take place at 25 °C is only a small percentage of the total number of collisions.

(B–A*)

....

.... [2 marks]

5 a Modern cars are fitted with catalytic converters. Describe what a catalyst does.

....

.... [2 marks]

(G–E)

  b Why are modern cars fitted with catalytic converters?

....

.... [2 marks]

  c Catalytic converters reduce the level of unburned hydrocarbons that are emitted from cars. Write a word equation for the reaction they catalyse.

(D–C)

.... [1 mark]

6 a Explain how the honeycomb design of car catalytic converters enables them to give the best performance.

....

.... [2 marks] *(B–A*)*

  b Write a balanced equation to show how catalytic converters reduce the quantity of carbon monoxide emitted from cars.

.... [2 marks]

1 Calculate the relative formula mass of the following compounds. Use a separate piece of paper for your working if necessary.

a HCl .... [1 mark]

b Br_2 .... [1 mark]

c $NaNO_3$ .... [1 mark]

d $Ca(OH)_2$ .... [1 mark]

2 Calculate the percentage by mass of the following. Use a separate piece of paper for your working if necessary.

a Carbon in CO_2 .... [2 marks]

b Oxygen in $KBrO_3$ .... [2 marks]

c Nitrogen in $Mg(NO_3)_2$ .... [2 marks]

3 A group of students carried out an experiment to calculate the formula for copper oxide. They heated some copper powder in an open crucible to turn it into copper oxide. The results are recorded in the table below.

Mass of empty crucible (g)	10.10 g
Mass of crucible + copper before heating (g)	15.05
Mass of copper (g)	
Mass of copper + crucible after heating (g)	16.30
Mass of copper oxide (g)	

a Complete the table of results. [2 marks]

b Calculate the mass of oxygen that was added to the copper during heating.

.... [1 mark]

c Calculate the empirical formula of the copper oxide.

.... [3 marks]

4 The theoretical yield for a reaction is 65 g. The actual yield was 43 g. Calculate the percentage yield for the reaction.

.... [2 marks]

5 George is making oxygen from hydrogen peroxide. The theoretical yield from 10 cm³ of his hydrogen peroxide solution is 100 cm³ of oxygen. The percentage yield for the reaction is 50%. What volume of hydrogen peroxide solution must George use to make 100 cm³ of oxygen?

.... [2 marks]

6 What mass of copper sulfate can be made from 5 g of copper oxide in the following reaction?
$CuO(s) + H_2SO_4 (aq) \longrightarrow CuSO_4 (aq) + H_2O (l)$

.... [3 marks]

7 Nylon can be made in two different ways. Method 1 is slow and produces water as a waste product. Method 2 is fast and produces hydrochloric acid as a waste product.

Suggest **one** reason why manufacturers might choose method 1 and **one** why they might chose method 2.

....

.... [2 marks]

Zain is given three white powders. All have different structures. One is sucrose (sugar), one is barium chloride (toxic) and one is powdered sand.

Plan an experiment that Zain could carry out to decide which is which. You should describe any apparatus that is needed and explain why the substances will give different results.

✏ *The quality of written communication will be assessed in your answer to this question.*

[6 marks]

1 a Katy adds sodium hydroxide solution to some water containing iron 3 + ions (Fe^{3+}). What will she see? Circle the correct answer. **[1 mark]**

    i A white precipitate.

    ii Red litmus paper turning blue.

    iii Blue litmus paper turning red.

    iv A brown precipitate.

b Victor and Fatima want to measure the concentration of copper ions (Cu^{2+}) in a sample. Victor says they should use a quantitative test but Fatima thinks a qualitative test would be better. Say who is right and explain why.

....

.... **[3 marks]**

c The government analyst tests a sample of water from a pond by adding sodium hydroxide solution. A white precipitate forms. She knows this means that two ions could be present.

    i Which two ions might be in the pond water?

    .... **[2 marks]**

    ii What test should she do next to see which one of the two ions is actually present?

    .... **[2 marks]**

2 a Describe a chemical test that could be used to confirm that a solution contained ammonium ions.

....

.... **[4 marks]**

b When Jon added silver nitrate and nitric acid to a solution containing ammonium ions, a pale yellow precipitate formed. Which *other* ion was in the solution?

.... **[1 mark]**

c What was the name of the compound dissolved in the solution?

.... **[1 mark]**

3 Students tested an unknown solution by adding sodium hydroxide solution. A white precipitate formed.

a Explain why this information is not enough to allow the students to identify the compound in the solution.

....

....

.... **[2 marks]**

b Suggest further tests that might help to identify the compound.

....

.... **[2 marks]**

4 Write an ionic equation for the reaction between potassium iodide and silver nitrate. Include state symbols.

$$KI + AgNO_3 \longrightarrow AgI + KNO_3$$

.... **[3 marks]**

1 a Why do chemists do tests for ions in drinking water?

....

.... **[2 marks]**

b Hospital biochemists test blood to see if it contains the correct amount of calcium. Name a chemical test that can detect calcium, and say what you would see if the blood does contain calcium.

....

.... **[2 marks]**

2 An industrial chemist thinks that the local river water might contain copper carbonate. The results of tests on the water are shown below:

Chemical test	Result
Add sodium hydroxide	Blue precipitate
Add sodium hydroxide, warm and test the gases with red litmus paper	No change
Add silver nitrate and nitric acid	White precipitate
Add weak acid	No change
Put a sample into a flame	Green flame

a Does the water contain copper carbonate? Explain your answer.

....

....

.... **[3 marks]**

b What **type** of test would need to be done to decide the concentration of copper ions in the water?

.... **[1 mark]**

3 Fill in the gaps on the flowchart below.

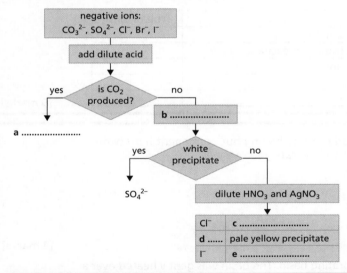

[5 marks]

4 Hospital biochemists use atomic absorption spectroscopy to measure the amount of potassium ions in human blood samples. List two advantages of this method over a simple flame test.

....

....

.... **[3 marks]**

1 a Which of these ions are present in hard water? Circle the correct answers.   [2 marks]
magnesium   sodium   chloride   calcium   sulfide   potassium

b What is the difference between when soap is used with hard water and with soft water?

....   [1 mark]

2 Jamie and Ola did an experiment to investigate the effect of calcium ions on making lather. They used the following instructions:

i Set up four test tubes containing the solutions shown in the table

Tube	Distilled water (cm³)	Soap solution (cm³)	Calcium chloride solution (cm³)
1	5.0	1	0
2	4.5	1	0.5
3	4.0	1	1.0
4	3.5	1	1.5

ii Put a bung on the tube and shake.

iii Measure the height of the lather produced.

a Name the dependent variable and one control variable in this experiment.

....

....   [2 marks]

b Predict the results of this experiment.

....   [1 mark]

3 Explain how ion exchange resin is able to turn hard water into soft water.

....

....   [2 marks]

4 Mark the following statements true or false.

	True or false
Temporary hard water can be made soft by boiling	
Permanent hard water cannot be made soft using ion exchange resin	
Temporary hard water contains calcium carbonate	
Filtered water is always soft	
Limescale is calcium or magnesium carbonate	

[5 marks]

5 Explain why temporary hard water can be made soft by boiling but permanent hard water cannot. Use chemical formulae and equations to illustrate your answer.

....

....

....

....   [4 marks]

6 A student put a sample of water into an evaporating basin. The basin was gently heated over a Bunsen burner until all the water was evaporated. The results of the experiment are shown below

	Mass (g)
Mass of the evaporating basin	63.2
Mass of the evaporating basin + water	83.2
Mass of the basin after the water had evaporated	63.3

a What mass of water was used?

....   [1 mark]

b What mass of dissolved ions was present in the water?

....   [1 mark]

1 a Circle the correct answer: [1 mark]

If a bottle is labelled 0.5 g/dm³ NaOH then it means:

   i The bottle contains 0.5 g of NaOH.   **iii** It contains 1 dm³ of solution.

   ii Only half of the bottle is NaOH.   **iv** The concentration of the solution is 0.5 g/dm³.

b Jack dissolved 2 g of KCl in 0.5 dm³ of water. What is the concentration of the solution he made?

.... [2 marks]   **G–E**

c Sandi and Kemi have to make a solution of NaCl with a concentration of 2 g/dm³. Sandi says they should add 0.2 g of NaCl to 100 cm³ water. Kemi thinks they need to add 2 g to 100 cm³. Who is correct and why?

....

.... [2 marks]

2 a Shomit needs a solution of $CuSO_4$ with a concentration of 2.5 g/dm³. He has 500 cm³ of water. What mass of $CuSO_4$ should he add? Show your working.

....

.... [2 marks]

b Next he dissolves 0.5 g of $CaCl_2$ in 100 cm³ of water. What is the concentration of the solution?

.... [2 marks]

3 Tracy and Joe obtained the following results from an experiment to discover the mass of solute in 25 cm³ of solution:

	Mass (g)
Mass of the evaporating basin	60.5
Mass of the evaporating basin + solution	85.5
Mass of the basin after the water had evaporated	61.5

a Calculate the mass of the solution.

.... [2 marks]   **D–C**

b Calculate the mass of solute in the solution.

.... [1 mark]

c Calculate the original concentration of the solution in g/dm³.

.... [1 mark]

4 a 25 cm³ of a solution contains 0.3 g of NaCl. What is the concentration of the solution in g/dm³?

.... [1 mark]

b The student evaporated the water from 40 cm³ of the solution. What mass of solute would remain?

.... [1 mark]

5 When Jon was describing his experiment, he wrote, 'We used the same amount of carbon as iron.' His teacher underlined 'amount' and wrote 'unclear'. What is wrong with Jon's description? What would have been a better way to describe the experiment? Use the words *mass*, *particles* and *mole* in your answer.   **B–A***

....

....

....

.... [4 marks]

1 Limestone is mostly calcium carbonate. Limestone is converted into quicklime by a thermal decomposition reaction.

$$CaCO_3 \longrightarrow CaO + CO_2$$

a Calculate the M_r of calcium carbonate.

.... [1 mark]

b If two moles of calcium carbonate are used in the decomposition reaction, what mass will be used?

.... [1 mark]

c If two moles of calcium carbonate are used in the decomposition, how many moles of calcium oxide will be produced?

.... [1 mark]

d What will be the mass of the calcium oxide produced?

.... [3 marks]

2 Chrome yellow is a pigment that is used to paint yellow lines on the road. It can be produced by reacting sodium chromate with lead nitrate.

$$Na_2CrO_4(aq) + Pb(NO_3)_2(aq) \longrightarrow PbCrO_4(s) + 2NaNO_3(aq)$$

a What name is given to this type of reaction?

.... [1 mark]

b A chemist uses 1 kg of Na_2CrO_4 in this reaction. How many moles were used?

....

.... [3 marks]

c How many moles of $PbCrO_4$ would be produced?

.... [1 mark]

d What mass of $PbCrO_4$ would be produced?

.... [2 marks]

e How many moles of $Pb(NO_3)_2$ would be needed for this reaction?

.... [1 mark]

3 Simon is following instructions in a project book for how to make electricity from chemical reactions. He is instructed to make up a solution of zinc sulfate and a solution of copper sulfate. Both should have a concentration of 1 mol/dm³.

a How many moles would Simon need if he were making up 1 dm³ of the solutions?

.... [1 mark]

b What mass of zinc sulfate ($ZnSO_4$) should he weigh out to make 1 dm³ of 1 mol/dm³?

.... [1 mark]

c Simon finds he does not need 1 dm³ of zinc sulfate solution but only needs 200 cm³. What mass of zinc sulfate should he weigh out?

....

.... [1 mark]

d Dawn says that he should use the same mass of copper sulfate ($CuSO_4$) to make up the copper sulfate solution. Is this correct? Explain your answer.

....

.... [2 marks]

1 a What is the name of the salt which is made when sodium hydroxide and hydrochloric acid
   react together? Circle the correct answer. **[1 mark]**

   i Sodium chloride.

   ii Sodium sulfate.

   iii Hydrogen hydroxide.

   iv Chlorine hydride.

b Write the name of the following ions: **[4 marks]**

   i SO_4^{2-} ....

   ii OH^- ....

   iii NO_3^- ....

   iv Cl^- ....

G–E

2 Zinc sulfate can be made by reacting an acid and a base. Sally decided to make zinc sulfate
using zinc oxide.

   a Write the name and the formula of the acid she should use.

   .... **[2 marks]**

   b Sally warmed the acid and then added zinc oxide until no more would dissolve. Why did she
   warm the acid?

   .... **[1 mark]**

   c She then removed the excess zinc oxide from the mixture. Draw a diagram of the apparatus
   she could use to do this. **[3 marks]**

D–C

3 a Complete the following word equation:

   Acid + _____ ⟶ _____ + water **[2 marks]**

   b Suggest two compounds that would react together to form magnesium chloride.

   .... **[2 marks]**

4 a Describe the difference between a base and an alkali and give examples of both.

   ....

   ....

   .... **[4 marks]**

   b Describe a method that could be used to prepare a sample of pure potassium nitrate.
   You should draw a diagram of apparatus and explain what is happening at each stage of
   the method.

B–A*

   ....

   ....

   ....

   .... **[5 marks]**

1 a Look at the word equation and circle the correct answers below

nitric acid + sodium hydroxide ⟶ sodium nitrate + water

  i This reaction is neutralisation/redox reaction.

  ii Sodium nitrate is an acid/salt/alkali.

  iii Sodium hydroxide is an acid/salt/alkali   **[3 marks]**

b Complete the symbol equation:

$H^+ + OH^- \longrightarrow$ .... **[1 mark]**

2 Put the following statements describing a titration in the correct order.

  a Add a few drops of indicator.

  b Open the tap and slowly add the solution from the burette.

  c Pipette the alkali into the conical flask and fill the burette with acid.

  d Close the tap when you see a colour change.

.... **[3 marks]**

3 Olga found the following results from the titration of 25 cm³ of an unknown concentration of nitric acid against 1.5 mol/dm³ sodium hydroxide.

Burette reading	Rough (cm³)	Titration 1 (cm³)	Titration 2 (cm³)	Titration 3 (cm³)
Start	00.0	19.0	31.0	00.0
Finish	19.0	33.6	45.4	14.8
Volume NaOH added				

a Complete the table by calculating the volume of sodium hydroxide added.   **[2 marks]**

b Calculate the average volume added. Show your working.

....

.... **[2 marks]**

c Calculate the average number of **moles** of NaOH added.

.... **[2 marks]**

d Write the equation for the reaction that has taken place.

.... **[3 marks]**

e Use your equation to calculate the number of moles of acid that were in the flask.

.... **[1 mark]**

f Calculate the concentration of the acid in mol/dm³.

....

.... **[3 marks]**

g Calculate the concentration of the acid in g/dm³.

....

.... **[3 marks]**

1 a Lead bromide is an ionic compound. Which ions does it contain?

.... [2 marks]

b When lead bromide is melted it is able to conduct electricity. Why does lead bromide not conduct electricity when it is solid?

.... [2 marks]

c When electricity passes through lead bromide the ions begin to move towards the electrodes. Which ion moves towards the cathode?

.... [1 mark] **G–E**

2 a Sodium is used in nuclear reactors. What is it used for?

.... [2 marks]

b What properties of sodium make it useful in a nuclear reactor?

.... [2 marks]

c In which group of the periodic table can sodium be found?

.... [1 mark]

3 a Some street lamps are based on sodium. What colour is the light given off by a sodium street lamp?

.... [1 mark]

b Sodium is a very reactive metal. How can sodium be extracted from sodium compounds?

.... [1 mark]

c Draw a dot and cross diagram of a sodium ion.

D–C

[2 marks]

d Why is a sodium ion called a **cation**?

.... [1 mark]

4 a Unlike gold, sodium is never found in the ground as the metal but always as a metal compound. Explain why it is not possible for sodium to exist in the ground as the element.

....

.... [2 marks]

b During the electrolysis of molten sodium chloride, ions move towards the electrodes.

i Describe the movement of the two ions.

....

.... [2 marks] **B–A***

ii Explain what happens to the ions once they reach the electrodes.

....

....

.... [4 marks]

c Sodium is used in some types of nuclear reactor as a coolant. Other nuclear reactors use water as a coolant. Suggest two advantages of using sodium rather than water as a coolant.

....

.... [2 marks]

1 a Which of the following reactions show oxidation?

    i Copper ions gain electrons and become copper ions.

    ii Zinc atoms lose electrons and become zinc ions.

    iii Magnesium reacts with oxygen and becomes magnesium oxide.

    iv Hydrogen is burned in air to become water.

    .... **[2 marks]**

b i Iron + oxygen $\longrightarrow$ iron oxide. Explain why this reaction is described as an oxidation reaction.

    .... **[1 mark]**

    ii Iron oxide $\longrightarrow$ iron + oxygen. What type of reaction is described by this equation?

    .... **[1 mark]**

---

2 During the electrolysis of hydrochloric acid, hydrogen and chlorine are produced at the electrodes.

    a What is the name of the two ions that are present in hydrochloric acid?

    .... **[2 marks]**

    b Which ion will move towards the cathode?

    .... **[1 mark]**

    c Which ion will be oxidised?

    .... **[1 mark]**

3 a Draw a labelled diagram of the apparatus that could be used to electrolyse hydrochloric acid.

    [3 marks]

    b What type of reaction occurs at the anode?

    .... **[1 mark]**

---

4 a Write an ionic equation for the following balanced formula equations:

    i $CuSO_4 + Zn \longrightarrow Cu + ZnSO_4$.

    .... **[3 marks]**

    ii $PbBr_2 \longrightarrow Pb + Br_2$.

    .... **[3 marks]**

    iii $2AgNO_3 + Cu \longrightarrow Ag + Cu(NO_3)_2$.

    .... **[3 marks]**

    b Write two half equations for equation **i**.

    ....

    .... **[2 marks]**

    c Which substance is oxidised in this reaction?

    .... **[1 mark]**

G–E

D–C

B–A*

Electrolysing sodium chloride solution

1 a Sodium chloride is a compound containing two ions: sodium and chloride.

  i Which ion could be described as a cation?

  .... **[1 mark]**

  ii Which ion would move towards the anode when sodium chloride is used as an electrolyte?

  .... **[1 mark]**

  iii Sodium chloride does not conduct electricity when it is solid. Why is this?

  ....

  .... **[2 marks]**

b i During the electrolysis of sodium chloride a green gas bubbles up at the anode. What is the name of this gas?

  .... **[2 marks]**

  ii During electrolysis of sodium chloride hydrogen bubbles up at the cathode. How could you show that this colourless gas is hydrogen?

  .... **[2 marks]**

G–E

---

2 a Write a word equation for the electrolysis of sodium chloride solution.

  .... **[5 marks]**

b Explain why sodium is not one of the products.

  ....

  .... **[2 marks]**

c Mark the following statements about the electrolysis of sodium chloride solution as true or false:

  i Chloride ions are reduced at the anode ....

  ii Hydroxide ions remain in solution ....

  iii The gas produced at the anode will bleach damp indicator paper ....

  iv The solution left after electrolysis will turn red litmus paper blue .... **[4 marks]**

D–C

---

3 a i Write a half equation for the reduction of chloride ions during the electrolysis of sodium chloride.

  .... **[2 marks]**

  ii Are chloride ions oxidised or reduced? Explain your answer.

  .... **[2 marks]**

  iii Explain why sodium ions are described as spectator ions in this reaction.

  .... **[2 marks]**

b When sodium chloride solution is electrolysed in industry great care is taken to prevent the products at the two electrodes from coming into contact. Suggest a reason for this precaution.

  ....

  ....

  .... **[3 marks]**

c Suggest two tests that could be used to demonstrate the presence of the two ions left in solution after the electrolysis of brine.

  ....

  ....

  .... **[3 marks]**

B–A*

---

1 a James used the apparatus shown in the diagram below to electrolyse copper sulfate solution.

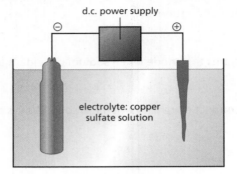

d.c. power supply

⊖   ⊕

electrolyte: copper sulfate solution

i What will happen to the piece of copper at the anode?

.... **[1 mark]**

ii At the start of the experiment the mass of the anode plus the cathode was 20g. Will this increase, decrease or stay the same at the end of the experiment?

.... **[1 mark]**

iii At the end of the experiment James removed the cathode and weighed it. He found that it weighed more than expected. What had caused it to gain weight?

.... **[2 marks]**

b Kate used inert electrodes and passed electricity through some solutions. Draw a line between the correct reactants and products. **[2 marks]**

Solution	Products
Copper sulfate	hydrogen and oxygen
Sodium sulfate	copper and chlorine
Copper chloride	copper and oxygen

2 a Sujaen wants to prepare a sample of chlorine by electrolysis. Name an electrolyte that he could use.

.... **[2 marks]**

b Has the chlorine formed as a result of oxidation or reduction?

.... **[1 mark]**

c What will form at the other electrode?

.... **[1 mark]**

3 a Oxygen collects at the anode when sodium sulfate is electrolysed. The formula for sodium sulfate is Na_2SO_4. Explain where the oxygen has come from.

.... **[1 mark]**

b Write the half equation for the formation of oxygen.

.... **[2 marks]**

c A reduction reaction occurs at the cathode. Write the half equation for this reaction.

.... **[2 marks]**

d What is left in the solution at the end of the electrolysis reaction?

.... **[1 mark]**

e Which substance is oxidised in this reaction?

.... **[1 mark]**

1 a Isabel does an experiment using the apparatus shown below.

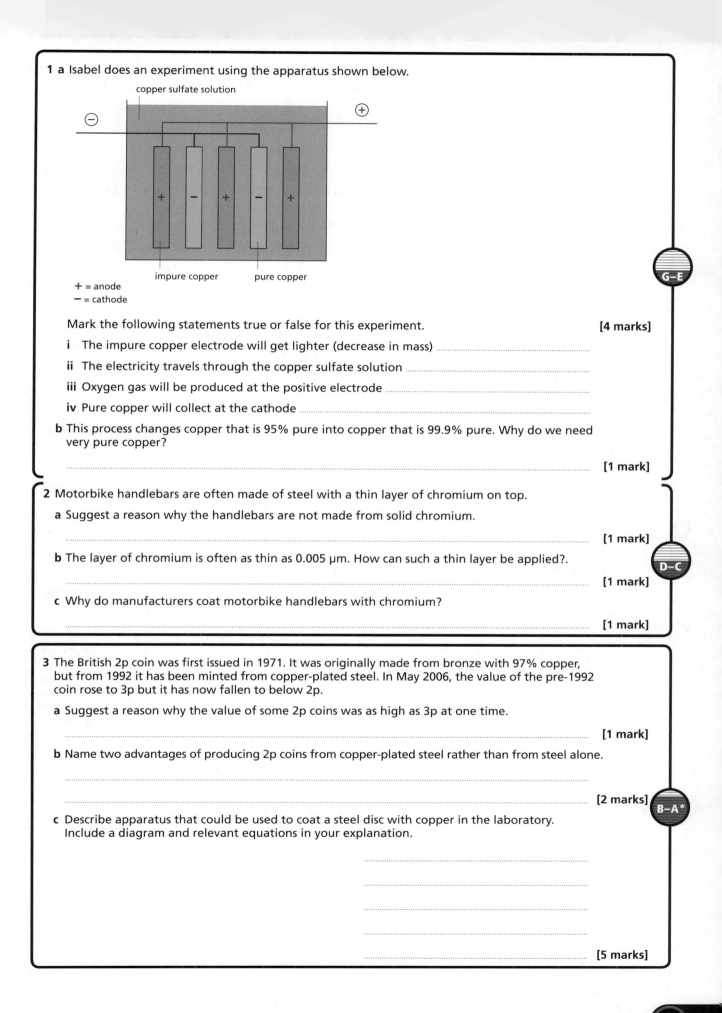

copper sulfate solution

$\ominus$ $\oplus$

impure copper   pure copper

+ = anode
− = cathode

G–E

Mark the following statements true or false for this experiment.   **[4 marks]**

i The impure copper electrode will get lighter (decrease in mass) ....

ii The electricity travels through the copper sulfate solution ....

iii Oxygen gas will be produced at the positive electrode ....

iv Pure copper will collect at the cathode ....

b This process changes copper that is 95% pure into copper that is 99.9% pure. Why do we need very pure copper?

.... **[1 mark]**

2 Motorbike handlebars are often made of steel with a thin layer of chromium on top.

a Suggest a reason why the handlebars are not made from solid chromium.

.... **[1 mark]**

b The layer of chromium is often as thin as 0.005 μm. How can such a thin layer be applied?.

.... **[1 mark]**

D–C

c Why do manufacturers coat motorbike handlebars with chromium?

.... **[1 mark]**

3 The British 2p coin was first issued in 1971. It was originally made from bronze with 97% copper, but from 1992 it has been minted from copper-plated steel. In May 2006, the value of the pre-1992 coin rose to 3p but it has now fallen to below 2p.

a Suggest a reason why the value of some 2p coins was as high as 3p at one time.

.... **[1 mark]**

b Name two advantages of producing 2p coins from copper-plated steel rather than from steel alone.

....

.... **[2 marks]**

B–A*

c Describe apparatus that could be used to coat a steel disc with copper in the laboratory. Include a diagram and relevant equations in your explanation.

....

....

....

....

.... **[5 marks]**

1 Camping gas cylinders contain gas stored under pressure. The gas is released and expands when the valve on the bottle is opened. The larger bottles of gas contain 2.72 kg of pure butane (C_4H_{10}), while the smaller bottles contain a mixture of propane and butane.

   a How many moles of butane are there in a large container of gas?

   ....

   .... **[3 marks]**

   b What volume of gas would a large container produce if all the contents were released at room temperature and pressure?

   Note: 1 mole of gas occupies 24 dm³ at room temperature and pressure.

   .... **[2 marks]**

   c Smaller bottles of gas contain 4.5 moles of a mixture of butane and propane. If the gas were pure propane then the volume at room temperature and pressure would be 108 dm³. Explain how this volume would change if the mixture were a 50/50 mixture of butane and propane.

   ....

   .... **[2 marks]**

   d When the butane is burned it produces carbon dioxide and water only. Write a balanced equation for the combustion of butane.

   ....

   .... **[3 marks]**

   e If 20 g of butane is used making a cup of tea, what volume of butane is this at room temperature and pressure?

   .... **[1 mark]**

   f What volume of carbon dioxide would this produce?

   .... **[1 mark]**

2 a Hydrogen cars rely on burning hydrogen in oxygen to provide energy. Write a balanced formula equation for the reaction between hydrogen and oxygen.

   .... **[2 marks]**

   b A hydrogen car tank contained 48 dm³ of hydrogen. What volume of oxygen (at the same temperature and pressure) would be needed to convert all the hydrogen into water?

   .... **[2 marks]**

   c Suggest a test that could be used to show that the product was water.

   ....

   .... **[2 marks]**

   d What mass of water would be produced if all the hydrogen in the tank was burned?

   ....

   .... **[4 marks]**

3 When limestone is converted into quicklime carbon dioxide is released:

$$CaCO_3 \longrightarrow CaO + CO_2$$

   a What mass of limestone would produce 12 dm³ of carbon dioxide?

   ....

   .... **[4 marks]**

   b A country produces 11.2 tonnes (11.2×10^6 g) of calcium oxide from calcium carbonate per year. What volume of carbon dioxide would be released as a result of this production?

   ....

   .... **[2 marks]**

B–A*

1 a Ammonium nitrate is an example of a nitrogenous fertiliser. Which of the following is the best reason for why farmers add nitrogenous fertilisers to the soil? Circle the correct answer. **[1 mark]**

   i To neutralise acid soil.

   ii To prevent nutrients leaching from the soil.

   iii To destroy weeds.

   iv To increase crop yields.

b Ammonium nitrate is a salt. It can be made by a neutralisation reaction.

   i Which two **types** of substance react together in a neutralisation reaction?

   .... **[1 mark]**

   ii Nitric acid is one of the reactants that are used to make ammonium nitrate. Name the other reactant.

   .... **[1 mark]**

G–E

2 The Government Environment Agency publishes fertiliser recommendations for crops. This helps farmers to decide the cheapest way of applying fertiliser and understand how to prevent pollution of the land and waterways.

a What advantage do farmers get by using fertilisers?

.... **[1 mark]**

b Give two disadvantages of using too much fertiliser.

.... **[2 marks]**

c Describe how using fertiliser may pollute waterways.

....

....

.... **[3 marks]**

D–C

3 Ammonium nitrate NH_4NO_3 and urea $CO(NH_2)_2$ are both nitrogenous fertilisers.

a Calculate the percentage of nitrogen in NH_4NO_3.

.... **[2 marks]**

b Calculate the percentage of nitrogen in $CO(NH_2)_2$.

.... **[2 marks]**

c In 2012 the cost of ammonium nitrate was about £0.33 per kg and urea was £0.425 per kg. Show which fertiliser would have provided the cheapest source of 1 kg of **nitrogen** in 2012.

....

.... **[4 marks]**

4 Ecologists have noticed that large areas of ocean have become 'dead zones'. The oxygen levels in these areas are so low that the water does not support any marine life. One such dead zone in the Black Sea suddenly became much smaller between 1991 and 2001. During this time the quantities of fertiliser used by countries surrounding the Black Sea also fell dramatically due to economic circumstances.

a Suggest a reason why dead zones appear in oceans.

....

....

.... **[5 marks]**

b How does the information in the passage support the hypothesis that dead zones are caused by eutrophication?

....

.... **[1 mark]**

B–A*

1 The reaction for the manufacture of ammonia is shown below:

$$\text{Nitrogen} + \text{hydrogen} \rightleftharpoons \text{ammonia}$$

a What does the symbol $\rightleftharpoons$ mean?

.... [1 mark]

b Where do manufacturers get the nitrogen and hydrogen from? Circle the correct answers.

i Hydrogen comes from: air   steam   natural gas   ammonia

ii Nitrogen comes from : air   water   methane   ammonia   [3 marks]

2 In 1919 Fritz Haber was awarded the Nobel Prize for his work on converting nitrogen in the air into nitrogen compounds, known today as the Haber process.

a What is the product in the Haber process?

.... [1 mark]

b Write a balanced formula equation for the Haber process.

.... [2 marks]

c Name one use for the products of the Haber process.

.... [1 mark]

3 a The reaction in the Haber process never goes to completion but reaches a state of dynamic equilibrium. Explain what is meant by **dynamic equilibrium**.

....

.... [2 marks]

b When ammonia is made in the Haber process under conditions of 200 °C and 100 atm, the yield of ammonia is around 25%. What would happen to the yield if the pressure were increased to 200 atm?

.... [1 mark]

c Suggest why manufacturers do not usually use pressures above 150 atm in the Haber process.

.... [2 marks]

d Decreasing the temperature would increase the percentage of ammonia at equilibrium. Suggest why low temperatures are not used in the Haber process.

.... [1 mark]

e Name the catalyst used for the Haber process and describe the effect that it has on the process.

....

.... [2 marks]

4 The reaction between methane and steam is called steam reforming. This reaction is endothermic:

$$CH_4 + H_2O \rightleftharpoons CO + 3H_2$$

a Explain why this reaction will never convert all of the methane and steam into hydrogen and carbon monoxide.

.... [1 mark]

b Describe and explain what will happen to the yield of hydrogen if pressure in the reaction chamber is increased.

....

.... [2 marks]

c Explain why the yield of ammonia will increase if the temperature is increased.

....

....

.... [3 marks]

G–E

D–C

B–A*

1 The instructions on a wine-making kit include:

   i Fill the container with grape juice.

   ii Use a thermometer to check that the temperature is above 22 °C.

   iii Sprinkle the yeast on top and stir.

   iv Put a lid on the container that is fitted with an airlock. This allows gases to escape but no air to enter.

   a What name is given to the process of making ethanol using yeast?

   .... [1 mark]

   b Which substance in the grape juice does the yeast convert into ethanol?

   .... [1 mark]

   c Why is it important that the temperature is not too low?

   .... [1 mark]

   d Which gas needs to escape from the container?

   .... [1 mark]

   e Why is it important that air does not enter the container?

   .... [1 mark]

G–E

2 The table shows the ethanol content of whisky at various stages of production

| Compound | Boiling point (°C) | % ethanol | | | |
		In the wash	Following distillation	After maturation	In the bottle
Water	100	92	30	40	60
Ethanol	78	8	70	60	40

   a During the first stage of whisky-making, yeast is mixed with a sugar solution made from malted grain. The mixture is allowed to ferment for about 72 hours. Write a word equation to show what happens to the glucose during this time.

   .... [2 marks]

   b The solution produced at the end of fermentation is known as the wash. This is then sent for distillation to increase the ethanol content. Explain what is meant by distillation and how this increases the ethanol percentage.

   ....

   ....

   .... [3 marks]

   c The spirit produced by distillation is left to mature in oak casks for 10 years. Small amounts of gases are able to pass through the cask. During this time the ethanol content of the whisky decreases. This is known as the 'angel's share'. Suggest why the ethanol content decreases.

   .... [1 mark]

D–C

3 In Brazil it is compulsory to blend petrol with at least 18% ethanol, a mixture known as gasohol. The ethanol is made by fermentation of sugar from sugar cane.

   a Suggest why Brazil decided to use blended fuel but gasohol is not used in the UK.

   .... [2 marks]

   b Give 2 environmental advantages of using ethanol as a fuel rather than pure petrol.

   ....

   .... [2 marks]

   c Describe a method of producing ethanol other than by fermentation.

   .... [2 marks]

   d Give one advantage of this method over fermentation.

   .... [1 mark]

B–A*

1 a Which of the following is the correct name for this molecule? Circle the correct answer. [1 mark]

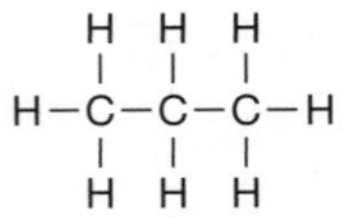

$$H-\underset{\underset{H}{|}}{\overset{\overset{H}{|}}{C}}-\underset{\underset{H}{|}}{\overset{\overset{H}{|}}{C}}-\underset{\underset{H}{|}}{\overset{\overset{H}{|}}{C}}-H$$

    i Ethane   **iii** Hydrocarbon

    ii Ethene   **iv** Propane

b i Draw the structural formula of the alkane with one carbon atom. [2 marks]

  ii What is the name of the molecule that you have drawn?

[1 mark]

c Put the following molecules in order of boiling point, lowest boiling point first:

propane   methane   butane   ethane

[2 marks]

---

2 a Name the homologous series that has the general formula C_nH_{2n}.

[1 mark]

b The first member of this series has the formula C_2H_4. Draw the full structural formula of this molecule. [1 mark]

c What test could you do to show that a compound is a member of this homologous series?

[2 marks]

---

3 The table below shows some properties of alcohols

Name	Formula	Boiling point (°C)	Relative viscosity
Methanol	CH_3OH	66	0.64
Ethanol	C_2H_5OH	78	1.52
Propanol	C_3H_7OH		1.94
Butanol	C_4H_9OH	118	2.95

a Write the general formula for alcohols.

[1 mark]

b Suggest a value for the boiling point of propanol.

[1 mark]

c Describe the trend in viscosity for alcohols.

[1 mark]

4 a Explain why the molecules methanoic acid, ethanoic acid, propanoic acid are known as a homologous series.

[2 marks]

b Describe one chemical reaction that you would expect to be the same for all members of the series.

[2 marks]

c Explain why propanoic acid has a higher boiling point than methanoic acid.

[2 marks]

1 Ethanoic acid is a weak acid. Circle the following statements which are true about ethanoic acid

  i It will turn blue litmus paper red.   **iii** It will fizz if mixed with magnesium.

  ii It will turn universal indicator blue.   **iv** It will neutralise hydrochloric acid.   **[2 marks]**

2 Jake is worried that his sister Ella drinks too much alcohol. Ella tells him that there is nothing to worry about because she only drinks lager and not spirits like vodka.

  a Give three reasons why drinking too much alcohol is a bad idea.

  ....

  .... **[3 marks]**

  b Why does Ella think that lager is less harmful than spirits?

  .... **[1 mark]**

  c The label on a bottle of lager says 5%. What does this mean?

  .... **[1 mark]**

G–E

  d If Ella drinks 3 pints of lager (1 704 cm³), what volume of pure alcohol has she taken?

  .... **[2 marks]**

  e The vodka bottle is labelled 50%. What volume of vodka contains the same amount of alcohol as 3 pints of lager?

  .... **[2 marks]**

  f A shot of vodka contains 25 cm³. How many shots of vodka contain the same amount of alcohol as 3 pints of lager?

  .... **[2 marks]**

D–C

3 Billy and Katy did an experiment where they gently warmed a mixture of ethanol and ethanoic acid. After heating, the mixture had a sweet, fruity smell.

  a Write a word equation for the reaction.

  .... **[1 mark]**

  b What **type** of compound did they make?

  .... **[1 mark]**

  c Name a use for this type of compound.

  .... **[1 mark]**

4 a Vinegar can be made from wine. Which molecule in the wine is converted into vinegar?

  .... **[1 mark]**

  b One instruction in an article titled 'Make your own vinegar' is: put the wine into a container with a large surface area. Suggest a reason for this instruction.

  .... **[1 mark]**

  c Write the name of the major component of vinegar and draw the structure.

  .... **[3 marks]**

B–A*

  d Vinegar is often recommended as a cleaning product for brass which has become tarnished by copper oxide. Suggest a word equation for the reaction that removes the tarnish.

  ....

  .... **[2 marks]**

1 a Artificial pineapple flavouring is the ester ethyl butanoate. Which properties of esters make them useful as flavours?

.... [2 marks]

b What else can esters be used for as well as flavouring?

.... [1 mark]

2 The table below shows the estimated world production of polyesters in 2008.

Product type	Million tonnes
Textile PET	39
Resin PET	16
Film PET	1.5
Special polyester	2.5

a What percentage of the polyester was made into textiles?

.... [2 marks]

b Suggest a use for polyester textiles.

.... [1 mark]

c One use of resin PET is making carbonated drink bottles. What properties must PET resin have to make good bottles?

.... [1 mark]

d Name one product that recycled PET can be used for.

.... [1 mark]

3 Fats and oils can be broken into smaller molecules by heating with sodium hydroxide. One product is glycerol and the others are the salts of long chain carboxylic acids.

a What name is usually given to the salts of long chain fatty acids?

.... [1 mark]

b What **type** of molecule are fats and oils?

.... [1 mark]

4 a Ethyl ethanoate is an ester which is used to decaffeinate coffee beans. It can be made from ethanoic acid and ethanol. Write an equation for this reaction showing the structural formulae of the reactants and products.

....

.... [4 marks]

b After soaking the beans in ethyl ethanoate the liquid is drained off and any remaining ethyl ethanoate is removed by steaming the beans. What property of ethyl ethanoate allows it to be removed by steaming?

.... [1 mark]

5 Use the diagram of a soap molecule shown below to explain how soap helps to remove grease from clothes.

....

....

.... [4 marks]

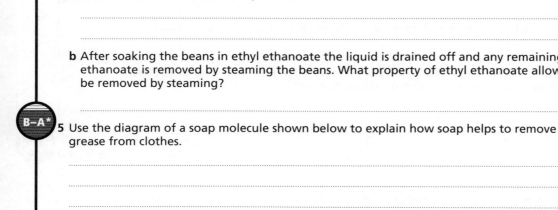

One method of producing hydrogen is by electrolysing sodium chloride solution. The cost of electricity for the process is high but the process is made economic by the fact that all the products of electrolysis are useful. Explain how hydrogen is produced during the electrolysis and describe the other products. Use equations where appropriate.

The quality of written communication will be assessed in your answer to this question.

[6 marks]

I can describe how the Earth's early atmosphere and oceans were formed.	
I can describe the composition of today's atmosphere and the early atmosphere.	
I can describe how carbonate rocks formed from carbon dioxide.	
I can describe the formation of igneous, metamorphic and sedimentary rock and give an example of each.	
I can describe the chemical name for limestone, chalk and marble as calcium carbonate.	
I can list some uses of limestone, and some advantages and disadvantages of quarrying.	
I can write a word equation for the thermal decomposition of calcium carbonate.	
I know that atoms are rearranged in chemical reactions, not created or destroyed.	
I can explain that hydrochloric acid is naturally present in the stomach and why indigestion remedies are used.	
I can explain that acids are neutralised by bases, which are metal oxides, hydroxides or carbonates.	
I understand that a salt is produced in a neutralisation reaction.	
I can describe electrolysis as using electricity to split up compounds.	
I can describe the tests for hydrogen, chlorine and oxygen and can list some uses of chlorine.	
I can explain that most metals are extracted from metal compounds that are in rocks, but that a few metals are found as elements.	
I can explain that most metals are extracted by heating with carbon or by electrolysis.	
I can describe oxidation as gain of oxygen and reduction as loss of oxygen.	
I can list some reasons for recycling metals.	
I can describe some properties and uses of aluminium, copper, gold and steel.	
I understand that metals can be mixed to make alloys to improve their properties.	
I can describe hydrocarbons as molecules that contain hydrogen and carbon only.	
I can describe how crude oil is split up by fractional distillation.	
I can write a word equation for the combustion of hydrocarbons, and name the products of incomplete combustion.	
I can describe what a greenhouse gas does.	
I understand that fossil fuels are a non-renewable resource but biofuels are renewable.	
I can describe hydrogen as a good fuel and explain what makes it a difficult fuel to use.	
I can name the first three alkanes.	
I can describe an alkane as a molecule that is unsaturated, decolourises bromine water and that is used to make polymers.	
I can describe how cracking converts long chain alkanes into shorter alkanes and alkenes.	
I can explain what polymerisation means and list some uses for particular polymers.	
I can explain why disposing of polymers is a problem and list some solutions.	
I am working at grades G/F/E	

I can explain how rocks provide a record of the atmosphere from years ago.	
I can explain how photosynthesis decreases the amount of carbon dioxide and increases the amount of oxygen in the atmosphere.	
I can use experimental results to calculate the amount of oxygen in the atmosphere.	
I can explain why there are small changes in the composition of the modern atmosphere.	
I can describe the difference between intrusive and extrusive igneous rock.	
I can explain why sedimentary rock may have fossils and be easily eroded.	
I can describe an experiment to compare how easily different metal carbonates decompose to metal oxides.	
I can describe the use of limestone products to neutralise soil and acidic gases from power stations.	
I know that the products of a reaction have different properties to the reactants, but that the mass of reactants and products is the same.	
I can describe how to compare the effectiveness of different indigestion remedies.	
I can describe chlorine as a toxic gas that can be obtained by electrolysis of seawater.	
I know that the electrolysis of water produces oxygen and hydrogen and that the hydrolysis of dilute hydrochloric acid produces chlorine and hydrogen.	
I can describe the extraction of a metal from its oxide as reduction and corrosion as oxidation.	
I can explain why some metals are extracted by electrolysis.	
I can draw a diagram to explain why alloying increases the strength of a metal.	
I can explain some reasons for turning iron into steel alloys.	
I can describe some properties and some uses for each fraction of crude oil.	
I can describe some causes of and some effects of acid rain.	
I can describe the relationship between atmospheric carbon dioxide levels and global temperatures.	
I can list some advantages and disadvantages of biofuels.	
I can describe an experiment to compare the energy released from different fuels.	
I can draw a labelled diagram of how to crack liquid paraffin.	
I can draw the structure of methane, ethane, propane, ethene and propene.	
I can list the properties of poly(ethene), poly(chloroethene), poly(propene) and poly(tetrafluoroethene)	
I can explain why a particular polymer might be chosen for a particular use.	
I can evaluate some solutions to the problem of disposing of polymers.	
I am working at grades D/C	

I can explain how the evolution of life changed the atmosphere.	
I can describe and explain an experiment to find the amount of oxygen in the atmosphere.	
I can explain how the crystal size of igneous rocks shows where the rock formed.	
I can suggest ways in which the negative effects of quarrying can be minimised, and write a balanced argument for and against limestone quarrying.	
I can explain the use of calcium carbonate to prevent the release of acidic gases from power stations.	
I can write equations for the thermal decomposition of calcium carbonate, the reaction between water and calcium oxide and the addition of carbon dioxide to limewater.	
I can identify when a formula equation is not balanced.	
I can predict the mass of a product given the mass of all other reactants and products.	
I can name the salt that would be produced by reacting an acid and a base.	
I can describe an experiment to electrolyse hydrochloric acid.	
I can relate the reactivity of a metal to the method chosen to extract it and to the ease with which it corrodes.	
I can discuss why chemists develop new materials and explain how shape memory alloys are suited to particular functions.	
I can explain why different fractions of crude oil have different boiling points.	
I can explain why the products of incomplete combustion are dangerous.	
I can explain how greenhouse gases warm the Earth, and evaluate the evidence supporting the theory of climate change.	
I can explain some methods of reducing acid rain and atmospheric carbon dioxide levels.	
I can write the reaction equation for the fermentation of glucose into ethanol.	
I can write arguments for and against replacing fossil fuels with biofuels.	
I can discuss the difficulties of using hydrogen as a fuel and describe a hydrogen fuel cell.	
I can explain why cracking is necessary.	
I can write an equation for the polymerisation of ethene.	
I can describe some recent developments in developing biodegradable polymers.	
I am working at grades B/A/A*	

I can describe the structure of an atom showing the position of protons, neutrons and electrons.	
I can explain that the number of electrons is the same as the number of protons.	
I can explain the meaning of atomic mass and atomic number.	
I can describe an element as metal or non-metal by looking at the periodic table.	
I can describe how Mendeleev organised his periodic table and how the modern periodic table is arranged.	
I can describe how positive and negative ions are formed.	
I can explain that ionic bonding is electrostatic attraction between oppositely charged ions.	
I can write the formula for an ion, and say which ions are present in an ionic compound from its name.	
I know that ionic substances are crystalline and have high melting and boiling points.	
I can use the solubility rules to decide if an ionic substance is soluble.	
I can list the flame colours of sodium, potassium, calcium and copper.	
I can describe a covalent bond as a shared pair of electrons and name some covalent molecules.	
I can draw a dot and cross diagram for hydrogen, hydrogen chloride, water and methane.	
I can list some differences in properties between ionic and covalent substances.	
I can describe how to separate two immiscible liquids.	
I can describe an experiment to separate colours using paper chromatography.	
I can list the physical properties of ionic, covalent and metallic substances.	
I can draw a diagram of metallic structure as a regular arrangement of ions surrounded by a sea of delocalised electrons.	
I can describe the properties of alkali metals as soft and reactive.	
I can explain that the reactivity of the alkali metals gets higher going down the group.	
I can describe the colour and physical state of the halogens.	
I can describe the properties of the noble gases.	
I can name a use for helium and for argon, and describe the properties that make it good for this use.	
I can describe the difference between an exothermic and endothermic reaction.	
I can use experimental results to decide if a reaction is exothermic or endothermic.	
I can list the factors that affect the rate of a reaction.	
I can explain what is meant by a catalyst, and describe why catalytic convertors are used in vehicles.	
I can calculate the relative formula mass of a compound or element.	
I can explain why the yield of a reaction is never 100% of what it could be.	
I can explain why industry must dispose of waste products carefully.	
I am working at grades G/F/E	

I can list the mass and charge of protons, neutrons and electrons.	
I can explain the meaning of isotope.	
I can describe how Mendeleev predicted the existence and properties of unknown elements by looking at the properties of known elements.	
I can write the electron arrangement of an atom using the periodic table and the 2.8.8 system.	
I can write the electronic structure of an ion and describe the properties of ionic substances.	
I can use the name of an ionic compound to write its formula.	
I can write a formula equation for a precipitation reaction using the correct state symbols.	
I can describe an experiment to make an insoluble salt.	
I can describe tests and results for the presence of carbonates, sulfates and chloride ions.	
I can explain why covalent bonds form and why carbon usually makes four bonds and hydrogen makes one bond.	
I can explain why simple covalent substances have a low melting point but giant covalent substances have a high melting point.	
I can explain that fractional distillation can be used to separate miscible liquids.	
I can analyse the results from a paper chromatogram to decide what is present in a mixture.	
I can use physical properties of an unknown substance to decide what structure it has.	
I can use the structure of metals to explain why they are malleable and can conduct electricity.	
I can describe the reaction of alkali metals with water and write the formula equations.	
I can write equations for the reactions of halogens with hydrogen and metals.	
I can describe the observations, hypothesis and experiments that led to the discovery of the noble gases.	
I can describe an experiment to measure the energy change in a reaction.	
I can describe experiments to show how the rate of a reaction is affected by concentration, surface area, temperature and catalysts.	
I can draw graphs to show the expected results from experiments about rates of reaction.	
I can explain how the design of catalytic converters helps them to work more effectively.	
I can write word equations for the reactions catalysed by catalytic converters.	
I can calculate the percentage by mass of an element in a compound.	
I can calculate the percentage yield of a reaction from the actual yield and the theoretical yield.	
I am working at grades D/C	

I can state the number of protons and neutrons in an atom given the periodic table.	
I can calculate the relative atomic mass of an element given the abundance of each isotope.	
I can predict the properties of an element given the properties of another element with the same number of electrons in the outer shell.	
I can predict whether an element will form a positive or negative ion and how many charges it will carry.	
I can write a balanced formula equation from a word equation.	
I can explain why ionic substances conduct electricity when dissolved or molten.	
I can suggest suitable reactants to make an insoluble salt.	
I can explain the use of barium sulfate in X-rays	
I can explain how scientists use emission spectroscopy.	
I can predict the formula of a simple covalent molecule by looking at how many unpaired electrons each atom has.	
I can draw dot and cross diagrams for covalent molecules containing double bonds.	
I can draw the structure of diamond and graphite and use it to explain their different properties.	
I can explain why the components separate during fractional distillation of air.	
I can calculate Rf values from a paper chromatogram.	
I can explain why ionic substances are only able to conduct electricity when dissolved or molten.	
I can predict the outcome of a halogen displacement reaction.	
I can use the trend in properties to predict the properties of an unknown noble gas.	
I can draw an energy level diagram for an exothermic and endothermic reaction.	
I can explain why reactions are endothermic or exothermic using ideas about bond breaking and making.	
I can use to collision theory to explain why concentration, surface area and temperature affect the rate of a reaction.	
I can use reacting masses to work out the empirical formula of a compound.	
I can use a symbol equation to calculate the masses of each reactant and product.	
I can discuss some considerations that industrial chemists must weigh up when deciding about the economics of reactions.	
I am working at grades B/A/A*	

I can explain the difference between a qualitative test and a quantitative test.	
I can describe what happens when sodium hydroxide solution is added to copper, iron, calcium aluminium and ammonium ions.	
I can calculate the concentration of a solution in g/dm³.	
I can describe hard water areas as those that have dissolved calcium or magnesium ions in their tap water.	
I can describe the formation of scum instead of lather when soap is used with hard water.	
I can explain that hard water can be softened.	
I know that you can find out the mass of dissolved substances in a solution by evaporating off the water.	
I can name the negative ion that is made when an acid is neutralised.	
I can write the equation that shows hydroxide ions reacting with hydrogen ions to make water.	
I know that electrolytes are solutions of ions or molten ionic compounds that can conduct electricity.	
I can decide which ions will move towards the cathode and which will move to the anode.	
I can decide if something has been oxidised or reduced by seeing if it has lost or gained electrons.	
I know that sodium can be used in streetlights and as a coolant in nuclear reactors.	
I can describe how to electrolyse sodium chloride solution in the lab and name the products.	
I can draw a diagram to show how copper can be purified by electrolysis.	
I can explain why the cathode gains mass and the anode loses mass during the electrolysis of copper sulfate.	
I can explain that nitrogenous fertilisers put nitrogen into the soil, which improves plant growth.	
I understand that fertilisers are made from ammonia.	
I can recognise a reversible reaction from the equation.	
I know that ammonia is made by the Haber process, which reacts hydrogen and nitrogen together.	
I can write a word equation for the production of ethanol by anaerobic fermentation.	
I can list the conditions needed for fermentation as yeast, glucose, warmth and no oxygen.	
I can name types of drink with a low, medium and high alcohol content.	
I can describe some bad consequences of drinking alcohol.	
I understand that the alkanes are called a homologous series because they have the same general formula, similar chemical properties and show trends in physical properties.	
I can describe some properties that show that ethanoic acid is a weak acid.	
I can describe some uses of esters.	
I know that fats and oils are esters.	
I am working at grades G/F/E	

I can describe how to test for chloride, bromide and iodide ions in solution.	
I can use the results of ion tests to identify which ions are present in a salt.	
I can explain the difference between temporary and permanent hard water.	
I can explain why boiling removes temporary hardness but not permanent hardness.	
I can describe how ion exchange resins remove both temporary and permanent hardness.	
I can calculate what mass of solute needs to be added to the solvent to make up a solution.	
I can describe how to make a salt from an insoluble base and an acid.	
I can describe how to carry out a titration.	
I can describe how sodium is produced from the electrolysis of molten sodium chloride.	
I can describe the reduction reaction at the cathode and the oxidation reaction at the anode that occur during electrolysis of molten sodium chloride.	
I can describe the reactions at the anode and cathode that make the products of electrolysis of sodium chloride solution.	
I can name the products of electrolysis of molten lead bromide and of solutions of copper sulfate, copper chloride and sodium sulfate using inert electrodes.	
I can describe the process of purification of copper by electrolysis using an impure anode and a pure cathode.	
I can explain what is meant by electroplating and give some examples of the use of electroplating.	
I can describe how excessive use of fertilisers causes eutrophication.	
I can explain what is meant by dynamic equilibrium.	
I can describe how to increase the concentration of alcohol in a solution by fractional distillation.	
I can explain that ethanol can be oxidised to ethanoic acid and that this is the main component of vinegar.	
I can write a word equation to show the formation of an ester from ethanoic acid and ethanol.	
I can define the meaning of 'homologous series'.	
I can write the names, formulae and structures of the first four members of the alkanes and the first two members of the alkenes.	
I can describe some uses of polyesters and how they can be recycled.	
I can describe soaps as the salts of long chain fatty acids that can be made by boiling fats and oils with alkali.	
I am working at grades C/D	

I can write out an ionic equation for precipitation reactions of chloride, bromide and iodide ions with silver ions.	
I can explain why hard water causes soap to be wasted and how limescale forms.	
I can convert moles into mass and mass into moles.	
I can convert a concentration given in mol/dm³ into a concentration in g/dm³ and vice versa.	
I can describe how to make a pure soluble salt from an acid and an alkali and explain the reason for each step.	
I can calculate the concentration of a solution from the results of a titration.	
I can write half equations for the reactions at the anode and the cathode during the electrolysis of molten sodium chloride.	
I can explain why the products of electrolysis of sodium chloride solution are chlorine and hydrogen, not chlorine and sodium.	
I can write half equations for the electrolysis of solutions of copper sulfate, copper chloride, sodium sulfate and molten lead bromide using inert electrodes.	
I can identify oxidation and reduction by looking at half equations.	
I can explain how an article can be electroplated and write half equations for the reduction reaction.	
I can explain what is happening at the anode and cathode during the purification of copper by electrolysis and write half equations for the reaction.	
I understand that all gases occupy the same volume at the same temperature and pressure so the mole ratio is the same as the volume ratio.	
I can calculate the volume of any gas at room temperature and pressure given the mass and the formula.	
I can calculate the volume of reactants and products in a gas reaction given the volume of one reactant or product and the reaction equation.	
I can use the example of the Haber process to explain the effect of changing temperature and pressure for a system at equilibrium.	
I can explain why low temperatures are not used for equilibrium reactions even when this would increase the percentage of product at equilibrium.	
I can describe some reasons why in industry, a compromise pressure is chosen for reactions that go to equilibrium.	
I can explain how a catalyst helps to produce an acceptable yield in an acceptable time in industrial equilibrium reactions.	
I can write an equation to show the production of ethanol from ethene and steam.	
I can explain some factors that are important in deciding whether to manufacture ethanol from ethene or by fermentation.	
I can write an equation using structural formulae, to show the esterification reaction between ethanol and ethanoic acid.	
I can describe the dehydration reaction that converts ethanol to ethene.	
I can write the names, formulae and structures of the first three members of the alcohols and carboxylic acids.	
I can describe the structure of a soap molecule and explain how it is able to remove grease.	
I can explain how liquid oils can be converted into solid fats for margarine-making by hydrogenation of the carbon–carbon double bonds.	
I am working at grades B/A/A*	

The Periodic Table

Key

relative atomic mass
1
H atomic symbol
hydrogen — name
1 — atomic (proton) number

Group	1	2	3	4	5	6	7	8
								4 **He** helium 2
	7 **Li** lithium 3	9 **Be** beryllium 4	11 **B** boron 5	12 **C** carbon 6	14 **N** nitrogen 7	16 **O** oxygen 8	19 **F** fluorine 9	20 **Ne** neon 10
	23 **Na** sodium 11	24 **Mg** magnesium 12	27 **Al** aluminium 13	28 **Si** silicon 14	31 **P** phosphorus 15	32 **S** sulfur 16	35.5 **Cl** chlorine 17	40 **Ar** argon 18

1	2											3	4	5	6	7	8
39 **K** potassium 19	40 **Ca** calcium 20	45 **Sc** scandium 21	48 **Ti** titanium 22	51 **V** vanadium 23	52 **Cr** chromium 24	55 **Mn** manganese 25	56 **Fe** iron 26	59 **Co** cobalt 27	59 **Ni** nickel 28	63.5 **Cu** copper 29	65 **Zn** zinc 30	70 **Ga** gallium 31	73 **Ge** germanium 32	75 **As** arsenic 33	79 **Se** selenium 34	80 **Br** bromine 35	84 **Kr** krypton 36
85 **Rb** rubidium 37	88 **Sr** strontium 38	89 **Y** yttrium 39	91 **Zr** zirconium 40	93 **Nb** niobium 41	96 **Mo** molybdenum 42	[98] **Tc** technetium 43	101 **Ru** ruthenium 44	103 **Rh** rhodium 45	106 **Pd** palladium 46	108 **Ag** silver 47	112 **Cd** cadmium 48	115 **In** indium 49	119 **Sn** tin 50	122 **Sb** antimony 51	128 **Te** tellurium 52	127 **I** iodine 53	131 **Xe** xenon 54
133 **Cs** caesium 55	137 **Ba** barium 56	139 **La*** lanthanum 57	178 **Hf** hafnium 72	181 **Ta** tantalum 73	184 **W** tungsten 74	186 **Re** rhenium 75	190 **Os** osmium 76	192 **Ir** iridium 77	195 **Pt** platinum 78	197 **Au** gold 79	201 **Hg** mercury 80	204 **Tl** thallium 81	207 **Pb** lead 82	209 **Bi** bismuth 83	[209] **Po** polonium 84	[210] **At** astatine 85	[222] **Rn** radon 86
[223] **Fr** francium 87	[226] **Ra** radium 88	[227] **Ac*** actinium 89	[261] **Rf** rutherfordium 104	[262] **Db** dubnium 105	[266] **Sg** seaborgium 106	[264] **Bh** bohrium 107	[277] **Hs** hassium 108	[268] **Mt** meitnerium 109	[271] **Ds** darmstadtium 110	[272] **Rg** roentgenium 111							

Elements with atomic numbers 112–116 have been reported but not fully authenticated.

* The Lanthanides (atomic numbers 58–71) and the Actinides (atomic numbers 90–103) have been omitted.

Cu and Cl have not been rounded to the nearest whole number.

C1 Chemistry in our world

Page 74 The early atmosphere and oceans

1 iii Oxygen

2 The early atmosphere was made by volcanoes; if scientists know which gases come from volcanoes they can tell what was in the early atmosphere

3 a Oxidation

b Iron sulfide rocks form when there is little oxygen in the atmosphere; iron oxide rocks form when there is a lot of oxygen in the atmosphere; the amount of oxygen in the atmosphere has increased between 4 billion and 1.8 billion years ago

4 a There was much more carbon dioxide in the early atmosphere / less carbon dioxide in the modern atmosphere

b Any two from: carbon dioxide dissolved into the oceans; it was used by marine animals to make shells; it was used by early plants for photosynthesis

5 a $100 - (75 + 5 + 2)$; $= 18\%$

b It is (3%) lower than the modern atmosphere

c The equation shows the reaction in photosynthesis; when plants evolved they took in carbon dioxide so the level of carbon dioxide in the atmosphere dropped; they gave out oxygen so the level of oxygen in the atmosphere rose; carbon dioxide gas from the atmosphere dissolved into the oceans (aq)

Page 75 Today's atmosphere

1 a iii Digital thermometer

b Burning fossil fuels; cutting down forests/trees

c So they can detect any changes.

2 a iii Combustion of hydrocarbons has released carbon dioxide

b i It increases carbon dioxide; and decreases oxygen levels

ii Trees do lots of photosynthesising so fewer trees means less photosynthesis; less carbon dioxide is taken up and less oxygen is produced

3 a $CH_4 + 2O_2 \longrightarrow CO_2 + 2H_2O$ (1 mark for each 2 in the correct place; 1 mark for including **no** balancing number in front of **both** CH_4 and CO_2)

b Show state symbols on the equation as liquid (l) and gas (g)

c No carbon is oxidised and no carbon dioxide is produced, only water; $2H_2 + O_2 \longrightarrow 2H_2O$ (1 mark for the explanation, 1 mark for the correct formula, 1 mark for the correct balancing numbers)

Page 76 Types of rock

1 a iii It forms when rock comes under heat and pressure

b The size of the crystals reveals whether the rock cooled under the ground or on the surface; small crystals mean it cooled on the surface and large crystals mean it cooled underground

c The plankton died and the skeletons settled on the bottom of the ocean; many more layers fell on top, causing pressure; the layers hardened into rock

2 a Tube 1; because has the biggest difference in temperature between tube and surroundings

b Tube 2

c Agree (1 mark); any three explanations from: tube 2 cooled slowly; because it was insulated; cooling magma underground is insulated by rock; cotton wool is like the rock underground; it formed large crystals like granite; granite is intrusive igneous rock, which cools slowly

3 a $0.78 + 0.92 + 1.20 + 0.93 + 1.1 + 0.86 + 0.76 + 0.61 = 7.16$
$7.16 \div 8 = 0.90 \ (0.895)$;
$2.15 + 1.76 + 0.89 + 1.24 + 0.98 + 1.35 + 1.29 + 1.17 = 10.83$
$10.83 \div 8 = 1.35 \ (1.354)$;
$1.35 - 0.90 = 0.45 \ mm \ / \ 1.354 - 0.985 = 0.369 \ mm$

b Any four from: slow cooling gives large crystals; because particles have time to move and join on to a few crystals; cooling underground is slow because surrounding rocks provide insulation; Hell Roaring Mountain rock is intrusive because crystals are large; Tower Falls rock is extrusive because crystals are smaller; particles form many crystals at the same time; Obsidian Cliffs cooled very fast so there was not enough time for crystals to form

Page 77 Sedimentary rock and quarrying

1 a Cementation = Concentrated solutions of salts stick rock fragments together
Weathering = Rocks break into small fragments.
Sedimentation = Small fragments of rock are deposited on the sea bed
Erosion = Rock fragments are removed from the surface of the rock

b Weathering, erosion; sedimentation, cementation

c Heat; and pressure; below the ground

2 Organisms fall into sediments; they are covered and leave an impression/caste; the caste fills with minerals; evidence is that they are only found in sedimentary rock / limestone was under the sea and contains sea shells

3 a Layers can be seen, which mean it has eroded so must be soft

b Answer must include the idea of different hardness of layers; and different rates of erosion

4 Any three from: dust; noise; damage to roads by heavy lorries; increased traffic; destruction of local wildlife habitats

5

Ingredient	Glass	Cement	Concrete
Limestone	✓	✓	✓
Sand	✓		✓
Clay		✓	✓
Gravel			✓
Water			✓
Sodium carbonate	✓		

(Each column completely correct for 1 mark)

6 Answer should include suggestions for: noise reduction; dust reduction; improving traffic flow; reclaiming the land

Page 78 Atoms and reactions

1 ii Atoms from one element change to another element during a chemical reaction

2 a The grey metal changed to white powder so its properties changed; a bright light was produced indicating energy change

b 2.0 g

3 Physical: green / solid / melting point of 200 °C; Chemical: decomposes/reacts with acid to form salt

4 a 395.65 g

b KNO_3 is soluble and PbI_2 is insoluble / KNO_3 is colourless and PbI_2 is yellow

5 Other measurements – the mass at the end of the reaction; calculation – starting mass minus end mass; CO_2 is a gas so will escape from the beaker; other products remain in the beaker; since mass is conserved, any decrease in mass is due to carbon dioxide

Page 79 Thermal decomposition and calcium

1 a Calcium carbonate ($CaCO_3$)

b By heating (strongly)

c Carbon dioxide

d Thermal decomposition

2 Magnesium carbonate; because metal carbonates decompose; to give metal oxides

3 a $Ca(OH)_2$ (1 mark for correct symbols for Ca and OH, 1 mark for $(OH)_2$)

b Limewater detects carbon dioxide (CO_2); calcium oxide reacts with carbon dioxide to make calcium carbonate ($CaCO_3$); which is insoluble; so is cloudy

4 a Zinc carbonate ⟶ zinc oxide; + carbon dioxide

b Put the *same mass* of zinc and copper carbonate in separate boiling tubes; heat using the *same flame* in the apparatus shown; *time* how long it takes for the limewater to become cloudy

c Copper carbonate will decompose first; because it decomposes at a lower temperature than zinc carbonate

5 a To increase the pH of the soil

b Calcium oxide is fast-acting; less is needed

c Three times more limestone would be needed so transportation costs would be higher; calcium oxide is difficult to handle/harmful

Page 80 Acids, neutralisation and their salts

1 a ii Sodium chloride

b acid + base; ⟶ salt + water

c Alkali

d The acid is neutralised when the pH reaches 7; the more drops of alkali needed to reach pH7, the more acid the vinegar contains

2 a Measure a known volume of acid (any sensible volume); weigh the antacid tablet or use the number of tablets recommended as one dose for that brand; measure the pH of the acid before and after mixing with the tablet

b The higher the rise in pH, the more acid was neutralised by the tablet and therefore the more effective the tablet

c Either Yes, because this is similar to taking antacid tablets in real life: you would keep adding until the acid was neutralised; by crushing up the tablet you can add smaller amounts each time, which is more accurate; **or** no, because in real life you would take whole tablets not parts of tablets so spatulas of crushed powder are not an accurate measure; you don't neutralise all the stomach acid in real life

3 a Hydrochloric acid

b $CaCO_3 + 2HCl ⟶ CaCl_2 + CO_2 + H_2O$ (1 mark for the correct formula of hydrochloric acid, 1 mark for the remaining formulae and 1 mark for correct balancing)

Page 81 Electrolysis and chemical tests

1 a iv Electrolysis

b Chlorine is toxic (poisonous); any two from: breathing apparatus; any named protective clothing or safety goggles; regular health checks; regular checks of chlorine levels in the working atmosphere

c Poly(chloroethene) / polyvinyl chloride (PVC)

2 a i Chlorine can be collected from the cathode

b The electrodes have different charges – the anode is positive and the cathode is negative; the particles in solution are charged; and are attracted to the oppositely charged electrode

3 a Anode = 3.3 cm³; cathode = 7.3 cm³

b It contains more of one element than the other (approximately twice as much)

c Oxygen at the anode; hydrogen at the cathode; oxygen will relight a glowing splint; hydrogen will give a squeaky pop with a lighted splint

d They continued the electrolysis for different lengths of time

e Group 5 – they failed to capture all the gas at the anode / they allowed air to enter the tube at the cathode

Page 82 Metals – sources, oxidation and reduction

1 a ii A naturally occurring compound

b Gold is very unreactive

2 a The abundance of the ore; the percentage of metal in the ore; the cost of extraction

b Electrolysis is passing electricity through (molten) ore; it is used to extract some metals from their ores

3 a To reduce; the metal oxide

b Orange specks; in black powder

c It would work with lead or tin (allow iron and zinc); it would not work with aluminium, magnesium, calcium, sodium, potassium

4 a Al is oxidised; Fe_2O_3 is reduced

b It is more expensive than reduction with carbon

c Reduction with carbon; $2Fe_2O_3$ (s) + 3C (s); ⟶ 4Fe (s) + $3CO_2$ (g) / iron oxide + carbon; ⟶ iron + carbon dioxide; heating to high temperature / heating in a blast furnace

5 a Steel corrodes when it comes into contact with oxygen and water; coating forms a barrier

b Any two from: zinc is more reactive than iron; it provides sacrificial protection; it corrodes first even when damaged

Page 83 Metals – uses and recycling

1
Gold	Does not corrode	Electronic connectors
Aluminium	Low density	Aircraft
Copper	Malleable	Plumbing

2 a An alloy

b It makes the metal stronger; diagram should show layers of metal atoms of the same size, able to slide over each other; and layers of atoms of different sizes

c Chromium; it would make it resistant to corrosion

3 By alloying with a white metal; which makes the gold stronger/harder; and less expensive

4 Any three from: use recycled metal; recycle the scrap metal produced in the plant; recycling reduces the energy used in extracting/transporting/mining; only 5% of energy is needed to recycle

5 Answer should include references to the following: metal ores as a finite resource; mining and extraction are damaging to the environment; the high energy cost of extraction by electrolysis; the percentage energy saving

Page 84 Hydrocarbons and combustion

1 a Crude oil contains many different molecules; made from carbon and hydrogen only; which are not chemically bonded / can be easily separated

b Different boiling points

2 It must be divided into fractions (with similar boiling point); uses should include two from: refinery gases for heating and cooking; petrol for transport fuel; kerosene for aircraft fuel; fuel oil for ships and power stations; diesel for lorries, some cars and trains; bitumen for roads and roofs

3 Any four from: crude oil is a mixture of molecules of different sizes; the larger the molecule the stronger the intermolecular forces holding the molecules as a liquid; increasing the temperature increases kinetic energy of the molecules; smaller molecules require less kinetic energy to break away as gases / larger molecules require more energy to become gases; different-sized molecules become gases at different temperatures / have different boiling points so can be separated by gradually increasing the temperature and collecting the gases /gradually cooling the vaporised oil

4 a i It is a reduction reaction

b They are both (invisible) gases; carbon dioxide and water

5 a The wax combusted/was oxidised/turned to products

b The oxygen had all reacted

c Carbon dioxide; and water

d Carbon monoxide

e Carbon dioxide: limewater test (becomes cloudy); cobalt chloride (paper): changes from pink to blue

6 a When there is not enough oxygen; it is toxic

b Yellow flame and soot; this happens because there is not enough oxygen; it is called incomplete combustion

7 Incomplete combustion of hydrocarbons; which absorb/reflect light from the sun

Page 85 Acid rain and climate change

1 a iv It reduces the yield of some crops

b The sulfur dioxide; is carried away in the atmosphere (to northern Norway)

2 a Hydrocarbon fuels contain sulfur; which reacts with oxygen during combustion; to form sulfur dioxide / acid rain

b Damages leaves; makes soil acidic

3 a Clams and snails

b Perch depend on mayfly species as a food source

4 Any three from: minimise energy use; choose low-sulfur fuels; remove sulfur from fuels before burning; capture sulfur dioxide by scrubbing waste gases

5 iii, i, iv, ii (iii before i = 1 mark; i before iv = 1 mark; all correct = 3 marks)

6 a The temperature has risen

b There is a correlation between the levels of carbon dioxide and the temperature; burning fossil fuels has increased the level of carbon dioxide

7 Any four from: seeding oceans with iron will increase growth of algae; because iron is a limiting factor for algal growth; algae take carbon dioxide from the atmosphere for photosynthesis and for making carbonate shells; carbon dioxide from the atmosphere will be stored within algae; carbon dioxide is a greenhouse gas; reducing carbon dioxide in the atmosphere will reduce the amount of energy trapped on the planet

Page 86 Biofuels and fuel cells

1 a Any three from: fossils fuels are non-renewable; supplies are running out; fossil fuels produce a lot of pollution; fossils fuels are becoming more expensive

b Ethanol

c Growing fuel crops will use up land needed to grow food

2 Any three from: high energy release; low carbon dioxide production; low polluting emissions/sulfur dioxide/nitrogen oxides; low ash/smoke; ease of transport; ease of storage; cost; cost of technology needed to use it

3 Any four from: wood residue requires too much land use to be sustainable as a fuel source; algae use little land; high farmland use for sugar cane and rapeseed is likely to have a significant effect on food production; although algae uses little land the energy cost are high and therefore the benefit of using biofuel in terms of reducing greenhouse gas emissions is reduced; use a mixture of sources, e.g. where there is surplus farmland use sugar cane or rapeseed; use waste wood residue from other industries; research less energy intensive ways of producing biodiesel from algae

4 It is a renewable resource / can be made from water; it does not produce polluting gases

5 a They used the water from the first experiment that was already heated

b Fuel 1; it gave the highest temperature rise

c Any one of: use a heat shield; take the mass of the fuel before and after burning; control the size of the flame; stir the water

6 Producing the hydrogen has an energy cost; most electricity is generated using fossil fuels; which produce carbon dioxide

Page 87 Alkanes and alkenes

1 a C

b A and C (methane and ethane)

c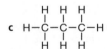

d Each carbon has 4 bonds; to 4 different groups

2 a

Substance	Mass (g)	% of total
Natural gas	80 g	100
Methane	64	80
Ethane	8	10
Propane	2.4	3
Butane	5.6	7

b Methane has only 1 carbon; propane has 3 carbons (and 4 more hydrogens)

c It is a gas at room temperature; increasing the pressure converts it to a liquid, which takes up less space

3 C_2H_6; the atoms are held together by covalent bonds; which are shared pairs of electrons.

4

Propene...	True	False
Has four carbon atoms		✓
Is an unsaturated molecule	✓	
Contains a double bond	✓	
Does not react with bromine water		✓

5 Any three from: burning fuel produces polluting gases; oil is a finite resource so we should preserve it; oil is a raw material for the chemical industry; it is used to make (any named product); there is no other energy source as effective as crude oil

6 a iii Butene   **b** Ethene; C_2H_4

Page 88 Cracking and polymers

1 a

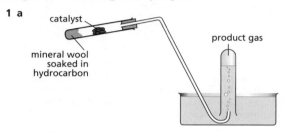

catalyst

mineral wool soaked in hydrocarbon

product gas

b Heat; the catalyst/aluminium oxide

c Alkanes; alkenes

2 a To reduce energy costs / to reduce the temperature of reactions

b Catalysts are not used up in the reaction; so the platinum can be reused

3 Any four from: cracking as breaking long chain alkanes into shorter alkanes and alkenes; describe the petrol/gases fraction that is the most valuable; the supply is less than the demand and why; cracking can increase the supply; fuel oil/bitumen supplies are far greater than demand

4 a Poly(propene)

b Poly(ethane)

c Poly(tetrafluoroethene)

d Poly(chloroethene)

5 iii, ii, iv, i (1 mark each for putting ii before iv and i after iv)

6 Any two from: polymers are made from oil and we will run out of oil; recycling polymers does not use oil; polymers can be burned but this produces toxic gases, or buried in landfill sites but we are running out of sites; polymers are not biodegradable so they stay in the ground for a very long time; recycling polymers saves energy, which is good for the environment

7 a Starch; cellulose

b Plant polymers are biodegradable

c Preserves oil supplies / renewable resource used

Page 89 C1 Extended response question

0 marks
Insufficient or irrelevant science. Answer not worthy of credit.

1–2 marks
Answer may be simplistic. There may be limited use of specialist terms. Errors of grammar, punctuation and spelling prevent communication of the science.

3–4 marks
For the most part the information is relevant and presented in a structured and coherent format. Specialist terms are used for the most part appropriately. There are occasional errors in grammar, punctuation and spelling.

5–6 marks
All information in answer is relevant, clear, organised and presented in a structured and coherent format. Specialist terms are used appropriately. Few, if any, errors in grammar, punctuation and spelling.

C2 Discovering chemistry

Page 90 Atomic structure and the periodic table

1 a iii It is where the neutrons are found

b Same: both contain protons and electrons / both have a nucleus with electrons surrounding it; different: helium has neutrons and hydrogen does not / helium has two protons and electrons and hydrogen has one

c Atoms contain subatomic particles / protons, neutrons and electrons; most of an atom is space / atoms are not solid

2 a Protons have a positive charge; neutrons have no charge

b 7

3 a Mg

b i 9 **ii** 12 **iii** 4

4 a They have different numbers of neutrons

b They have the same number of protons / they have the same atomic number; the number of protons decides the element

5 There are different isotopes of magnesium; which have different numbers of neutrons (different atomic masses); relative atomic mass is the average mass of an atom of the element; taking into account the abundance of all isotopes

Page 91 Electrons

1 a

Element symbol	Electronic configuration
F	2.7
Al	**2.8.3**
S	2.8.6

b i Electron **ii** 11 **iii** Electron shells

2 a Magnesium; 2.8.2

b Group 7; number of protons is the same as the number of electrons so there would be 17 electrons; 2 electrons in the first shell and 8 in the second means 7 in the outer shell; the group number is the number of electrons in the outer shell

c Ne = 2.8; Ar = 2.8.8

d The electronic configuration shows that they each have 8 electrons in their outer shell; they are in the same group in the periodic table; elements in the same group have similar properties

e Magnesium

f Period 4

3 a Mendeleev knew about the chemical properties of the elements; he grouped elements according to their properties; he knew the atomic masses and listed elements in order of atomic mass; the chemical properties depend on the electronic structure

b Mendeleev realised that not all elements had been discovered; he left gaps to allow for undiscovered elements; he predicted the properties of the undiscovered elements; when the elements were discovered, his predictions were found to be correct

Page 92 Ionic bonds and naming ionic compounds

1 a Electrostatic attraction = force that holds ions together; negative ion = atom that has gained electrons; positive ion = atom that has lost an electron; ionic compound = made from positive and negative ions

2 a The 2 electrons; in the outer shell; of magnesium are transferred to; the outer shell of oxygen; 1 mark for correct diagram

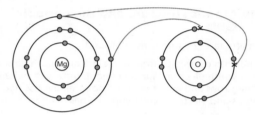

b F = F$^-$; Na = Na$^+$; S = S^{2-}; Ca = Ca^{2+}

c Potassium has 1 electron in its outer shell (and loses it to form a 1+ ion); chlorine has 7 electrons in its outer shell (and gains one more to form a 1– ion)

3 a Cation = Ca^{2+}; anion = CO$_3$$^{2-}$

b Diagram should show 2 electrons in the inner shell and 8 in the outer shell; charge should be shown as negative

c A sodium ion has a full outer shell of electrons; a sodium atom only has 1 outer electron

4 a

Name	Ions	Elements
Sodium chloride	Sodium and chloride	Sodium and chlorine
Potassium fluoride	**Potassium and fluoride**	Potassium and fluorine
Calcium oxide	**Calcium and oxide**	Calcium and oxygen
Magnesium nitrate	Magnesium and nitrate	**Magnesium, nitrogen, oxygen**

b Calcium hydroxide; ammonium chloride; magnesium bromide; sodium carbonate

c Potassium sulfide contains potassium and sulfur only; potassium sulfate contains potassium, sulfur and oxygen

Page 93 Writing chemical formulae

1 a

Name of ion	Charge	Formula
Sulfide	2–	S^{2-}
Fluoride	1–	F$^-$
Hydrogen	1+	H$^+$
Ammonium	1+	NH$_4$$^+$
Potassium	1+	K$^+$
Sulfate	2–	SO$_4$$^{2-}$
Carbonate	2–	CO$_3$$^{2-}$
Hydroxide	1–	OH$^-$
Nitrate	1–	NO$_3$$^-$
Tin	2+	Sn^{2+}
Copper	2+	Cu^{2+}
Silver	1+	**Ag$^+$**
Iron	3+	**Fe^{2+}**
Iron	2+	**Fe^{2+}**

b Barium sulfate is an ionic compound that contains barium and <u>sulfur</u> ions. The barium ion is a <u>polyatomic</u> cation and the <u>sulfate</u> ion is a monoatomic <u>cation</u>. (1 mark for underlining sulfur **or** sulfate)

2 a CaCl$_2$ / James; Cl$^-$ has one negative charge; Ca^{2+} has two positive charges; two negative ions are required for each positive ion to make a neutral compound

b Potassium fluoride = KF; calcium nitrate = Ca(NO$_3$)$_2$; aluminium oxide = Al$_2$O$_3$; ammonium sulfate = (NH$_3$)$_2$SO$_4$

3 a Two ammonia molecules are used in the equation

b Two hydrogen atoms are in the formula

c The brackets show that the whole ammonium ion is multiplied by two

4 a i Sodium chloride + silver nitrate → silver chloride + sodium nitrate (1 mark for each correct reactant; 1 mark for the correct product)

ii Potassium hydroxide + hydrogen chloride/ hydrochloric acid → potassium chloride + water (1 mark for each correct reactant; 1 mark for the correct product)

b i Na$_2$(SO$_4$) + BaCl$_2$ → BaSO$_4$ + 2NaCl (3 correct formulae, 3 marks; 2 in front of NaCl, 1 mark)

ii Mg(NO$_3$)$_2$ + 2NaOH → Mg(OH)$_2$ + 2NaNO$_3$ (3 correct formulae, 3 marks; 2 in front of either NaOH or Mg(OH)$_2$, 1 mark)

Page 94 Ionic properties and solubility

1 a iii Forms crystals, high melting point

b Diagram should show alternating positive and negative ions; ions must be labelled as specific substances

2 No it is not an ionic compound; because it melted at a low temperature/in a Bunsen flame

3 a Aluminium oxide has a giant lattice structure; large amounts of energy are needed to break strong ionic bonds; it must be melted because it does not conduct electricity as a solid

b Calcium oxide; it is the only compound where both ions have a double charge; this makes a stronger ionic bond so more energy is needed to break the bonds

4 Soluble – sodium chloride; magnesium nitrate; ammonium carbonate; insoluble – calcium carbonate; silver chloride

5 iii AgNO$_3$ (aq) + NaCl (aq) → AgCl (s) + NaNO$_3$ (aq)

6 ii Silver nitrate and sodium chloride

Page 95 Preparation of ionic compounds

1 a Choose the two **soluble** compounds. Then dissolve them and mix them together. The insoluble salt that you want will be **precipitated as a solid**.

b Precipitation reaction

2

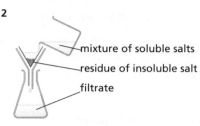

— mixture of soluble salts
— residue of insoluble salt
— filtrate

3 Barium sulfate is X-ray opaque; it leaves a silhouette of the bowel on the X-ray so doctors can spot any abnormalities; it is not absorbed as it is insoluble

4 Calcium = brick red; sodium = yellow/orange; potassium = lilac; copper = green/blue

5 a Dip nichrome wire into acid then the solution; put in flame; yellow/orange flame means sodium; add silver nitrate and nitric acid; white precipitate means chloride is present

b The white powder is a carbonate; test the gas with limewater; cloudy limewater confirms that the gas is carbon dioxide

6 Helium has a unique spectrum; which did not match the spectrum of any known element; so it must be an unknown element

Page 96 Covalent bonds

1 a iv iron oxide

b i H_2O

ii 2

2 a The atoms are held together by a shared; pair of electrons

b To become more stable

3 a To become stable by having a full outer shell of electrons

b Hydrogen has 1 electron in its outer shell; it needs 2 to fill the outer shell; there is no space for more than 2 electrons so it can only bond with one atom

4

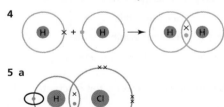

5 a

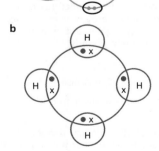

b

c i 8

ii 2

iii Carbon needs 8 electrons to have a full outer shell; but hydrogen only needs 2 electrons to have a full outer shell

6 a Two shared pairs of electrons; between the same two atoms

b

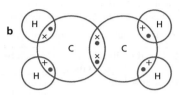

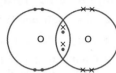

Page 97 Properties of elements and compounds

1 a ii It is white

b Diagram showing a circuit; including a power source; light bulb or ammeter; two separated electrodes in a beaker of solution

c Sucrose

d Simple – water/ammonia; methane/any named alkane/glucose/carbon dioxide; giant – diamond/graphite/silicon dioxide/silicon/silicon carbide

2 a 1 simple covalent; 2 ionic; 3 giant covalent (structure and bonding must both be correct for 1 and 3)

b Test whether the solution conducts electricity; if it is ionic it will conduct electricity; test whether it melts in a Bunsen flame/at a low temperature; ionic will not melt

c Ionic substances contain charged particles; which can move when molten or dissolved; covalent substances have no charged particles

3 a Graphite has a layered structure; with weak bonds between layers; the layers easily slide over each other; **or** a clearly labelled diagram of the structure of graphite showing weak bonds between layers

b Silicon dioxide has a giant structure; because it has a high melting point (since it is solid at room temperature); carbon dioxide has a simple structure; because it has a low boiling point/is a gas at room temperature; giant covalent structures have high melting points/require large amounts of energy to break bonds between particles, simple covalent structures have low melting points/require little energy to break forces between particles

Page 98 Separating solutions

1 Put into a separating funnel; allow to settle into two layers; open the tap and allow the lower layer to run into collecting vessel

2 iii, ii, iv, i, v (completely correct = 3 marks; **iii** before **ii** = 1 mark; **ii** before **i** = 1 mark)

3 Cool air to below –219 °C; remove solid carbon dioxide and allow temperature to rise; nitrogen turns to gas first (at –196 °C); argon turns to gas next (at –186 °C); oxygen can be collected as a liquid

4 Diagram should show a pencil line or cross near the bottom; with two spots higher up

5 Glucose; fructose

6 a Substance A

b Substance C

c Run a chromatogram using a pure sample of phenylalanine; measure the Rf value / see how far the spot travels; if it matches one of A, B or C then that confirms the identity

Page 99 Classifying elements

1 a i Metallic **ii** Ionic lattice

b Simple molecular covalent

2 a Giant lattice; of alternating sodium and chloride ions / positive and negative ions (or a clearly labelled diagram)

b Lots of energy; is needed to break strong ionic bonds

3

	Melting point	Solubility	Electrical conductivity	Structure
Silicon carbide	2 730 °C	**Insoluble**	Non-conductor	**Giant molecular covalent**
Boron trifluoride	–127 °C	Very soluble	Non-conductor	**Simple molecular covalent**
Copper(II) oxide	1 201 °C	Insoluble	**Only conducts when molten**	Ionic
Cerrosafe	74 °C	**Insoluble**	Conducts as solid	**Metallic**

4 a Alkali metals

b Group 0

c i It has a low melting point

5 a Labelled diagram showing: a regular arrangement; positive ions; sea of electrons

b Metals are malleable because layers of ions slide over each other; in the sea of electrons; metals conduct electricity because electrons can move; when a voltage is put across them

6 Two pairs from below (the reason must match the explanation):

Mobile sea of electrons; means it conducts electricity

Layers of ions slide over each other in the sea of electrons; therefore ductile/easily made into wires

Regular lattice of positive ions has strong metallic bonds; therefore has a high melting point so does not melt when electricity is put through it

Page 100 Alkali metals

1 a Line D

b Any two from: low melting point; soft; react with water

2 a i Fizzing

ii Lighted splint; gives a squeeky pop

iii Either: test the pH; lithium hydroxide would have a high value; **or**: add indicator; the water is alkaline

iv $2Li\ (s) + 2H_2O\ (l) \longrightarrow 2LiOH\ (aq) + H_2\ (g)$ (1 mark each for: formula for LiOH; formula for H_2; balanced correctly; left-hand side state symbols; right-hand side state symbols)

b (1 mark each for: correct number of shells; correct number of electrons; loss of one outer electron leaves a 1+ ion; which leaves a full/stable shell of electrons)

3 a Reactivity increases down the group

b Potassium has two more shells of electrons; the outer electron is further from the nucleus in potassium; the inner shells of electrons shield the outer electron from the positive pull of the nucleus; the outer electron is more easily lost (in potassium)

c Rubidium would have a very vigorous reaction/more vigorous than lithium, sodium or potassium; produces hydrogen/rubidium hydroxide; $2Rb + 2H_2O \longrightarrow 2RbOH + H_2$

4 a Atomic mass increases; as reactivity increases

b At conferences; in scientific journals

Page 101 Halogens and noble gases

1 Fluorine = yellow gas; chlorine = green gas; bromine = brown liquid; iodine = grey solid (1 mark each for three correct lines in left column and three in right)

2 a iii $H_2\ (g) + Br_2\ (l) \longrightarrow 2HBr\ (g)$

b Low pH (any number below 4)

3 a Chlorine water + potassium bromide, a colour change from green/colourless to brown; $Cl_2 + 2KBr \longrightarrow Br_2 + 2KCl$; iodine water and potassium would have no reaction

b Chlorine is more reactive than bromine, so it displaces bromine from potassium bromide; iodine is less reactive than bromine since it does not displace bromine from potassium bromide; therefore the order of reactivity is Cl>Br>I

4 He, Ne, Ar, Xe (1 mark each for any two in the correct order)

5 a Neon 2.8; argon 2.8.8

b Both neon and argon have 8 electrons in their outer shell/have a full outer shell; they do not need to share, lose or gain electrons; to increase stability

6 a Any value between 1.5 and 4.5 g/dm^3

b Use the periodic table to find the atomic number/mass of radon (in group 0); plot a graph of the atomic number/mass; against the boiling point; extend the line/extrapolate and read off the boiling point at the atomic number/mass of radon

Page 102 Endothermic and exothermic reactions

1 a iv The reaction takes in energy overall

b i Endothermic **ii** Exothermic

iii Endothermic **iv** Exothermic

2 a Diagram should show an insulated container; and a thermometer

b Temperature before and after mixing the reactants

c The temperature would rise

3 Reactions start by breaking bonds (of reactants)/taking in energy; next, new bonds are made/energy is given out; for exothermic reactions more energy is given out in making bonds; than is taken in when breaking bonds

4 a Exothermic

b $(22 + 24) \div 2 = 23$; $43 - 23 = 20$; °C; increase

c Silver nitrate + sodium chloride; $\longrightarrow$ silver chloride + sodium nitrate

d Reactants and products are labelled; energy is labelled at the y-axis; energy of products is below energy of reactants

5 The energy needed to break bonds; in oxygen and methane; is less than the energy needed to make bonds; in carbon dioxide and water

Page 103 Reaction rates and catalysts

1 ii Cut the carrots into small pieces.

2 A lower concentration of acid in the water; reduces the rate of reaction

3 a Diagram should show **either**: flask/test tube containing magnesium and acid; sealed connection; to inverted measuring cylinder under water/gas syringe; **or** flask containing magnesium and acid; with cotton wool in the neck; on a balance

  b The change in volume/mass; every (number) seconds/minute

  c As a line graph

  d The higher the concentration; the steeper the (initial) gradient (or a graph showing this)

4 Only collisions with sufficient energy; result in a reaction

5 a A catalyst increases the rate of a reaction; without being used up by the reaction

  b To reduce; polluting emissions/carbon monoxide and unburned hydrocarbons

  c Hydrocarbon + oxygen $\longrightarrow$ carbon dioxide and water

6 a Open structure allows gases to pass through; and increases the surface area of the catalyst

  b $2CO + O_2 \longrightarrow 2CO_2$ (1 mark for correct formula; 1 mark for correct balancing)

Page 104 Mass and formulae

1 a 36.5

  b 160

  c 85

  d 74

2 a $(12 \div 44) \times 100\%$; 27.3%

  b $(48 \div 167) \times 100\%$; 28.7%

  c $(28 \div 148) \times 100\%$; 18.9%

3 a Mass of copper = 4.95 g; mass of copper oxide = 6.20 g

  b $6.20 - 4.95 = 1.25$

  c $4.95 \div 63.5 = 0.078$; $1.25 \div 16 = 0.075$; formula CuO

4 $(43 \div 65) \times 100\%$; = 66.2%

5 Actual yield from 10 cm³ = (50% of 100) 50cm³ oxygen; volume required to make 100 cm³ = **20cm³** hydrogen peroxide

6 M_r CuSO$_4$ = 160; M_r CuO = 80; $(160 \div 80) \times 5 = 10$ g

7 H_2O is not damaging to the environment / no problems disposing compared to HCl; faster process means more profit

Page 105 C2 Extended response question

0 marks
Insufficient or irrelevant science. Answer not worthy of credit.

1–2 marks
Answer may be simplistic. There may be limited use of specialist terms. Errors of grammar, punctuation and spelling prevent communication of the science.

3–4 marks
For the most part the information is relevant and presented in a structured and coherent format. Specialist terms are used for the most part appropriately. There are occasional errors in grammar, punctuation and spelling.

5–6 marks
All information in answer is relevant, clear, organised and presented in a structured and coherent format. Specialist terms are used appropriately. Few, if any, errors in grammar, punctuation and spelling.

C3 Chemistry in action

Page 106 Testing for ions

1 a **iv** A brown precipitate

b Victor is right/a quantitative test is right; a quantitative test will measure how much/what concentration of copper is in the sample; a qualitative test only shows if there is any copper present or not

c **i** Aluminium ions; magnesium ions

ii Add more sodium hydroxide; and see if the precipitate dissolves

2 a Add sodium hydroxide; warm/heat; test the gas given off with red litmus paper; red litmus turns blue

b Bromide ions/Br^-

c Ammonium bromide

3 a Adding sodium hydroxide only gives information about the cations/positive ions/metal ions; compounds contain positive and negative ions/you have to test for anions/negative ions as well; the test is not specific/a white precipitate could mean either Ca^{2+} or Al^{3+}

b Any **2** from: adding silver nitrate and nitric acid; adding more sodium hydroxide to see if the precipitate dissolves; warming the solution and testing the gas with red litmus paper; flame tests; adding barium chloride; adding sulfuric acid/acid

4 I^- (aq) + Ag^+ (aq) $\longrightarrow$ AgI (s) (1 mark for correct reactants; 1 mark for correct products; 1 mark for correct state symbols)

Page 107 Ions in industry

1 a High levels; of some ions may be bad for health

b Flame test; brick red colour

2 a No, there is no positive test for carbonate/no fizzing when acid is added; there is a positive test for copper, blue precipitate with sodium hydroxide/green flame colour; there is a copper chloride/positive test for chloride ions, or copper carbonate may be present at too low a concentration to detect

b Quantitative test

3 a Carbonate ions/CO_3^{2-}

b (HCl and) $BaCl_2$

c White precipitate

d Bromide ions/Br^-

e Yellow precipitate

4 It gives a quantitative answer; flame tests give a qualitative answer; it is able to measure very low concentrations/flame tests need large amounts of sample

Page 108 Hard water

1 a Magnesium; calcium

b Scum is formed in hard water/it does not lather; soft water forms lather

2 a Dependent variable = height of lather; control variables = volume of soap solution/total volume of mixture/diameter of test tubes

b The more calcium chloride solution the less lather/negative correlation between calcium chloride solution and lather height

3 Ion exchange resins remove calcium and magnesium ions; and replace them with sodium ions

4

	True or false
Temporary hard water can be made soft by boiling	true
Permanent hard water cannot be made soft using ion exchange resin	false
Temporary hard water contains calcium carbonate	false
Filtered water is always soft	false
Limescale is calcium or magnesium carbonate	true

5 Any **3** from: Temporary hard water contains calcium/magnesium hydrogencarbonate; this decomposes on heating; to calcium carbonate; which precipitates out/forms a solid.

And any **1** from: Permanent hard water contains calcium/magnesium sulfate; ions which do not decompose

6 a 20.0 g

b 0.1 g

Page 109 Measuring masses

1 a **iv**: The concentration of the solution is 0.5 g/dm³

b 2/0.5; = 4 g/dm³ (units must be shown)

c Sandi; (0.2 ÷ 100) × 1000 = 2 g/dm³/or (2 ÷ 100) × 1000 = 20 g/dm³

2 a 2.5 g in 1 dm³; 1 dm³ = 1 000 cm³/500 cm³ = 0.5 dm³; 2.5 ÷ 2 = 1.25 g/ (2.5 ÷ 1) × 0.5 = 1.25 g

b (0.5 ÷ 100) × 1000 = 5 g/dm³

3 a 85.5 − 60.5 = 25.0; g

b 61.5 − 60.5 = 1 g

c 1 ÷ 0.025 = 40 g/dm³

4 a 12 g/dm³

b 0.48 g

5 Any **4** points from: Amount could mean more than one thing; it could mean the same mass or the same number of particles/moles; mass is the amount in grams; mole is 6×10^{23} particles; it would be better to say we used the same number of moles of carbon as iron; it would be better to say we used the same mass of carbon as iron

Page 110 Mass, molecules and concentrations

1 a 40 + 12 + (16 × 3) = 100

b 2 × 100 = 200 g

c 2 moles

d M_r CaO 40 + 16 = 56; 2 × 56 = 112; g

2 a A precipitation reaction

b 1 kg = 1 000 g; M_r Na_2CrO_4 (2 × 23) + 52 + (16 × 4) = 162; 1 000 ÷ 162 = 6.17 moles

c 6.17 moles

d M_r $PbCrO_4$ 207 + 52 + (16 × 4) = 323; 6.17 × 323 = 1 993 g/ 1.99 kg

e 6.17 moles

3 a 1 mole

b M_r $ZnSO_4$ $65 + 32 + (16 \times 4) = 161$ g

c $161/1\,000 \times 200 = 32.2$ g

d No, because the mass of one mole/M_r; of copper sulfate is not the same as the mass of one mole of zinc sulfate

Page 111 Salts from acids

1 a i: Sodium chloride

b i sulfate; **ii** hydroxide; **iii** nitrate; **iv** chloride

2 a Sulfuric acid; H_2SO_4

b To make the reaction faster

c Diagram of a filter funnel; filter paper; container beneath/beaker/evaporating basin/test tube

3 a Acid + base/alkali ⟶ salt + water

b Magnesium/magnesium oxide/hydroxide/carbonate; hydrochloric acid

4 a An alkali is a base that is soluble. Alkali = sodium/potassium hydroxide/ammonia/sodium/potassium carbonate/sodium/potassium hydrogencarbonate; Base = any metal oxide/hydroxide or carbonate or ammonia if not given as example of alkali

b Diagram of burette; conical flask; add small portions of acid to alkali (or other way around); check the pH after each addition; stop adding when pH=7/neutral; evaporate water

Page 112 Acid-base titrations

1 a i This reaction is <u>neutralisation</u>/redox reaction

ii Sodium nitrate is an acid/<u>salt</u>/alkali

iii Sodium hydroxide is an acid/salt/<u>alkali</u>

b $H^+ + OH^- \longrightarrow H_2O$

2 c a b d

3 a

Burette reading	Rough (cm³)	Titration 1 (cm³)	Titration 2 (cm³)	Titration 3 (cm³)
Volume NaOH added	19.0	14.6	14.4	14.8

(1 mark each for titrations 1 and 2)

b $(14.6 + 14.4 + 14.8) \div 3$; = 14.6 cm³

c $14.6 \div 1,000 = 0.0146$ dm³; $0.0146 \times 1.5 = 0.0219$ mols NaOH

d $HNO_3 + NaOH \longrightarrow NaNO_3 + H_2O$ correct reactant formula; correct products formula; balancing

e 0.0219 mols HNO_3

f $0.0219 \div 0.025$; 0.875; mol/dm³

g M_r $HNO_3 = 1 + 14 + (16 \times 3) = 63$; mass HNO_3 in 1 dm³ = 63×0.875; = 55.2 g/dm³

Page 113 Electrolytes and sodium

1 a Lead; brom<u>ide</u>

b The ions cannot move; no free electrons

c Lead

2 a Coolant; to carry heat away

b Any **2** from: liquid at reactor temperatures/not corrosive/ good heat conductor

c Group 1

3 a Orange/yellow

b By electrolysis

c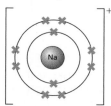

or with outer shell electrons only/or with no electrons (empty outer shell)

d It has a positive charge/moves towards the cathode during electrolysis

4 a Very reactive/only one electron in outer shell; would have reacted with oxygen in air/other elements in rocks

b i Sodium moves to cathode/negative electrode; chloride moves to anode/positive electrode

ii Sodium ions gain an electron; and become an atom/ metallic sodium; chloride ions lose an electron; and become chlorine molecules/elemental chlorine/ chlorine gas

c Any **2** of: Does not cause corrosion but water does; better conductor of heat than water; higher boiling point than water so need not be pressurised

Page 114 Oxidation and reduction

1 a ii, iii, iv (2 correct scores 1 point, 3 correct scores 2 marks)

b i Gain of oxygen/loss of electrons; **ii** reduction

2 a Hydrogen ion; chloride ion

b Hydrogen ion

c Chloride

3 a The diagram should show 2 electrodes; in a solution of hydrochloric acid (must be labelled); power source

b Oxidation

4 a i $Cu^{2+} + Zn \longrightarrow Cu + Zn^{2+}$ (marks for correct charges on ions; correct reactants; correct products)

ii $Pb^{2+} + 2Br^- \longrightarrow Pb + Br_2$ (marks for correct charges on ions; correct reactants; correct products)

iii $2Ag^+ + Cu \longrightarrow 2Ag + Cu^{2+}$ (marks for correct charges on ions; correct reactants; correct products)

b $Cu^{2+} + 2e- \longrightarrow Cu$; $Zn \longrightarrow Zn^{2+} + 2e-$

c Zinc

Page 115 Electrolysing sodium chloride solution

1 a i Sodium ion

   ii Chloride ion

   iii The ions; cannot move/there are no free electrons

 b i Chlorine

   ii Test for hydrogen gas (lighted splint, squeaky pop)

2 a Sodium chloride + water $\longrightarrow$ hydrogen + chlorine + sodium hydroxide (1 mark for each reactant or product in the correct position)

 b Hydrogen ions; are reduced/accept electrons more easily than; sodium ions

 c i False; **ii** True; **iii** True; **iv** True

3 a i $2Cl^- \longrightarrow Cl_2 + 2e^-$

   ii Oxidised; electrons are lost

   iii They do not take part in the reaction/are neither oxidised nor reduced; they remain (unchanged) in solution

 b To prevent; hydrogen and chlorine; reacting together/ forming hydrogen chloride

 c Any **3** from: Two ions are sodium and hydroxide; test for sodium with flame test; yellow colour produced; test for hydroxide; add to copper/iron/aluminium/magnesium ions; precipitate forms

Page 116 Products of electrolysis

1 a i Increase in mass

   ii Stay the same

   iii Copper ions from the solution; had become copper atoms

 b

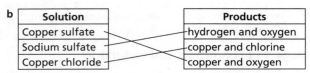

Solution	Products
Copper sulfate	hydrogen and oxygen
Sodium sulfate	copper and chlorine
Copper chloride	copper and oxygen

2 a Sodium chloride/copper chloride/any named metal chloride except silver; solution or <u>molten</u> lead chlorine/ any named molten metal chloride

 b Oxidation

 c Sodium chloride = hydrogen/copper chloride = copper/ lead chloride = lead/if metal is less reactive than hydrogen then the metal forms, if more reactive then hydrogen

3 a From ions/hydroxide ions/OH^- in the water

 b $4OH^- \longrightarrow O_2 + H_2O + 4e^-$

 c $2H^+ + 2e^- \longrightarrow H_2$

 d Sodium sulfate

 e Hydroxide ions

Page 117 Industrial electrochemistry

1 a i True; **ii** true; **iii** false; **iv** true

 b For electrical wiring

2 a Chromium is very costly

 b Electroplating

 c To improve appearance/reduce corrosion

3 a The value of copper increased

 b Steel rusts, copper does not; steel is grey, copper is orange/red/to give a distinctive colour.

 c Diagram of electrolysis apparatus; power source; steel disk as cathode; copper ions in solution; $Cu^{2+} + 2e^- \longrightarrow Cu$

Page 118 Volumes of gases

1 a M_r butane = 58; moles butane = (2.72 × 1 000) ÷ 58; = 46.9 moles

 b 46.9 × 24; = 1 126 dm³

 c No difference; one mole of any gas occupies the same volume at the same temperature and pressure

 d $C_4H_{10} + 6.5 O_2 \longrightarrow 4CO_2 + 5H_2O$ (marks for reactants correct; products correct; correctly balanced (or multiples of))

 e 20 ÷ 58 = 0.34; 0.34 × 24 = 8.3 dm³

 f 4 × 8.3 = 33.1 dm³

2 a $2H_2 + O_2 \longrightarrow 2H_2O$ (marks for formulae correct; balancing correct)

 b 48 ÷ 2; = 24 dm³ O_2

 c Anhydrous copper sulfate; turns from white to blue/blue cobalt chloride; turns to pink

 d 48 ÷ 24 = 2 moles H_2; mole ratio hydrogen to water = 1:1; M_r water = 18; 2 × 18 = 36 g water

3 a Any **3** from: 12 ÷ 24 = 0.5 moles; mole ratio CO_2: $CaCO_3$ = 1:1; M_r $CaCO_3$ = 100; **and** 0.5 × 100 = 50 g limestone

 b 11 200 000 ÷ 56 = 200 000 moles; 200 000 × 24 = 4 800 000 dm³ CO_2

Page 119 Fertilisers

1 a iv: To increase crop yield

 b i Acid and base/alkali

   ii Ammonia

2 a Improved plant growth

 b Increases costs; causes pollution/nitrates in drinking water/eutrophication

 c Any **3** from: Washed from soil; causes water plants to overgrow/clog waterways; decay of plants causes decomposers; to use up oxygen in water/results in no oxygen in water

3 a M_r NH_4NO_3 = 80; (28 ÷ 80) × 100 = 35%

 b M_r $CO(NH_2)_2$ = 60; (28 ÷ 60) × 100 = 47%

 c NH_4NO_3 033 ÷ 0.35; = £0.94 (per kgN); $CO_2(NH_2)_2$ 0.425 ÷ 0.47; = £0.90 (per kgN) urea is cheaper

4 a Any **5** from: fertiliser from agriculture; is washed into the water; plants/algae grow excessively; then die and are decomposed; which uses all the oxygen in the water; so marine life dies

 b There is a positive correlation between fertiliser use and area of dead zone/when less fertiliser is used the dead zone is smaller

Page 120 Dynamic equilibrium

1 a The reaction is reversible

  b i Steam; natural gas

    ii Air

2 a Ammonia

  b $3H_2 + N_2; \rightleftharpoons 2NH_3$

  c Fertilisers/explosives

3 a Both reactions are occurring at the same time; the rate of the forward reaction is the same as the rate of the backward reaction

  b If would increase

  c It would cost more; it becomes more hazardous

  d The rate of the reaction is too slow

  e Iron; increases the rate of both forward and backward reactions/increases the rate at which equilibrium is reached

4 a It comes to equilibrium

  b It will decrease the yield of hydrogen/decrease the quantity of products at equilibrium; there are more moles of gas in the products than in the reactants

  c The forward reaction is endothermic; increasing the temperature moves the position of equilibrium; towards the endothermic side/towards products

Page 121 Ethanol production

1 a Fermentation

  b Glucose

  c The enzymes in the yeast will not work at low temperatures

  d Carbon dioxide

  e No ethanol is produced unless the fermentation is anaerobic

2 a Glucose $\longrightarrow$ ethanol; + carbon dioxide

  b The mixture is heated; ethanol evaporates because it has a lower boiling point than the water; the vapour travels to a condenser and then turns back to liquid and runs into a separate container; water is left behind

  c Ethanol evaporates but water does not

3 a Brazil has a cheap supply of sugar cane; the UK does not

  b Carbon dioxide is absorbed when the sugar cane grows so less net carbon dioxide is released; decreased demand on crude oil (non-renewable)

  c Reacting ethene; with steam

  d No need to distil/purer product

Page 122 Homologous series

1 a iv: Propane

  b i

$$H-\overset{\displaystyle H}{\underset{\displaystyle H}{\overset{|}{\underset{|}{C}}}}-H$$

    ii Methane

  c Methane ethane propane butane (all correct 2 marks, 2 correct 1 mark)

2 a Alkenes

  b

$$\overset{\displaystyle H \qquad\quad H}{\underset{\displaystyle H \qquad\quad H}{C=C}}$$

  c Shake with bromine water; if it is an alkene there will be a colour change from brown to colourless

3 a $C_nH_{2n+1}OH$

  b Any value between 85 and 110 (actual value = 97)

  c Viscosity increases as number of carbons increases

4 a Any **2** from: They have the same general formula/functional group; they differ from each other by CH_2; they show a trend in physical properties

  b Fizzes; when added to sodium carbonate/any carbonate/magnesium **or** reacts with alcohol; to form an ester

  c There are stronger intermolecular forces in propanoic acid; so more energy is needed to overcome them

Page 123 Ethene, ethanoic acid, ethanol and society

1 i: It will turn blue litmus paper red; iii: it will fizz if mixed with magnesium (1 wrong answer cancels out a correct answer. No negative marks.)

2 a Any **3** from: Damages liver; damages brain; increases the risk of accidents; increases anti-social behaviour

  b It contains less alcohol

  c 5 cm³ ethanol in every 100 cm³ of drink

  d $(1\,704 \div 100) \times 5$; = 85.2 cm³

  e 85.2×2; = 170.4 cm³

  f $170.4 \div 25$; = 6.8 shots/7 shots

3 a Ethanol + ethanoic acid $\longrightarrow$ ethyl ethanoate + water

  b Ester

  c Perfume/flavour compound

4 a Ethanol

  b To allow the air to oxidise the ethanol

  c Ethanoic acid

$$H-\overset{\displaystyle H}{\underset{\displaystyle H}{\overset{|}{\underset{|}{C}}}}-C\overset{\displaystyle \diagup\!\!\diagup O}{\underset{\displaystyle \diagdown O-H}{}}$$

  d Copper oxide + ethanoic acid; $\longrightarrow$ copper ethanoate + water

Page 124 Esters, fats and soaps

1 a Sweet-smelling; low boiling point

  b Solvent/perfume

2 a 3.9 + 16 + 1.5 + 2.5 = 59 million tonnes;
($39 \div 59$) × 100 = 66%

b Making clothes/ bedding/curtains − any sensible suggestion

c Strong/not allow gases to pass through/unreactive/ insoluble

d Fleece/new bottles − any other sensible suggestion

3 a Soaps

b Esters

4 a (1 mark each correct structure for ethanoic acid, ethanol, ethyl ethanoate and water)

$$H_3C - C \overset{O}{\underset{O-H}{}} + H_3C - CH_2-O-H \longrightarrow H_3C - \overset{O}{\overset{\|}{C}} - O-CH_2-CH_3 + H_2O$$

b Low boiling point/boiling point lower than water

MALPAS

12·10·13.

5 Diagram labelled 'hydrophilic head' at left end of molecule; 'hydrophobic tail' at right end of molecule; hydrophilic end dissolves in water; hydrophobic end dissolves in grease

Page 125 C3 Extended response question

0 marks
Insufficient or irrelevant science. Answer not worthy of credit.

1–2 marks
Answer may be simplistic. There may be limited use of specialist terms. Errors of grammar, punctuation and spelling prevent communication of the science.

3–4 marks
For the most part the information is relevant and presented in a structured and coherent format. Specialist terms are used for the most part appropriately. There are occasional errors in grammar, punctuation and spelling.

5–6 marks
All information in answer is relevant, clear, organised and presented in a structured and coherent format. Specialist terms are used appropriately. Few, if any, errors in grammar, punctuation and spelling.